32.50
set

MUSCLE AS A FOOD

Proceedings of an International Symposium
Sponsored by the University of Wisconsin
July, 1965
With the support of United States Public Health Service
Research Grant EF-00727-01, from the
Division of Environmental Engineering and Food Protection
And a special grant from
The American Meat Institute Foundation

The Physiology and Biochemistry of Muscle as a Food

EDITED BY

E. J. Briskey

R. G. Cassens

J. C. Trautman

THE UNIVERSITY OF WISCONSIN PRESS

Madison, Milwaukee, and London, 1966

Published by

The University of Wisconsin Press

Madison, Milwaukee, and London

U.S.A.: Box 1379, Madison, Wisconsin 53701

U.K.: 26–28 Hallam Street, London, W. 1

Printed in the United States of America by

North Central Publishing Co., St. Paul, Minnesota

Library of Congress Catalog Card Number 66-22849

C. E. Allen
Department of Meat and Animal Science
University of Wisconsin
Madison, Wisconsin

F. A. Andrews
Bjorksten Research Laboratories
Fish Hatchery Road
Madison, Wisconsin

A. F. Anglemier
Department of Food Science
Oregon State University
Corvallis, Oregon

J. R. Bendall
Low Temperature Research Station
Downing Street
Cambridge, England

E. Birmingham
Swift Research Center
Packers at Exchange
Chicago, Illinois

T. N. Blumer
Department of Food Science
North Carolina State University
Raleigh, North Carolina

R. J. Bouthilet
Wilson and Company, Inc.
4200 South Marshfield
Chicago, Illinois

E. J. Briskey
Department of Meat and Animal Science

University of Wisconsin
Madison, Wisconsin

M. H. Brooke
Medical Neurology Branch
National Institute of Neurological Diseases and Blindness
National Institute of Health
Bethesda, Maryland

H. Buttkus
Fisheries Research Board of Canada
6640 N.W. Marine Drive
Vancouver 8, British Columbia, Canada

A. F. Carlin
School of Home Economics
Iowa State University
Ames, Iowa

Z. L. Carpenter
Department of Animal Science
Texas Agriculture and Mechanics University
College Station, Texas

R. G. Cassens
Department of Meat and Animal Science
University of Wisconsin
Madison, Wisconsin

Jean Charpentier
Laboratoire Viande
C.N.R.Z.
Jouy-En-Josas, France

R. E. Davies
Department of Animal Biology
University of Pennsylvania
Philadelphia, Pennsylvania

D. de Fremery
U.S. Department of Agriculture
Western Regional Research
  Laboratory
800 Buchanan Street
Albany, California

T. H. Donnelly
Swift Protein Laboratory
4633 Grand Avenue
Western Springs, Illinois

O. R. Fennema
Department of Dairy and Food
  Industries
University of Wisconsin
Madison, Wisconsin

R. L. Fischer
Campbell Soup Company
Camden, New Jersey

D. E. Goll
Department of Animal Science
Iowa State University
Ames, Iowa

G. A. Goll
Department of Animal Science
Purdue University
West Lafayette, Indiana

E. Gould
Bureau of Commercial Fisheries
Emerson Avenue
Gloucester, Massachusetts

M. L. Greaser
Department of Meat and Animal
  Science
University of Wisconsin
Madison, Wisconsin

R. Hamm
German Meat Research Institute
Kulmbach, Germany

B. Harmon
Department of Animal Science

University of Illinois
Urbana, Illinois

E. Helander
Medical School
University of Gothenburg
Gothenburg, Sweden

R. L. Henrickson
Department of Animal Science
Oklahoma State University
Stillwater, Oklahoma

H. K. Herring
Department of Meat and Animal
  Science
University of Wisconsin
Madison, Wisconsin

W. G. Hoekstra
Department of Biochemistry
University of Wisconsin
Madison, Wisconsin

P. F. Hopper
Devro
Southside Avenue
Sommerville, New Jersey

J. M. Jay
Biology Department
Wayne State University
Detroit, Michigan

T. F. Johnson
College of Medicine, Department of
  Physiology
Howard University
Washington, D.C.

M. D. Judge
Department of Animal Science
Purdue University
West Lafayette, Indiana

R. G. Kauffman
Department of Animal Science
University of Illinois
Urbana, Illinois

C. H. Kim
Wilson and Company, Inc.

4200 S. Marshfield
Chicago, Illinois

F. J. King
Bureau of Commercial Fisheries
Emerson Avenue
Gloucester, Massachusetts

C. D. Kochakian
University of Alabama
    Medical Center
Birmingham, Alabama

J. J. Lalich
Department of Pathology
University of Wisconsin
Madison, Wisconsin

H. A. Lardy
Institute for Enzyme Research
University of Wisconsin
Madison, Wisconsin

R. Lauck
Stauffer Chemical Company
11th and Arnold Street
Chicago Heights, Illinois

R. A. Lawrie
Food Science Department
University of Nottingham
Loughborough
Leics, England

H. Lineweaver
U.S. Department of Agriculture
Western Regional Research
    Laboratory
800 Buchanan Street
Albany, California

B. J. Luyet
American Foundation for Biological
    Research
RFD 1
Madison, Wisconsin

J. K. McAnelly
Swift R. and D. Center
Packers at Exchange
Chicago, Illinois

A. P. Mackenzie
American Foundation for Biological
    Research
RFD 1
Madison, Wisconsin

B. B. Marsh
Meat Industry Research Institute of
    New Zealand
Hamilton, New Zealand

R. K. Meyer
Department of Zoology
University of Wisconsin
Madison, Wisconsin

W. F. H. M. Mommaerts
University of California
    Medical Center
Los Angeles, California

R. E. Morse
T. J. Lipton, Inc.
800 Sylvan Avenue
Englewood Cliff, New Jersey

S. M. Mozersky
U.S. Department of Agriculture
Eastern Regional Research
    Laboratory
Philadelphia, Pennsylvania

R. P. Newbold
Division of Food Preservation
C.S.I.R.O.
North Ryde, Australia

H. W. Ockerman
Department of Animal Science
Ohio State University
Columbus, Ohio

H. S. Olcott
Department of Nutritional Sciences
University of California
Berkeley, California

S. M. Partridge
Low Temperature Research Station
Downing Street
Cambridge, England

W. D. Paynter
Research Division
Oscar Mayer and Company
Madison, Wisconsin

A. M. Pearson
Department of Food Science
Michigan State University
East Lansing, Michigan

K. A. Piez
Laboratory of Biochemistry
National Institute of Dental Research
National Institute of Health
Bethesda, Maryland

J. F. Price
Department of Food Science
Michigan State University
East Lansing, Michigan

D. W. Quass
Department of Meat and Animal
  Science
University of Wisconsin
Madison, Wisconsin

R. Sair
Department of Meat and Animal
  Science
University of Wisconsin
Madison, Wisconsin

R. N. Sayre
U.S. Department of Agriculture
Western Regional Research
  Laboratory
800 Buchanan Street
Albany, California

C. J. Schram
Unilever Limited
Sharnbrook Bedford
England

B. S. Schweigert
Department of Food Science
Michigan State University
East Lansing, Michigan

W. C. Sherman
National Livestock and Meat Board
36 South Wabash Avenue
Chicago, Illinois

J. D. Sink
Department of Animal Industry and
  Nutrition
Pennsylvania State University
University Park, Pennsylvania

D. B. Slautterback
Department of Anatomy
University of Wisconsin
Madison, Wisconsin

R. B. Sleeth
Armour Food Research Division
801 West 22nd Street
Oak Brook, Illinois

H. E. Snyder
Department of Dairy and Food
  Industry
Iowa State University
Ames, Iowa

M. Solberg
Department of Food Science
Rutgers University
New Brunswick, New Jersey

G. F. Stewart
Department of Food Science
  and Technology
University of California
Davis, California

A. H. Sutton
Unilever, Limited
Greyhope Road
Aberdeen, Scotland

W. Sybesma
Research Institute Animal Husbandry
Driebergseweg 10 D
Zeist, The Netherlands

A. G. Szent-Györgyi
Dartmouth Medical School
Hanover, New Hampshire

PARTICIPANTS

A. L. Tappel
Department of Food Science
  and Technology
University of California
Davis, California

N. W. Thomas
Department of Animal Science
Purdue University
West Lafayette, Indiana

W. A. Thomson
Department of Food Science
North Carolina State University
Raleigh, North Carolina

N. Tomlinson
Fisheries Research Board of Canada
6640 N.W. Marine Drive
Vancouver 8, British Columbia,
  Canada

D. G. Topel
Department of Animal Science
Iowa State University
Ames, Iowa

J. C. Trautman
Research Division

Oscar Mayer and Company
Madison, Wisconsin

R. W. Usborne
Department of Animal Science
University of Kentucky
Lexington, Kentucky

A. Veis
Department of Biochemistry
Northwestern University
Evanston, Illinois

J. R. Whitaker
Department of Food Science
  and Technology
University of California
Davis, California

E. Wierbicki
U.S. Army Natick Laboratory
Kansas Street
Natick, Massachusetts

J. A. Will
NIH Research Fellow
Departments of Medicine and
  Veterinary Science
University of Wisconsin
Madison, Wisconsin

Preface

This text has been assembled from the proceedings of the symposium on the Physiology and Biochemistry of Muscle as a Food which was held on the University of Wisconsin campus, July 12–14, 1965. Leading scientists from a diversity of scientific disciplines reviewed the latest information on various aspects of the architectural machinery and function of muscle tissue. Because this symposium was organized as the first of a series, its subjects were rather diverse, in order to serve as a base for present and future discussions. Supplemental chapters were contributed by Dr. J. R. Bendall, Drs. H. Buttkus and N. Tomlinson, and Dr. D. de Fremery. Leading scientists were also selected as panel review members to direct the discussion sessions, which followed each set of papers, toward the use of muscle as a food.

The planning committee is grateful to all contributors for their effort and cooperation. Grateful acknowledgment is also made of the fine cooperation from all session chairmen and panel review members. Especial appreciation is extended to Dr. R. E. Davies and Dr. J. R. Bendall, who served as special discussants for this symposium, and to the symposium's Advisory Committee, consisting of Dr. R. W. Bray, Dr. C. H. Krieger, Dr. H. Lineweaver, Dr. B. S. Schweigert, Dr. A. D. Stevens, Dr. G. F. Stewart, and Dr. C. E. Weir. For the interest and cooperation of the graduate students and postdoctoral fellows in Muscle Chemistry and Physiology in the Department of Meat and Animal Science, University of Wisconsin, the planning committee is forever grateful.

Special appreciation is directed to the Public Health Service, for Public Health Service Research Grant EF-00727-01 from the Division of Environmental Engineering and Food Protection and to the American Meat Institute Foundation for a special symposium grant. Appreciation for supplemental support is also expressed to the American Meat Science Association; the Graduate School, University of Wisconsin; Jones Dairy, Fort Atkinson, Wisconsin; Meat and Animal Science Department, University of Wisconsin; and Oscar Mayer and Company, Madison, Wisconsin.

E. J. B.
R. G. C.
J. C. T.

Madison, Wisconsin
February, 1966

Contents

Part V: Connective Tissue Proteins in Muscle

Part VI: Response of Muscle to Physical and Chemical Treatment

MUSCLE AS A FOOD

Chapter 1

"Postmortem" Perspectives

G. F. STEWART

The symposium which produced this book is bound to influence developments in food science for the next decade. There is no doubt in my mind that it will have a profound and stimulating effect on research in meat science which might well set the standard for food science as a whole.

Meat science, like its mother field of food science, is interdisciplinary. The organizers of this symposium wisely recognized this fact and brought to bear contributions that could be made from all relevant basic disciplines and their applied counterparts. Thus there were speakers and discussants from many fields, including anatomy, biochemistry, biophysics, chemistry, meat science, medical science, nutrition, pathology, and physiology. The interplay of ideas and experiences was tremendous and will no doubt serve to accelerate developments not only in meat science, but very likely also in the basic disciplines themselves.

Another feature of this conference was its international character. Not only did key foreign scientists serve as speakers, but a number came to listen and take part in the extensive discussions. Such faraway places as South Africa, Australia, New Zealand, United Kingdom, and West Germany were represented at the symposium. However, scientists from Eastern Europe and Asia were missing, and no doubt this was a real loss in certain of the subjects under discussion. It is to be hoped that this gap can be closed at the next symposium on this topic.

Another unique feature of the meeting was the generous mingling of agricultural and medical scientists. This was a welcome and uncommon state of affairs which should lead to many benefits, not only to meat science but to the medical science as well. I observed many contacts being made among these two groups of scientists which are sure to blossom into productive collaborations in the years ahead.

Not the least of the unique features of this symposium was the blending of basic and applied subjects on the program, and it was heartening to see the active interest of the "pure" scientists in the applied problems being

3

discussed, and conversely the intense interest of the food and medical scientists in the basic problems. This seems to me a healthy reversal of the trend to the "ivory tower," especially by academic scientists.

To one whose active interest in meat science spans a third of this century, the progress brought to light by the symposium discussions seemed enormous, and yet our ignorance is colossal. Furthermore, our meat technology is still largely based on practical experience and tradition.

To highlight the results of this symposium let us recapitulate several of the subjects discussed at the conference:

MUSCLE STRUCTURE AND DEVELOPMENT

Numerous studies have been made on the structure, development, and function of muscle. Electron microscopy has been of invaluable help in bridging the gap between the gross structure evident to the eye and the molecular architecture of muscle. Somewhat startling, but still perfectly logical, are the findings that the gross structures seen by the eye are direct reflections of the integrated fine structures at the molecular level. Developments over the last decade or two have begun to clarify the biochemical events that accompany muscular development and muscular function. In particular we have reasonably good ideas of the energy metabolism that permits muscular function, and the biochemical details of muscular contraction and relaxation are becoming increasingly clear. Great discoveries are in the making, as was evidenced by the discussions of the active workers in the field.

HORMONAL, NUTRITIONAL, AND ENVIRONMENTAL EFFECTS ON MUSCLE

Spirited discussions of these topics reflected the dynamic state of research in this area. While the effects of androgens on muscle development were stressed here, it was made clear that the estrogens and other hormones also influence muscle greatly. Nutritional and environmental factors affecting muscle in living animals as well as in the postmortem state are under very active investigation by food scientists and medical scientists, and rapid progress seems assured. It was heartening to see the interest and collaboration developing among physiologists, biochemists, medical scientists, and food scientists in this area of research; and it is to be hoped that it will continue and even be expanded, since many of our meat quality problems have their solution in the interdisciplinary approach.

POSTMORTEM CHANGES IN MUSCLE

Partly due to its inherent complexities but also partly due to neglect, this subject is probably the least understood of all those dealt with in the symposium. However, it was good to note that some very competent scientists are now concentrating on this aspect of muscle biochemistry and physiology. Workers in the basic disciplines involved have largely developed the theory and tools to the point where we should be able to understand what is going on in muscle postmortem and its relationship to the quality of the resultant meat. No longer is the dictum of Sir William Hardy to stay out of the morass of muscle autolysis appropriate.

MUSCLE AS MEAT

The fact that only a minimum of discussion related to this most important topic was largely a reflection of the paucity of first-class work in the field. It is essential that studies in this area be pushed, because the primary purpose of producing animal muscle is to provide meat for human consumption. There is an urgent need for greatly accelerated programs of research in the biochemistry and microbiology of meat and meat products. There is also a need for better and wider use of valid techniques for evaluating the organoleptic qualities of meat. At the symposium there was little evidence of the need for this type of work and little realization that sound methodology exists for measuring certain of the sensory properties. Muscle is used as meat, not only in the relatively unprocessed form but increasingly in formulated and highly processed products. Very little basic work has been or is being done on the problems of using muscle in these products. As a result the technology in use today has almost all been developed on an empirical basis. This must be changed if we are to have technology soundly based on science. As I see it, this is one of the most urgent needs in meat science today.

In conclusion, this was a most successful symposium and one that will be long remembered by all who attended. It must be repeated in a few years, when we may hope that many of today's unanswered questions will have been solved and more work will have been done in the badly neglected areas. It is my hope that postmortem changes in muscle and the science and technology of converting muscle to meat and meat products will receive major attention from well-trained scientists in the years immediately ahead.

Chapter 2

Muscle as a Contractile Machine

J. R. BENDALL

The aim of this synopsis is to provide a setting for the biochemical and physiological discussions which constitute the following chapters. It is usual when describing the structure of muscle to begin with the intact tissue and then to analyze it down to its constituent parts. Here we shall take the opposite view and attempt to build the muscle up from these parts, beginning with the contractile system, and moving on to the system of sarcotubules responsible for excitation coupling within the fiber, to the enzyme systems supplying the energy for contraction, and finally to the connective-tissue components which bind the fibers together into a muscle, and in which run the nerves and vascular system.

THE CONTRACTILE SYSTEM

The contractile system is built up of interdigitating filaments of actin and myosin, which in the resting muscle can slide passively over one another, whereas during contraction the actin filaments are pulled actively over the myosin filaments, towards the center of the A band (see Fig. 2.1).

The filaments are arranged in a hexagonal array, so that at the point of overlap each myosin filament is surrounded by six actin filaments, and each actin by three myosins. The myosin filaments are built up of myosin molecules, arranged head to tail. The heads, which are made of heavy meromyosin, appear on the filaments as projecting feet with a sixfold screw axis of symmetry, whereas the tails of light meromyosin serve to bind the filaments together. The dimensions of the molecule are about 1500 Å by 20 Å, the "globular" heads being about 200 Å long. In the filaments, the feet are 435 Å apart in each row. At the center of each myosin filament in the A band, there is a bare patch without feet, and it is here that the backbone molecules of light meromyosin from each half filament are bound together (M band). Stretching in each direction from this patch, the feet are shown in Figure 2.1 arranged in arrow-head fashion, pointing towards the M band; in this position they would

7

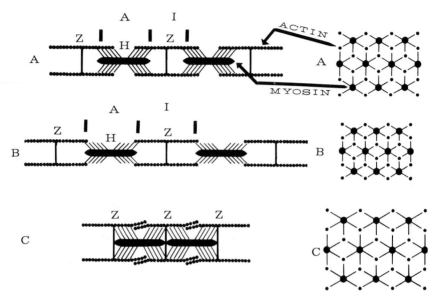

Fig. 2.1. — Fine structure of a sarcomere in longitudinal and cross section, showing myosin filaments with their protruding feet, and the beaded structure of actin (see text). Note that the length of the sarcomere has been reduced tenfold, for ease of drawing. Other features are approximately to scale. *A* is muscle at rest length $=l_0=2.4$ microns per sarcomere; *B* is muscle stretched to $l=1.3\ l_0$; *C* is muscle contracted to $l=0.6\ l_0$.

exert maximum tension as they pulled on the neighboring actin filaments. The ends of the filaments are tapered. Their diameter is about 120 Å.

The actin filaments, although shown in Figure 2.1 as a single chain of beads, actually consist of a double chain of globular G-actin monomers, helically arranged, so that the pitch of the helix is about 700 Å, and there are about 13 monomers per turn, with a spacing of about 55 Å. The thickness of the filament is about 70 Å. At the so-called Z line, the actin filaments from each half sarcomere are joined together in a complex crisscross fashion, to give the greater density observed at this point on electron micrographs. Tropomyosin may also be involved in the structure of the Z line.

One feature of the sliding filament model which is commonly overlooked but which follows from the fact, first observed in the seventeenth century, that muscle contracts at very nearly constant volume, is that the crystal lattice of actin and myosin filaments must also stay at constant volume during contraction. This has recently been confirmed from X-ray studies of living muscle; and it follows that the actin-to-myosin, center-to-center distance must increase on contraction and decrease on stretch, as shown in Figure 2.1, in proportion to the reciprocal of the square root of the

muscle length. Thus the myosin feet, where the active adenosine triphosphatase site is situated, must be able to extend further and further the
more the muscle contracts, in order to reach the surrounding actin filaments and pull them towards the center of the A band. When the feet
can extend no further, the limit of contraction has been reached.

Another feature of contraction, noted in the figure, is the overlap of
actin filaments which occurs as the muscle contracts below about 30%
of rest length. In some exceptional circumstances, such as thaw-contracture
and cold-shortening, the muscle contracts so far that the myosin filaments
are pulled up against the Z discs and eventually buckle up at this point,
to present an isotropic appearance in polarized light.

In meat science, one of the major preoccupations is what happens to
the structure during the process of rigor mortis. The sliding-filament
model, of Hanson and Huxley, provides an elegant explanation of the
great increase in modulus of elasticity which occurs as rigor is completed.
At this stage there is no longer ATP available to act as a plasticizer and
allow the two sorts of filaments to slide passively over one another, so
that the myosin feet then form firm cross bonds with the actin filaments,
wherever there is overlap. At very high degrees of stretch, beyond about
35%, however, there is almost no overlap of filaments, and no rigor bonds
can be formed until the muscle is released. In this condition, it is soft and
flabby, quite different from the usual rigid structure of meat in rigor.

EXCITATION COUPLING AND THE SARCOPLASMIC RETICULUM

The system which conducts the nervous impulse within the fiber to
set off the contractile explosion is the intricate network of transverse and
longitudinal tubules of the sarcoplasmic reticulum (SR). It is the surrounding longitudinal tubules and vesicles of this system which serve to bind the
constituent actin and myosin filaments of the fibril into a unit, containing
some 500 myosin and 1,000 actin filaments, in its cross section.

It is impossible in this short space to describe the intricacies of the
SR system, but the diagram in Figure 2.2 of a three-dimensional view of
two fibrils, one with SR intact and the other stripped, will help to en-
visage its complexity. Mammalian muscle has been chosen, and here the
transverse elements of the SR occur at the A–I junctions, whereas in
frogs, fish, and reptiles they occur at the Z lines. Note that the longitudinal
elements are here shown in glancing section as tubules arising from the
vesicles of the triads, whereas in fact they themselves are vesicular and
wrap the whole fibril round.

It has recently been shown that the transverse elements of the SR are in
fact tubules arising directly from the plasmalemma on the outside of the
fiber; they form a ring round each fibril, and give off branches to neigh-

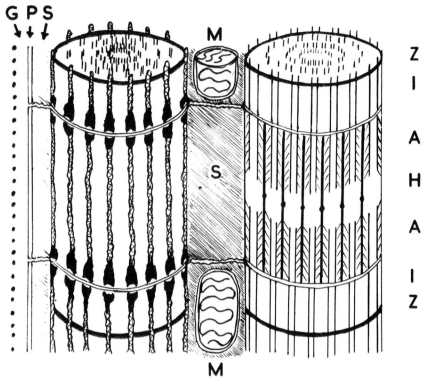

Fig. 2.2. — Two fibrils, to illustrate the sarcotubular system (SR). Only one complete sarcomere is shown in each case (about 2.4 microns from Z line to Z line). Left-hand fibril with SR intact; right-hand fibril partly stripped to show underlying actin and myosin filaments in the outer layers. The transverse elements of the SR can be seen arising from the plasmalemma (*P*). The longitudinal elements are shown as tubules, arising from the large dark vesicles of the triad system, at the A–I boundary. Two mitochondria are shown at the level of Z line. In the outer layers of the fiber proper, there is first ground substance (*G*), then a layer of fine connective tissue, shown as dots. With-in the fiber, sarcoplasmic fluid (*S*) bathes the fibrils.

boring fibrils. The nervous impulse is conducted along these elements in the form of an Na/K depolarization wave or action potential, as in nerve fibers and the plasmalemma itself. When the action potential arrives at the triads of the longitudinal system, however, it sets off a different type of depolarization wave, consisting of the release of Ca^{++} from these tubules. It is when these Ca^{++} arrive, by diffusion, at the active enzyme sites on the myosin feet that the splitting of ATP and the configurational changes in the feet begin, to exert a pulling action on the actin filaments towards the center of the A band. Contraction begins when the Ca^{++} concentration rises above 10^{-7} M.

Even before contraction has been set in motion in this manner, the plasmalemma and the transverse elements of the SR have already become repolarized, by the action of a Na/K pump in the membranes, driven by the energy from the splitting of ATP. As a result the status quo in the longitudinal elements is restored, by reversal of the earlier depolarization, so that the Ca pump in their membranes, also driven by ATP, can begin to pump Ca^{++} back into the tubules. When the Ca^{++} concentration has been reduced in this way below 10^{-7} M, the contractile adenosine triphosphatase activity ceases, and the muscle begins to relax, providing that sufficient ATP is still available, or can be quickly resynthesized at the sites from creatine phosphate (via creatine kinase), to act as a plasticizer.

It was, of course, fragments of the SR system which made up the original relaxing factor of Marsh; these fragments acted as a rather inefficient Ca pump, in the same way as the intact system does in vivo.

THE ENERGY SUPPLY

As we have seen, ATP is used up during the contractile process in three ways: to drive the Na/K pump in the plasmalemma; to drive the Ca pump in the longitudinal elements of the SR; and last, but not least, as the immediate source of contractile energy. The latter is overwhelmingly the most expensive of the three, and probably uses during a single twitch more than 1,000 times the energy needed to reverse the depolarization of the membranes during the passage of one action potential, and at least ten times that needed to drive the Ca pump. Thus very efficient resynthetic mechanisms are required to maintain the energy supply in a working muscle.

In muscles working slowly, the system of oxidative rephosphorylation, sited mainly on the mitochondria (see Fig. 2.2), can work extremely efficiently to maintain the ATP and creatine phosphate supply, but in rapidly contracting muscles, for example during a sprint, the oxygen supply rapidly becomes insufficient, and ATP must then be resynthesized anaerobically via the glycolytic system of soluble enzymes in the sarcoplasm, bathing the fibrils (see Fig. 2.2). The end product of this process is, of course, lactic acid, which itself inhibits further contraction as it accumulates. The limit for contraction probably lies close to pH 6.5.

It is the glycolytic system which is working more or less slowly during the rigor process, driven by one or more adenosine triphosphatases of unknown origin. This slow adenosine triphosphatase activity could arise from the Ca pump which must always be working slowly, even in resting muscle, against the Ca diffusion gradient, or possibly from the cyclic formation and destruction of phosphorylase a, where ATP is used for the rephosphorylation of phosphorylase b. It is unlikely to be due to activity of the contractile adenosine triphosphatase.

ORGANIZATION OF THE FIBRILS WITHIN A FIBER, AND OF FIBERS INTO BUNDLES

The fibrils, which are about 1.0 micron in diameter and number about 2,000 in an average fiber of 50 microns diameter, are bound together within the fiber by the transverse elements of the SR, which serves to keep their striations in register. These elements all make direct or indirect contact with the plasmalemma (Fig. 2.2), which is a double layered membrane, about 100 Å thick, surrounding the fiber and containing phospholipid and protein. Outside this again is a layer of ground substance about 500 Å in thickness, probably made of mucopolysaccharides, and then a thin, spirally disposed layer of so-called reticulin. The latter is stained black by silver stains, unlike collagen proper. In fiber sections it appears to make up most of the endomysial layer (see Fig. 2.3a). It is not certain how this layer is connected to the thicker collagen elements of the perimysium and epimysium.

The fibers themselves are bound into bundles of about 30 or so by the fine collagen fibers of the perimysium, which are about 2 to 3 microns thick (see Fig. 2.3b). Secondary bundles of fibers may also be formed, and those in their turn are finally bound together into a muscle proper by the thicker collagen fibers of the epimysium and of the fascial sheaths. The outermost sheaths of thick collagen connect up and anastomose with the collagen of the tendons of origin and insertion, particularly in fusiform muscles.

Most of the connective tissue in large muscles thus consists of collagen and, to a lesser degree, reticulin, but in exceptional cases, such as the semitendinosus of beef, large amounts of elastin also occur in the epimysial and perimysial layers (about two-thirds the collagen content). Normally, however, the elastin-to-collagen ratio in most of the prime cuts of beef, pork, and lamb is less than 0.1. Thus it would seem that elastin cannot be regarded as a serious contributor to the toughness of meat. On the other hand, insufficient attention has been paid to the possible contribution of reticulin, which, although otherwise similar to collagen, is not easily destroyed by heat. At present, the only known way of estimating the reticulin content of a muscle is by histological methods, which is a serious limiting factor to exact determinations, particularly in large muscles.

NERVE SUPPLY AND VASCULAR SYSTEM

The nerve supply and vascular system run between the bundles of fibers and give off finer branches to each individual fiber. The nerve branch to a fiber may contain both motor and sensory elements, the

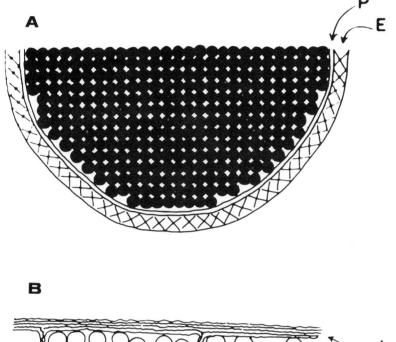

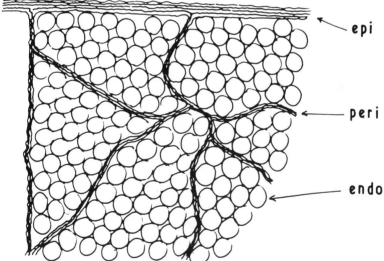

Fig. 2.3. — *A*, cross section of part of a muscle fiber, to show fibrils, plasmalemma proper (*P*), and the connective tissue of the endomysium (*E*). *B*, cross section of a muscle fiber bundle, to show endomysium (*endo*) around the fibers, perimysium (*peri*) around the primary bundles, and a thicker layer of epimysium (*epi*) on the outside.

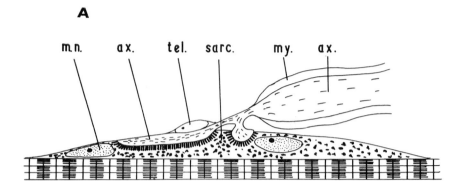

Fig. 2.4. — *A*, motor end-plate in contact with a fiber. The terminal nerve branches lie in synaptic gutters or troughs: *ax.* = axoplasm of the nerve; *my.* = myelin sheath; *tel.* = teloglia; *sarc.* = sarcoplasm with mitochondria; *m.n.* = muscle nuclei (fundamental nuclei). *B*, branching capillary system of a number of fibers. Individual fibers are seen lying in the spaces between capillaries.

latter arising from delicate stretch receptors (not illustrated), and the former terminating in motor end-plates on each fiber (see Fig. 2.4*a*). As the motor nerve-impulse arrives at the brushes on the end-plate, acetyl choline is released, and this triggers off an action potential in both directions along the fiber. As we have seen, this action potential is conducted within the fiber by the transverse elements of the SR. In many fusiform muscles, such as biceps brachii, the motor end-plates are situated in a ring towards the center of the muscle.

The vascular system of the fibers themselves consists of capillaries which intimately enwrap them (see Fig. 2.4b). These originate in arterioles and drain into venules. In many highly vascularized muscles, most of the elastin content is made up of the elastin of the arterioles and smaller arteries.

SUBSTRATES AND ENZYMES INVOLVED IN THE CONTRACTILE PROCESS

To attempt to list all the substrates and enzymes involved in muscle metabolism is quite outside the scope of this synopsis. The interested reader should consult a modern textbook of biochemistry. Here we shall only point out a few of the substrates and enzymes involved in the basic processes.

We note first that the substances directly involved in contraction are actin, myosin, ATP, Mg^{++}, and Ca^{++}, but that the enzyme creatine kinase, and possibly also myokinase, must also be sited fairly close to the contractile filaments, since the breakdown of ATP during a tetanus cannot be detected at all unless these enzymes, particularly the former, are inhibited by fluorodinitrobenzene. ATP is involved in two ways: when Mg^{++} only are present it acts as a plasticizer, allowing the actin and myosin filaments to slip passively past each other, when the muscle is stretched; secondly it acts as the fuel for contraction, when Ca^{++} are released beyond a concentration of 10^{-7}M. Mg^{++} are necessary for contraction, probably again because of their plasticizing effect.

The process of excitation-contraction coupling, as we have said, also involves ATP, first to drive the Na/K pump in the plasmalemma and the transverse elements of the SR, and secondly for the Ca pump in the longitudinal elements. The first of these adenosine triphosphatases is Na/K activated, and the second is Mg/Ca activated.

For the important enzymes and substrates involved in the process of excitation-contraction coupling, we can quote the following approximate values, taken for a typical resting mammalian muscle: myosin 10^{-4} mmoles/g fresh weight; ATP 10^{-2} mmoles/g; ADP, bound on actin, 8×10^{-4} mmoles/g; free creatine 2×10^{-2} mmoles/g; creatine phosphate 2×10^{-2} mmoles/g; Mg^{++}, mostly chelated by ATP, 10^{-2} mmoles/g; Ca^{++}, mostly bound in the SR system, 10^{-3} mmoles/g; K^+, inside the fiber, 12×10^{-2} mmoles/g; glycogen, as glucose, 3 to 8×10^{-2} mmoles/g.

Excluding the systems mentioned above, almost all the other enzymes and their substrates are involved in the supply of energy: in the mitochondria, for instance, cytochrome c, succinic dehydrogenase, and other enzymes of the Krebs cycle; in the sarcoplasm, the thirty or so enzymes of glycolysis, and traces of their substrates, except of course when lactic acid is accumulating; within the SR system, glycogen granules; beneath the plasmalemma, but probably close to it, myoglobin for transfer of oxygen to the mitochondria, and so on. The list is endless, and the complexity overwhelming, until we consider it in relation to the needs of the contractile machine, whether in its living state or on its way towards death, during the process of rigor mortis.

PART I

Muscle Development and Metabolic Processes

Chapter 3

General Consideration of Muscle Development

E. HELANDER

Muscle development may be defined as the changes which take place in the constitution, volume, and structure of skeletal muscle in normal and pathological states. Hypertrophy and hypotrophy (atrophy) are the two main types of development which we recognize.

The literature on changes observed in muscle development is vast, and the following factors must be given consideration: (1) age, (2) degree of activity, i.e., exercise and disuse, (3) hormonal state, (4) metabolic state, and (5) diseases in muscles and nervous system.

I will confine this paper to the influence on muscle development of age and muscle activity, because hormonal regulation, metabolic stresses, and disease syndromes will be discussed in detail in other chapters.

Muscle development has been studied by scientists of widely diverse disciplines. For example, the physician, working with patients with diseases affecting skeletal muscles, or exercising patients in physical medicine and rehabilitation, is intimately aware of the problems involved in muscle development. On the other hand, athletes are aware of muscle development with the aim of achieving the highest physical fitness. For food scientists, muscle development is studied in respect to producing muscle as a food.

The main constituents of skeletal muscle, shown in Table 3.1, should

TABLE 3.1
Main constituents of skeletal muscle

Water		76%	Fat		1%
Proteins		20	Glycogen		1
Myofilaments	11%		Salts (creatine, sodium,		
Sarcoplasm	6		phosphates, potassium,		
Connective tissue	3		chlorides, etc.)		2

Source: E. Helander, "On quantitative muscle protein determination," *Acta Physiol. Scand. 41(1957, suppl.):*141.

be reviewed at this point. While the figures in the table represent the average composition of skeletal muscle, the actual amounts of the constituents may vary a great deal.

AGE AND MUSCLE DEVELOPMENT

Certain age periods seem to be easily discernible in the life span of a human being or an animal: the fetal period, infancy and adolescence, maturity, and senescence. But it is far from easy to tell when the adult stage is reached or to determine specifically when old age begins. It is also very difficult to compare animals with humans, and it is not easy to distinguish normal from pathological aging. Age in some people is accompanied by good health and high muscular activity, and such people may be difficult to compare with more "normal" people. Accordingly, one should very carefully consider the following points concerning muscle changes with age.

Morphological changes

During the fetal period the amount of skeletal muscle per kilo of total body weight is rather small (Cowdry, ed. Lansing, 1952). This amount rises soon after birth and remains fairly constant after adolescence. Some authors have reported that during senescence the muscle volume remains of the same order (Frantzell and Ingelmark, 1951). Other authors maintain that during senescence all organs diminish in size, but the skeletal muscles proportionately more than other tissues (Binet and Bourlière, 1955; Korenchevsky, 1961). This has been confirmed by studies of the urinary creatinine excretion and of the total body potassium content, both of which fall with age (Garn and Harper, 1955; Allen, Anderson, and Langham, 1960; Norris, Lundy, and Shock, 1963). As these values are well correlated with the amount of skeletal muscle, the latter obviously decreases in senescent man. Tables 3.2 and 3.3 show the effects of age on some muscle characteristics of animals.

Although no major volume changes occur during maturity before senescence, microscopic changes are evident. All muscle cells are formed in the early fetal period. During infancy cells appear fairly uniform and have a comparatively small diameter, but later they increase in size, and thus the connective tissue appears to decrease, relatively, soon after birth (Yannet and Darrow, 1938). The muscles gain strength when used and their intracellular content increases. In senescence the fiber volume increases even more, but the number decreases (Bucciante and Luria, 1934). Thus skeletal muscle in old age contains a decreased number of cells, which are larger than those of the adult phase. This change might reflect partial atrophy, where some muscle fibers have disappeared and the re-

TABLE 3.2

Effect of age on skeletal muscle

Rats[a]			Chickens[b]		
No. animals in test	Age in days	Muscle fibers g/kg tissue	No. animals in test	Age in days	Muscle fibers g/kg tissue
20	15	688	10	3	600
23	30	818	10	7	767
22	60	861	10	28	867
16	90	883	10	124	884
15	120	879	8	270–427	926
13	180	885	5	566–1825	944
13	336	885			

[a] *Source*: H. M. Hines and G. C. Knowlton, "Effect of age upon the cellular phases of skeletal muscle," *Proc. Soc. Exp. Biol. Med. 42(1939)*:133.

[b] *Source*: J. S. Barlow, J. S. Slinger, and J. F. Manery, "The effect of age on the concentration of chloride and water in chick tissues," *J. Gerontol. 2(1947)*:110.

TABLE 3.3

Relative proportion and water content of skeletal muscle fibers in albino rats at different ages

No. of animals	Age in days	Proportion of muscle fibers	Water content %
23	3	389	88.5
32	12	707	79.9
19	18	797	77.5
52	23–33	805	77.3
35	38–48	797	77.5
37	55–90	856	75.9
205	112–630	875	75.4
16	689	875	75.4
10	768	881	75.2

Source: S. M. Horvath, "The influence of the aging process on the distribution of certain components of the blood and the gastrocnemius muscle of the albino rat," *J. Gerontol. 1(1946)*:213.

maining are hypertrophic. It has not been established that this is the reason for the increased diameter of the muscle cells occurring with rising age, but it is interesting in this connection that the number of myelinated spinal root fibers decreases with age (Corbin and Gardner, 1937; Gardner, 1940). This might signify that the primary cause of the microscopic change is combined with degeneration of nerve fibers resulting in atrophy and disappearance of some motor units and compensatory hypertrophy of those remaining.

Biochemical changes

Table 3.3 shows that in albino rats tested the water content decreased during early life, then remained unchanged from the 55th to the 768th day. This finding was also established by an earlier study (Murray, 1926). It has been shown that during the fetal period and immediately after birth the water content is some 5%–10% higher than in the adult. But it is well known that the water content in man is somewhat lower in old age than at more youthful stages (Norris *et al.*, 1963).

Age is accompanied by changes in the protein composition of skeletal muscles (Helander, 1957), as shown in Table 3.4. In the fetal period the muscles are richer in connective tissue and contain less sarcoplasmic

TABLE 3.4
Protein composition of skeletal muscle from cattle and rats

Age	Nitrogen components in mg N/g muscle tissue			
	Myofilamental protein	Sarcoplasmic protein	Stroma protein	Non-protein
Cattle				
(7 months)	8.2	7.8	10.0	2.0
7 days	15.5	7.2	4.5	2.8
18 months	18.2	7.9	3.4	3.4
11 years	16.2	9.3	3.9	3.4
Rats				
90–120 days	16.3	6.9	6.8	3.0
750–780 days	15.9	7.0	7.1	3.2

and myofilamental proteins. Soon after birth both the sarcoplasmic and myofilamental protein contents rise, especially the latter. This is due to the general muscular development after birth. The activity of skeletal muscles is very restricted during intrauterine life, and this is comparable to what is seen in adult muscles in which activity has been restricted, as for example with a plaster cast (Helander, 1957). The connective tissue decrease after birth is only relative (Yannet and Darrow, 1938). During adult life up to senescence very few changes are seen in the protein composition of skeletal muscles, provided muscular activity has been reasonably constant (Table 3.5). A small increase in connective tissue protein content is seen in old age and is accompanied by decrease of the myofilamental and sarcoplasmic proteins.

It is well known that the concentrations of K, Mg, and P decrease with age and that the concentrations of Na, Cl, and Ca increase (Horvath, 1945, 1946; Garn and Harper, 1955; Allen *et al.*, 1960; Norris *et al.*, 1963; Iob

TABLE 3.5
Changes in rat skeletal muscle with age

Age in days	H$_2$O g	Collagen + elastin g	Cl mEq	Acid-soluble P mM	Na mEq	K mEq
60	779	12	16	61	...	118
603	761	13	13	60	21	110
988	790	14	23	50	32	99

and Swanson, 1934). This suggests that the extracellular space has increased and the intracellular volume decreased. However, the amounts of elastin and collagen increase only slightly with age (see Table 3.5; also Cowdry, ed. Lansing, 1952).

In humans the amount of fat increases with age (Helander, 1959). This increase is most evident in the calf muscles (Table 3.6). The fat is almost wholly deposited around the intramuscular capillaries, and it tends to

TABLE 3.6
Mean percentage of fat in dry substance of skeletal muscles from humans

Age group	No. of analyses	Mean % of fat in dry substance	
		Gastrocnemius	Biceps brachii
0–9 yrs.	9	10.2	7.4
10–19	8	13.1	6.0
20–29	32	14.9	8.2
30–39	37	21.4	10.8
40–49	20	17.7	7.6
50–59	22	24.6	8.9
60–69	45	28.8	9.6
70–79	36	35.5	13.6
80–89	14	37.6	16.5
90–99	4	23.4	11.1

be more abundant in women. In animals such an increase of intramuscular fat is not found.

MUSCLE DEVELOPMENT IN RELATION TO ACTIVITY

Muscle activity will be considered here at three stages of intensity, i.e., during exercise, during "normal activity," and during disuse.

Of course it is very difficult to tell what "normal activity" is. In man the usual range is very wide; a normal man at leisure might walk only a few hundred feet a day, while another man, under other circumstances, might walk many miles in a day. In animals the difference between wild and laboratory animals is immense, so that any comparison is most difficult.

One should really compare only results from similar, uniform series in which functional conditions have been similarly changed. All experiments must be designed very carefully to exclude uncontrollable factors.

Morphological changes

It is well known that activity increases the total volume of muscles and inactivity leads to hypotrophy (Helander, 1957; Siebert, 1928). After exercise the capillary vascularization of muscles increases abundantly (Petrén, Sjöstrand, and Sylvén, 1936) and the muscle cells grow (Knipping and Vallentin, 1961). After disuse the number of capillaries is reduced and the fiber diameter is diminished. A small amount of fat may be seen in skeletal muscles in disuse atrophy (Helander, 1959).

Biochemical changes

Changes in the water and fat content occur in disuse atrophy (Helander, 1959), but are not found following exercise (Helander, 1961). The increased fat content with disuse is probably only relative; the absolute amount of fat per muscle is not altered.

To study the protein composition the following experiment was performed (Helander, 1958, 1961): 48 guinea pigs of uniform weight and age were divided into three groups of 16. The first group, comprising controls, were confined in a big cage. Group 2, the exercised animals, were kept in a similar cage, but were exercised every day. They ran 1,000 m a day, Monday through Saturday, on an endless belt, moving as fast as they could manage. The number of exercise days for each animal ranged from 95 to 105, with an average of 100. Group 3 comprised animals with restricted activity. They were kept in groups of three in cages which were just large enough for the animals and their food. After four months the animals were sacrificed, the calf muscles excised, and protein determinations performed. The results (Table 3.7) showed a minor, but significant,

TABLE 3.7
Results of exercise and disuse experiment in guinea pigs (16 animals in each test group)

Analysis	Control group	Exercised group	Restricted activity group
Body wt., g	980 ± 25	980 ± 17	980 ± 18
Combined wt., both calf muscles, g	6.33 ± 0.20	6.53 ± 0.19	6.06 ± 0.17
Water content, %	76.7 ± 0.25	75.2 ± 0.21	76.2 ± 0.22
Protein, mg/g wet tissue			
Myofilamental	15.0 ± 0.34	17.2 ± 0.30	15.0 ± 0.42
Sarcoplasmic	7.2 ± 0.25	7.1 ± 0.25	6.9 ± 0.30
Stroma	3.5 ± 0.43	2.7 ± 0.47	3.0 ± 0.89

increase of the myofilamental protein content of the calf muscles of the exercised animals compared to the controls and the inactive. No changes could be detected in the inactive animals, probably because the restriction of their activity was insufficient to change the protein composition.

Two other experiments were designed to study the effect of restricted activity. In the first, 17 rabbits each had one hind leg immobilized in a plaster cast (Helander, 1957). After 20 days the plaster was removed, the animal sacrificed, and the calf muscles of both legs were dissected, weighed, and extracted for muscle proteins. The results are shown in Table 3.8.

TABLE 3.8
Nitrogen yield from normal and immobilized muscles of the same rabbit (given as mg/g muscle tissue)

Nitrogen	Normal muscle	Immobilized muscle	Deviations immobilized in % normal
TOTAL	32.4 ± 0.35	30.4 ± 0.55	94 ± 1.3
Myofibril	18.7 ± 0.32	14.9 ± 0.52	79 ± 2.7
Sarcoplasm	7.9 ± 0.25	8.9 ± 0.28	115 ± 2.9
Nonprotein	3.3 ± 0.02	3.6 ± 0.04	110 ± 1.2
Stroma	2.7 ± 0.06	3.3 ± 0.10	122 ± 4.1
Dry weight %	23.7 ± 0.19	24.6 ± 0.20	

This experiment caused a selective decrease of the myofilamental proteins. The sarcoplasmic and stroma proteins appear to have increased, but considering the approximate 20% atrophy, the increased values appear to be only relative. The second of the inactivity experiments (Helander, 1961) comprised 25 rabbits, 16 of which were controls and 9 of which were kept in very small cages in order to restrict their activity. As the guinea pig experiment had proved insufficient, the duration of the rabbit experiment was prolonged, to six months for five of the animals, and to three years for four of them. No significant conclusions can be drawn from the experiment, but nonetheless interesting figures appeared (Table 3.9). It will be seen that a partial reconstitution of the muscle cells had occurred. The amount of sarcoplasmic proteins had increased and that of myofilamental proteins diminished. No atrophy was apparent; the amount of stroma had not changed.

It is consequently apparent that the protein composition of a muscle varies considerably. The amount of contractile protein increases after exercise and decreases with reduced activity. If the decreased activity sets in very rapidly and is severe, muscle atrophy ensues, selectively affecting the myofilaments. But if the reduction in activity is more gradual, there is no pronounced atrophy; sarcoplasm simply replaces myofilaments.

TABLE 3.9
Protein composition of thigh muscles from rabbits after various physical activity

Animal no.	Total nitrogen (mg/g of muscle tissue)	Nitrogen components (% of total N)			
		Myofilamental	Sarcoplasmic	Stroma	Nonprotein
Group 1: controls, killed at beginning of experiment					
1	32.8	59	26	5	10
2	32.1	58	25	7	10
3	34.0	60	24	6	10
4	32.6	62	23	6	10
5	31.8	57	27	7	10
6	33.1	56	27	6	11
7	32.9	61	23	6	10
8	32.4	60	24	6	11
9	32.7	59	24	6	11
10	33.4	62	22	7	9
Mean	32.8	59	25	6	10
Group 2: controls, kept six months without restriction of activity					
11	32.4	61	22	7	11
12	34.0	59	23	7	11
13	32.6	57	25	5	12
14	33.5	59	24	7	10
15	31.1	58	27	6	9
16	33.3	56	26	6	11
Mean	33.6	58	25	6	11
Group 3: kept six months in very small cages, to restrict activity					
17	33.4	52	31	6	11
18	32.9	52	33	4	10
19	34.1	51	33	6	10
20	32.0	49	34	6	11
21	32.8	53	31	7	10
Mean	33.0	51	32	6	10
Group 4: kept three years in same type of cages as Group 3					
22	34.3	40	44	6	11
23	35.2	39	44	6	11
24	32.6	44	41	5	10
25	34.2	41	43	6	10
Mean	34.1	41	43	6	10

SUMMARY

The skeletal muscle tissue responds in two ways to changes in functional activity. First, exercise is accompanied by hypertrophy and inactivity by hypotrophy. Second, the amount of contractile substance in the muscle cell changes, rising with exercise and diminishing with restricted activity. Apparently either of these processes can take place independently, but probably they are most often combined. That the number of myofilaments increases in hypertrophy has been confirmed recently by other authors using electron microscopy of heart muscles. In sectioned material, the number of myofilaments in each myofibril appeared to have increased and also new myofilaments might have been formed (Richter and Kellner, 1963). Both these processes exert a modifying influence on the contractile strength of the muscle. Textbooks describe this strength as directly proportional to the effective cross-sectional area of the muscle. But since the amount of contractile substance may vary from one cell to another it is evidently more correct to use the effective cross-sectional myofilamental area as the basis for calculation of the contractile strength. Experiments have also confirmed that there is a close relationship both in vivo (Helander and Thulin, 1962) and in vitro (Helander, 1962) between the myofilamental area and the isometric strength of a muscle. In such experiments the contractile power exerted by a single myofilament could also be measured: 1.6×10^{-6} dyne (Helander, 1962).

In this connection the question arises, How much can a single muscle cell be exercised and still go on hypertrophying? What limits the development of muscle fibers? Here several interesting facts may be discussed. For instance, the number of capillaries in the skeletal muscle tissue is probably limited. By exercise, closed capillaries may be opened, but probably no new ones are formed. Several authors are inclined to believe that all capillaries are formed during the early fetal life in accordance with the genetic information (Katz, 1954). Another fact is that an overly large muscle cell probably will have transport congestion like a modern metropolis: oxygen and glucose may not have sufficient time to diffuse through to the middle of the cell, and metabolic waste may not escape. During heavy contraction, the muscle cell is wholly secluded from its blood supply. Storage room in the cell may play a role here. Furthermore the muscle cells might, like all other cells, be limited in growth by genetic information.

In muscle development another important fact is that once atrophied, a muscle cell will not be recreated. The muscle as a whole can regain its strength only if the remaining muscle cells hypertrophy to such an extent that the myofilamental area is restored. This fact is important in medical rehabilitation (De Lorme, 1945; Bonde-Petersen, 1962).

In food science, recent as well as earlier investigations have shown that meat containing too much connective tissue and too many myofibrils is tough (Hill and O'Carroll, 1963; Hill, 1963). Thus exercise of a meat animal should be avoided. But too severe restriction of its activity should also be avoided, because then atrophy might supervene and increase the amount of connective tissue. The animals should not be kept after adolescence, because no further improvement in the amount of muscle tissue can be expected. The fibers will get thicker and tougher, and at advancing age atrophy will increase.

References

Allen, F. H., E. C. Anderson, and W. H. Langham. 1960. Total body potassium and gross body composition in relation to age. *J. Gerontol.* 15:348.

Barlow, J. S., J. S. Slinger, and J. F. Manery. 1947. The effect of age on the concentration of chloride and water in chick tissues. *J. Gerontol.* 2:110.

Binet, L., and F. Bourlière. 1955 *Précis de Gérontologie.* Masson & Cie, Paris.

Bonde-Petersen, F. 1962. *Commun. Test. Observ. Inst. Danish Nat. Ass. Infant. Paral.* 12:1.

Bucciante, L., and S. Luria. 1934. Transformasion nello struttura del muscoli ulentau dell' uomo nella senescenoza. *Arch. Ital. Anat. Embriol.* 33:110.

Corbin, K. B., and E. D. Gardner. 1937. Decrease in number of myelinated fibers in human spinal roots with age. *Anat. Rec.* 68:63.

Cowdry, E. V. 1952. *Problems of Aging: Biochemical and Medical Aspects* (3d ed., A. J. Lansing, ed.). Williams & Wilkins Co., Baltimore.

De Lorme, T. L. 1945. Restoration of muscle power by heavy resistance exercises. *J. Bone Joint Surg.* 27:645.

Frantzell, A., and B. E. Ingelmark. 1951.. Occurrence and distribution of fat in human muscles at various age levels: morphologic and roentgenologic investigation. *Upsala läkaref. förh.* 56:59.

Gardner, E. D. 1940. Decrease in human neurones with age. *Anat. Rec.* 77:529.

Garn, S. M., and R. V. Harper. 1955. Fat accumulation and weight gain in adult male. *Human Biol.* 27:39.

Helander, E. 1957. On quantitative muscle protein determination. *Acta Physiol. Scand.* 41(suppl.):141.

———. 1958. Adaptive muscular allomorphism. *Nature 182*:1035.

———. 1959. Fat content of skeletal muscle tissue. *Acta Morphol. Neerlando-Scandinavica* 2:230.

———. 1960. Muscular atrophy and lipomorphosis induced by immobilizing plaster casts. *Acta Morphol. Neerlando-Scandinavica* 3:92.

———. 1961. Influence of exercise and restricted activity on the protein composition of skeletal muscle. *Biochem. J.* 78:478.

———. 1962. Adenosine triphosphate induced isometric tension in glycerol-extracted muscle fibers in relation to the cross-sectional area of their myofilaments. *Biochim. Biophys. Acta 60:*265.

Helander, E., and C. A. Thulin. 1962. Isometric tension and myofilamental cross-sectional area of striated muscle. *Amer. J. Physiol. 202:*824.

Hill, F. 1963. Fibre composition of tough and tender muscles of meat animals. *Irish J. Agr. Res. 1:*319.

Hill, F., and F. M. O'Carroll. 1963. A comparison of the mincer and chew count methods of measuring meat toughness in relation to the evaluation of material from a feeding trial. *Irish J. Agr. Res. 1:*307.

Hines, H. M., and G. C. Knowlton. 1939. Effect of age upon the cellular phases of skeletal muscle. *Proc. Soc. Exp. Biol. Med. 42:*133.

Horvath, S. M. 1945. The distribution of phosphorus compounds in the gastrocnemius muscle as influenced by the aging process. *Amer. J. Physiol. 145:*77.

————. 1946. The influence of the aging process on the distribution of certain components of the blood and the gastrocnemius muscle of the albino rat. *J. Gerontol. 1:*213.

Iob, V., and W. W. Swanson. 1934. Mineral growth of the human fetus. *Amer. J. Dis. Child. 47:*302.

Katz, L. 1954. The mechanism of cardiac failure. *Circulation 10:*663.

Knipping, H. W., and H. Vallentin. 1961. Sports in medicine, p. 354. *In* S. H. Licht and E. W. Johnson (eds.), *Therapeutic Exercise.* Waverly Press, Baltimore.

Korenchevsky, V. 1961. *Physiological and Pathological Aging* (G. H. Bourne, ed.). S. Karger Publ. Co., New York.

Murray, H. A. 1926. Physiological ontogeny. A. Chicken embryos. XI. The pH, chloride, carbonic acid and protein concentrations in the tissues as functions of age. *J. Gen. Physiol. 9:*789.

Norris, A. H., T. Lundy, and N. W. Shock. 1963. Trends in selected indices of body composition in man between the ages of 30 and 80 years. *Ann. N.Y. Acad. Sci. 110:*623.

Petrén, T., T. Sjöstrand, and B. Sylvén. 1936. Der Einfluss des Trainings auf die Häufigkeit der Capillaren in Herz- und Skelettmuskulatur. *Arbeitsphysiologie 9:*376.

Richter, G. W., and A. Kellner. 1963. Hypertrophy of the human heart at the level of fine structure (an analysis and two postulates). *J. Cell Biol. 18:*195.

Siebert, W. W. 1928. Untersuchungen über Hypertrophie des Skelettmuskels. *Z. Klin. Med. 109:*350.

Yannet, H., and D. C. Darrow. 1938. The effect of growth on the distribution of water and electrolytes in brain, liver and muscle. *J. Biol. Chem. 123:*295.

Chapter 4

Regulation of Energy-Yielding Processes in Muscle

H. A. LARDY

Muscle is a highly specialized tissue, and its metabolic processes are accordingly less complex than those of liver, for example. Muscle has lost many of the synthetic processes that occur in less highly differentiated tissues. Liver has retained them and acquired exquisite control mechanisms for regulating the rate of these syntheses in accordance with cell needs. Control mechanisms exist also for regulating rates of metabolic processes that yield energy to cells. In this chapter I propose to review some of these mechanisms and to contrast them with the control processes involved in regulating biosynthetic reactions. Possible implications of these control phenomena for the production of high quality meats will be obvious to anyone familiar with the influence of postmortem glycolytic rates on protein denaturation and water retention, which culminate in problems like "pale, soft, exudative pork."

Presently, we know in considerable detail the pathways by which carbon chains of glucose, fatty acids, and other energy sources are rearranged and combusted so as to yield energy to all living cells. But we know very little about the actual mechanism of the energy capture in oxidative metabolism, or the mechanism by which chemical energy is transduced to muscular work. These limitations will restrict the scope of my presentation to consideration of glycolysis and substrate oxidation by mitochondria.

The rates of cellular metabolic processes are governed, like all chemical reactions, by concentrations of substrates and cofactors, by accumulation of end products, by pH, temperature, ionic strength, and obviously by the concentrations of catalysts — the various enzymes. In living cells, however, many of these parameters are fixed within relatively narrow limits, and the striking variations that occur in rates of metabolism must be the result of a more facile regulation.

One of the best-known types of enzyme regulation is that of feedback

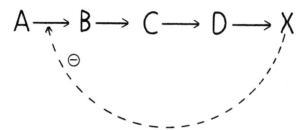

Fig. 4.1. — Feedback inhibition. The arrows indicate enzyme-catalyzed reactions. Feedback control is designated by
the segmented arrow, and a negative influence is indicated.

from end product to the first step in a biosynthetic pathway. I shall call
this the Yates-Pardee (1956) type of control, after the discoverers of this
phenomenon. In the sequence shown in Figure 4.1, a metabolite A is
converted by a sequence of reactions to B, C, D, and, eventually, X. For
many biosynthetic reactions, the end product X is an inhibitor of the
reaction $A \rightarrow B$. In most cases X also inhibits the *formation* of the enzyme that catalyzes $A \rightarrow B$. When $A \rightarrow B$ is a reaction common to the biosynthesis of several different cellular building blocks, X is frequently
found to inhibit the enzyme that catalyzes $B \rightarrow C$, i.e., the first step in the
pathway unique for its own biosynthesis.

Why has evolution selected this type of control mechanism for survival?
Undoubtedly, because it is the most economical for the cell. If X is an
amino acid, for example, and the reactions leading to the synthesis of
B, C, and D were not controlled, there would probably be an accumulation
of these intermediates with considerable wastage of energy going into
their formation and possibly with interference in many other reactions of
the cell. Imposition of control at any position other than the first unique
step for the biosynthesis of compound X would merely diminish the waste
but not eliminate it completely. Hence, the control mechanism that survived is the most efficient one, and X is synthesized only as rapidly as it is
needed by the cell. If it is not used in the synthesis of new protoplasm it
efficiently shuts off the formation of all the intermediates as well as of
itself. When X is used up or is lost from the cell, the biosynthetic process
starts up and the intermediates must accumulate to steady-state concentrations before X is produced at a reasonable rate.

Such a control mechanism would not be suitable as a means of regulating energy production by the cell. For example, let us consider the
conversion of glucose to lactic acid (Fig. 4.2) for the purpose of generating
ATP. If the cell employed only Yates-Pardee control of this process, the
end product, ATP, would inhibit hexokinase and the nine intermediate

Fig. 4.2. — Regulation of glycolysis by metabolites. Enzyme-catalyzed reactions are indicated by arrows. The broken lines designate regulatory influences: + indicates enhancement of rate; — indicates inhibition.

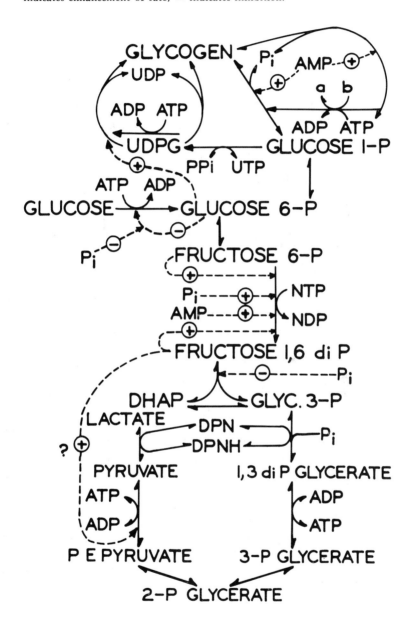

metabolites would diminish in concentration. When ATP concentrations diminish sufficiently as a result of its use, and the cell needs energy again, glucose would be phosphorylated, but before all the intermediates could be built up to their normal steady-state levels, ATP supplies would probably be depleted and the cell placed in jeopardy.

Considerations of this type have led Professor Theodore Bücher of Munich to postulate that energy-yielding systems must be regulated by multiple controls to keep the cell in a state of "physiological readiness." This is beautifully borne out by considering the regulation of glycolysis in muscle (Fig. 4.2). Glucose, inorganic phosphate, and ADP are the starting materials, and lactic acid and ATP are the end products. The question is, What shuts down glycolysis when ATP is not required by muscle? And what initiates the process as soon as some work has been accomplished?

Both inorganic phosphate and ADP have been implicated as regulators of glycolytic rates by virtue of the fact that they are essential metabolites (Lynen, 1942; Johnson, 1941); of these, inorganic phosphate is the first detectable end product of contraction, and is produced in relatively large, amounts (Cain and Davies, 1962). Triose phosphate cannot be oxidized without a stoichiometric supply of inorganic phosphate, nor can glycogen be phosphorylized to glucose 1-phosphate. In some cells, rates of glycolysis are limited by availability of inorganic phosphate for triose phosphate dehydrogenase (Wu and Racker, 1959). A single twitch of muscle produces enough inorganic phosphate (5×10^{-4} M) to enhance the rate of these reactions significantly.

In addition to this stoichiometric function, inorganic phosphate facilitates glycolysis by exerting a regulating influence on some other reactions as well, in keeping with the Bücher concept of "physiological readiness."

The rate of glucose phosphorylation in many animal cells is controlled by the concentration of glucose 6-phosphate, which is a powerful inhibitor of hexokinase. Rose, Warms, and O'Connell (1964) found that in erythrocytes, inorganic phosphate has no effect on hexokinase in the absence of glucose 6-phosphate but overcomes the inhibition of this enzyme by glucose 6-phosphate. If this release of inhibition applies also to muscle hexokinase, it might provide a means of initiating and continuing the phosphorylation of glucose in the presence of a normal steady-state concentration of glucose 6-phosphate. However, at least in resting muscle, the regulation of glucose penetration may be a more important control mechanism than the rate of phosphorylation. It has not yet been established that inorganic phosphate influences permeability of intact cells as it does of isolated mitochondria.

Inorganic phosphate is also known to exert an allosteric activating effect on phosphofructokinase. Whether this is of physiological significance is not known. Recently, Rose (1965) has found that inorganic phosphate increases the K_m of aldolase for hexose diphosphate. This would cause glycolysis to proceed with a higher steady-state concentration of fructose diphosphate, and Rose has postulated that this would accelerate phosphofructokinase, for this enzyme was shown by Morrison, in 1961, to be activated by its product (Lardy, 1961). The increased steady-state concentration of fructose diphosphate could activate glycolysis at still another site. Hess (1965) has found that fructose diphosphate activates pyruvate kinase in yeast. In Hess's terminology, this is "feed-forward" control. While it is mediated by fructose diphosphate, it may be initiated by an increase of inorganic phosphate through the influence of the latter on the steady-state concentration of fructose diphosphate.

Thus, inorganic phosphate will enhance the rate of glycolysis by acting as a substrate at two sites, and if muscle enzymes are found to respond like those in certain other cells, it may exert a stimulatory influence at hexokinase, phosphofructokinase, and pyruvate kinase as well. Clearly it is important that the corresponding enzymes from muscle be examined for their possible susceptibility to these regulatory influences.

Slaughter methods which might diminish P_i liberation in muscle postmortem would surely have a beneficial effect in retarding glycolytic rate.

Adenosine diphosphate enhances glycolysis because it is an acceptor of phosphoryl groups from 1,3-diphosphoglycerate and from phosphoenolpyruvate (*PE Pyruvate* in Fig. 4.2).

A third factor of significance for regulating rates of glycolysis is the concentration of adenylic acid. This nucleotide is an allosteric activator of both forms of phosphorylase, a and b; it causes a decrease in the Michaelis constants for both inorganic phosphate and glycogen, thus permitting greater rates of glucose 1-phosphate formation when substrates are limiting (Helmreich and Cori, 1964). Adenylic acid is also an activator of phosphofructokinase under some conditions (Passoneau and Lowry, 1962).

A question of crucial importance is, How early in the process of steady muscular work does adenylic acid increase significantly?

We know from the work of Fleckenstein *et al.* (1954) and from Mommaerts (1954) that a single twitch of muscle releases no detectable ADP or AMP. Continued contractions do cause ADP production. But, assuming that ATP is the source of the inorganic phosphate liberated, the amount of ADP accumulating is far less than stoichiometric (Chance, Mauriello, and Aubert, 1962), indicating an extremely rapid removal by rephosphorylation. In addition to the glycolytic system, two other systems compete for ADP to rephosphorylate it — creatine kinase-phosphocreatine and oxidative phosphorylation. Despite the fact that the Michaelis constant for

ADP of the former system (Kuby, Noda, and Lardy, 1954*b*) is 40 times greater than that of oxidative phosphorylation, the high concentration of phosphocreatine and the great abundance and proximity of creatine kinase (Kuby *et al.*, 1954*a*) in muscle permit this system to rephosphorylate ADP so rapidly that only a small fraction of that released becomes available to the oxidative phosphorylation system of mitochondria.

Before leaving the subject of glycolytic reactions, there is one more type of control that may be of some practical interest. Citrate is known to be an inhibitor of phosphofructokinase (Parmeggiani and Bowman, 1963; Garland, Randle, and Newsholme, 1963; Passonneau and Lowry, 1963), which is a rate-limiting enzyme in glycolysis. I think it would be worth while to attempt perfusion of slaughter animals with citrate to determine whether it would retard the rate of postmortem glycolysis.

The aerobic metabolism of muscle is also closely regulated by the concentration of inorganic phosphate and ADP (Lardy, 1956). Asmussen, Christian, and Nielsen (1939) demonstrated that in man the resting leg muscles increase their oxygen consumption as much as seventyfold when caused to perform heavy work. An in vitro counterpart of this phenomenon is demonstrable with mitochondria isolated from muscle, liver, kidney, and other tissues (Lardy and Wellman, 1952; Lardy, 1956; Chance and Williams, 1956). There are, very likely, additional regulatory influences of inorganic phosphate and various nucleotides on respiratory rates of mitochondria. However, since only one enzyme of the oxidative phosphorylation machinery has been purified, we know very little about the more subtle types of regulation of phosphorylation and substrate oxidation rates.

From the practical point of view it is unlikely that the oxidative reactions can be manipulated usefully for the improvement of meat quality, for muscle masses become anaerobic very shortly after blood circulation stops.

It seems likely that the glycolytic system offers much better possibilities of alteration in an effort to improve meat quality. The combined efforts of pharmacologists, enzymologists, and physiologists should be able to manipulate the glycolytic pathway to suit whatever needs exist. They should be able to study the problems and to come up with practices which might aid the meat industry.

References

Asmussen, E., E. H. Christian, and M. Nielsen. 1939. Die O_2-Aufname der Ruhenden und der Arbeitenden Skelettmuskeln. *Skand. Arch. Physiol.* 82:212.

Cain, D. F., and R. E. Davies. 1962. Chemical events and contractile activity, p. 84.

In K. Rodahl and S. Horvath (eds.), *Muscle as a Tissue*. McGraw-Hill Book Co., New York.

Chance, B., G. Mauriello, and X. M. Aubert. 1962. ADP arrival at muscle mitochondria following a twitch, p. 128. *In* K. Rodahl and S. Horvath (eds.), *Muscle as a Tissue*. McGraw-Hill Book Co., New York.

Chance, B., and G. R. Williams. 1956. The respiratory chain and oxidative phosphorylation. *Advance. Enzymol. 17:*65.

Fleckenstein, A., J. Janke, R. E. Davies, and H. A. Krebs. 1954. Chemistry of muscle contraction: contraction of muscle without fission of adenosine triphosphate or creatine phosphate. *Nature 174:*1081.

Garland, P. B., P. J. Randle, and E. A. Newsholme. 1963. Citrate as an intermediary in the inhibition of phosphofructokinase in rat heart muscle by fatty acids, ketone bodies, pyruvate, diabetes and starvation. *Nature 200:*169.

Helmreich, E., and C. F. Cori. 1964. The role of adenylic acid in the activation of phosphorylase. *Proc. Nat. Acad. Sci. 51:*131.

Hess, B. 1965. *In* B. Chance (ed.), *A Symposium on Control of Energy Metabolism*. Academic Press, New York. (In press.)

Johnson, M. J. 1941. The role of aerobic phosphorylation in the pasteur effect. *Science 94:*200.

Kuby, S. A., L. Noda, and H. A. Lardy. 1954*a*. Adenosinetriphosphate-creatine transphosphorylase. I. Isolation of the crystalline enzyme from rabbit muscle. *J. Biol. Chem. 209:*191.

————. 1954*b*. Adenosinetriphosphate-creatine transphosphorylase. III. Kinetic studies. *J. Biol. Chem. 210:*65.

Lardy, H. A. 1956. Energetic coupling and the regulation of metabolic rates, p. 287. *Proc. 3d Int. Congr. Biochem.* (Brussels, 1955). Academic Press, New York.

————. 1962. In *Welch Foundation Conference on Chemical Research* (1961), 5:267.

Lardy, H. A., and H. Wellman. 1952. Oxidative phosphorylations: Role of inorganic phosphate and acceptor systems in control of metabolic rates. *J. Biol. Chem. 195:*215.

Lynen, F. 1942. Die Rolle der Phosphorsäure bei Dehydrierungsvorgärgen und ihre Biologische Bedeutung. *Naturwissenschaften 30:*398.

Mommaerts, W. H. F. M. 1954. Is adenosine broken down during a single muscle twitch? *Nature 174:*1083.

Parmeggiani, A., and R. H. Bowman. 1963. Regulation of phosphofructokinase activity of citrate in normal and diabetic muscle. *Biochem. Biophys. Res. Commun. 12:*268.

Passonneau, J., and O. Lowry. 1962. Phosphofructokinase and the pasteur effect. *Biochem. Biophys. Res. Commun. 7:*10.

————. 1963. P-fructokinase and the control of the citric acid cycle. *Biochem. Biophys. Res. Commun. 13:*372.

Rose, I. A. 1965. *In* B. Chance (ed.), *A Symposium on Control of Energy Metabolism*. Academic Press, New York. (In press.)

Rose, I. A., J. V. B. Warms, and E. L. O'Connell. 1964. Role of inorganic phosphate in stimulating the glucose utilization of human red blood cells. *Biochem. Biophys. Res. Commun. 15*:33.

Wu, R., and E. Racker. 1959. Regulatory mechanisms in carbohydrate metabolism: II. Limiting factors in glycolysis of ascites tumor cells. IV. Pasteur effect and crabtree effect in ascites tumor cells. *J. Biol. Chem. 234*:1029 and 1936.

Yates, R. A., and A. B. Pardee. 1956. Control of pyrimidine biosynthesis in Escherichia Coli by a feed-back mechanism. *J. Biol. Chem. 221*:757.

Chapter 5

The Ultrastructure of Cardiac and Skeletal Muscle

D. B. SLAUTTERBACK

It may be appropriate to begin a report of the ultrastructure of some striated muscle cells with the following observation. Among the vertebrates, and frequently in invertebrates too, muscle cells do not occur in the absence of connective tissue. This tissue is often voluminous and disposed in fascial sheets or trabeculae. Indeed, so pervasive is the collagenous mesh that it can be said that no vertebrate muscle cell exists without some part of its surface in contact with connective tissue. Such an intimate relationship is not surprising when it is recalled that both myofiber and fibroblast differentiate from the same melange of mesenchymal cells. In the adult, however, it is easy to lose sight of the fact that all substances entering or leaving the muscle cell must diffuse through a collagenous bed replete with active fibroblasts. Furthermore, the perivascular and perineural specializations of this bed carry into the muscle large numbers of endothelial cells, smooth muscle cells, neural processes, and a variety of wandering cells, as well as providing indirect communication with the connective beds of surrounding muscles and other tissues. I shall not dwell upon the properties of these less contractile elements in muscle, beyond pointing out that these cells (many of which also show some specialization for contraction) play a key role in regulating the environment in which the striated cells must function.

The striated muscle cell, then, is found in a sleeve of collagenous connective tissue to which it is attached by an amorphous or faintly filamentous basement membrane, a few hundred Ångströms thick (Figs. 5.1, 5.3, 5.5, 5.6). Like other basement membranes this one contains mucopolysaccharides and may serve as a filtering barrier to unwanted substances or perhaps as a preferential diffusion pathway. In either case, it probably contributes to the stability of the immediate cellular environment as well as "cementing" the cell to its contiguous connective tissue.

Fig. 5.1. — This low magnification micrograph of zebrafinch cardiac muscle in longitudinal section shows the A, H, I, and Z bands distinctly. Arrows indicate the dimensions of one of the cells. The abundance of mitochondria (*Mi*) and their tendency to cluster can be seen clearly. Interruptions by the sarcoplasmic reticulum (*SR*) show the varying transverse dimensions of cardiac myofibrils. Note the intercalated discs (*I*). Two capillaries (*C*) are present in the lower part of the figure. ×5,000.

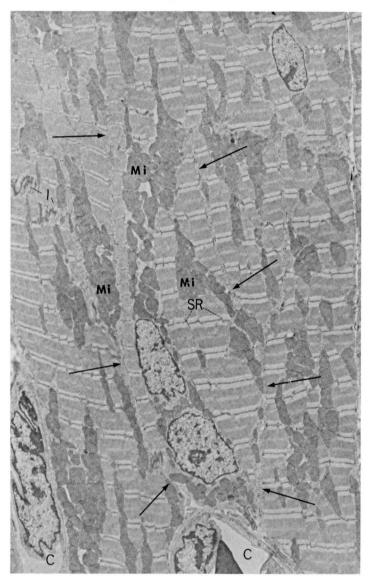

Fig. 5.2. — This micrograph is similar to Figure 5.1 except that it is a transverse section of canary cardiac muscle. Arrows define the limits of one of the cells. Notice the relatively large size of the centrally placed nucleus (*N*) with its prominent nucleolus (*Nu*). Lipid droplets (*Li*) of varying density are present among the mitochondria, as is another dense body (*Db*) of unknown composition, though it is believed to be proteinaceous. ×5,000.

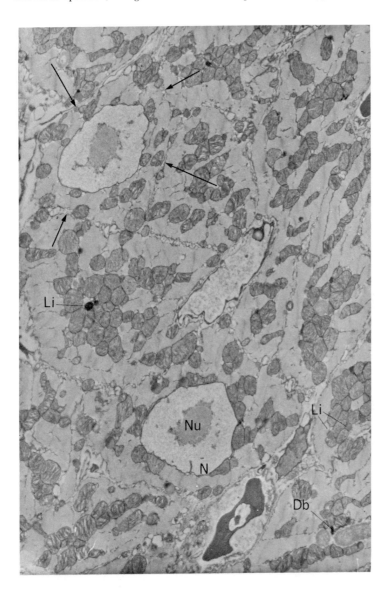

Fig. 5.3. — This is a transverse section of a papillary muscle from the heart of a turtle, cut near one of the poles of the nucleus. The distribution of mitochondria and particulate glycogen (*G*) is well shown, as is the variation in myofibril dimension. Separated from the muscle cell by two basement membranes (*BM*) and a narrow intervening space, is an endothelial cell (*E*) of the endocardium. It has a well-defined Golgi complex (*GC*) and centriole (*Ce*). The dense body in the lower left is an erythrocyte. × 15,000.

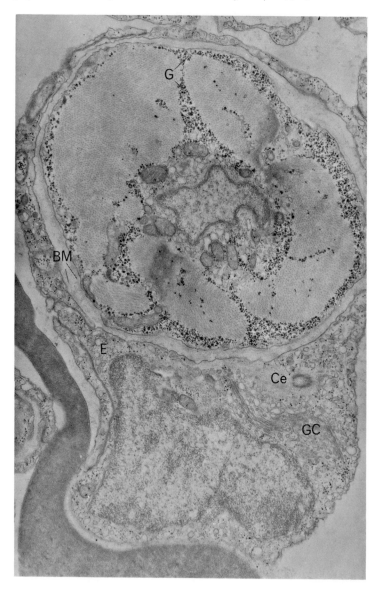

Fig. 5.4. — This longitudinal section through the nuclear region of a turtle cardiac muscle cell shows the pair of centrioles (*Ce*), Golgi complex (*GC*), and sarcoplasmic reticulum (*SR*). Note the desmosome-like (*D*) attachments to contiguous cells at the lateral interfaces. × 19,000.

Fig. 5.5. — The central element in this micrograph of shrew (*Blarina*) cardiac muscle is an endothelial cell (*E*) actively engaged in micropinocytosis
and surrounding a capillary lumen (*C*). The basement membranes separating this cell from the two muscle cells can be seen clearly. Compare the
mitochondria (*Mi*) of the two cell types. Those of the endothelial cell are
of a more usual dimension. Clear examples of the fenestrations of the
cristae can be seen, *en face* in the lower left, and edge-on in the upper right.
A good illustration of a dyad (*Dy*) is shown, with it central T tubule nearly
surrounded by an L tubule. ⨯ 17,000.

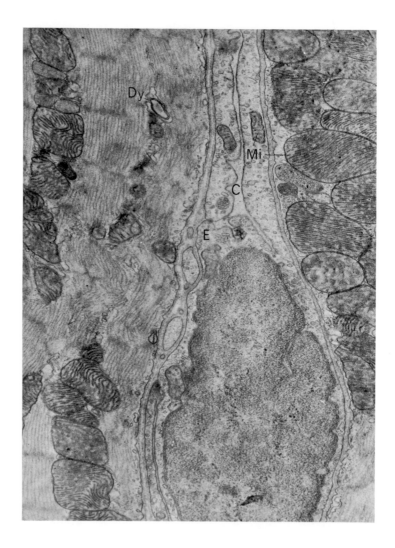

Fig. 5.6. — Longitudinal section of turtle cardiac muscle. Note especially the desmosome-like (*D*) lateral attachments, the abundant particulate glycogen (*G*), the irregular sarcoplasmic reticulum (*SR*), and the variation in myofibril diameter. × 19,000.

Inside these extraneous coats, the cardiac myofiber is a moderately large, mono- or binucleate cell in possession of all of the organelles common to animal cells. Unlike the skeletal muscles, cardiac muscle is cellular, not syncytial, and its nuclei are centrally rather than peripherally placed (Figs. 5.1, 5.2, 5.3). The structure of the large ellipsoidal nucleus is in no way remarkable (Figs. 5.1, 5.4). It is composed of a heterogeneous assemblage of fine granules and filaments. Some of these granules are aggregated into a prominent nucleolus and evidently are composed of a ribonucleoprotein. The karyoplasm is bounded by a pair of membranes which are held apart by the perinuclear cistern, a space of variable dimensions, which in protein secreting cells is often seen to be continuous with the cisternae of the endoplasmic reticulum (Figs. 5.3, 5.4.). Although this relationship can be seen in sections of striated muscle also, it is comparatively rare. The paired membranes of the nuclear envelope may be fused with each other in small circular areas to provide cylindrical channels through which the karyoplasm and cytoplasm are confluent. These nuclear pores may be very numerous in differentiating cells, but are less frequently seen in the adult.

Because of the prominence of the contractile elements, the free sarcoplasm is restricted to the two poles of the nucleus and to a subsarcolemmal layer of variable thickness (Figs. 5.1, 5.3, 5.4, 5.5). The most conspicuous occupants of these regions of the cell are the mitochondria (sarcosomes). In all of the striated muscles the mitochondria are large and numerous with long closely packed cristae and abundant matrix (Figs. 5.5, 5.15, 5.16). Although their size and shape are variable, they are commonly about 1 or 2 microns long by about 0.5 micron in diameter. They are enclosed by a pair of membranes, the outer one being smooth-contoured and the inner deeply invaginated to form the cristae. The mitochondria of cardiac muscle are especially numerous and less restricted in their distribution, and it is usual for their especially large cristae to be shelflike, fenestrated, and to extend across the full diameter of the mitochondrion (Fig. 5.5). The fenestrae may become so numerous and highly ordered in the fast hearts of small birds that the cristae assume the form of anastomotic tubules rather than shelves (Slautterback, 1965). The fine structure of the membrane of cardiac sarcosomes has been studied extensively, and it appears that the unit membrane concept does not adequately describe its organization. Fernandez-Moran et al. (1964), studying negatively stained preparations, have concluded that it is composed of tripartite subunits called elementary particles. Although Sjöstrand (1963) disputes the reality of these particles, calling them artifacts of prolonged exposure to unphysiological environments, it seems clear that there is some kind of repeating subunit in the mitochondrial membrane. Some additional support for this view is seen in the appearance of the membrane in ordinary tissue sections of canary cardiac sarcosomes (Slautterback, 1965).

At the poles of the nucleus of the cardiac myofiber other organelles are found. There is a diplosome, or pair of centrioles (Fig. 5.4). These bodies are made up of 27 tubular subunits about 200 Å in diameter and bound together in groups of three tubules in a row. The nine triplets thus formed are disposed around the circumference of a hollow cylinder and they are set so that a line joining the centers of the three tubules would intersect a tangent to the circumference at about 30°. Apart from the fact that centrioles are found at the poles of the mitotic spindle and at the bases of cilia, flagella, and sperm tails, nothing definite is known about their function. Since muscle cells are not normally mitotic nor are they ciliated, the presence of a pair of centrioles remains, as in many other cell types, unexplained.

Also at the poles of the nucleus is a small Golgi complex and numerous convoluted tubules which are evidently a part of a smooth-surfaced sarcoplasmic (endoplasmic) reticulum (Figs. 5.3, 5.4, 5.18). These are more prominent in the atrial myofiber. That the vesicles filled with dense material decrease with reserpine treatment was reported by Palade (1961), who thought these observations indicated secretion of catecholamines by the atrial cells. Subsequent efforts by Jamieson and Palade (1964) to verify this interpretation have thus far been unsuccessful. (More recent attempts to determine the identity of these granules have not yet become available to the author.)

Accumulations of tortuous tubules of the reticulum are also seen beneath the sarcolemma, woven in among the mitochondria (Figs. 5.5, 5.6). The abundance of these organelles and the intimacy of their relationship suggest interdependent function, but none has yet been found.

Variable deposits of particulate glycogen, small lipid droplets, and occasional free ribosomes complete the catalogue of the occupants of the main regions of free sarcoplasm (Figs. 5.2, 5.4, 5.6).

The most conspicuous element in the sarcoplasm of the striated muscle cells — excepting the Purkinje fiber (see Fig. 5.18; and Rhodin, del Missier, and Reid, 1961; Trautwein and Uchizono, 1963) — is the contractile protein itself (Fig. 5.1). This occurs in the form of three myofilaments in a highly ordered array which imparts to the cell the familiar cross-banded pattern (Figs. 5.6, 5.7). The largest of these is the A band filament. It is, at least in part, myosin and in a typical cardiac cell measures 160 Å thick by 1.1 microns in length. It has fine projections from its surface which appear to be helically arranged around the long axis of the myosin; there being six projections per turn of the helix. The filament which occupies the I band and projects a variable distance into the A band between the myosin filaments is actin, and typically has a diameter of 100 Å and a length of 0.7 micron. The third filament is found in the Z band (Figs 5.2, 5.7) and may also be made of myosin. It may be 100 Å thick and 0.6 micron long. (The existence of this filament is disputed by Franzini-Armstrong and Porter, 1964b.) Four of these filaments are attached to each I filament and connect with four separate I filaments in the next sarcomere. (Other reported dimensions for A and I filaments in mammalian skeletal muscle are, for example, A = 100 Å × 1.5 microns, I = 50 Å × 2 microns.)

It is evidently the absence of actin filaments from the central region of the A band which accounts for the relatively less dense H line (Figs. 5.7, 5.11). However, the M line is produced by an unexplained thickening of the myosin filament midway along its length (Fig. 5.11). Unlike the other bands, the N line, when seen, is attributable to accumulations of inter-fibrillar material of increased density (Figs. 5.6, 5.7, 5.11, 5.12). Transverse sections of striated muscle through the region of A–I interpenetration reveal the beautifully ordered array in which these two filaments are disposed (Fig. 5.8). In the cardiac muscles which form the basis of this report the filaments are so disposed that every actin filament is related to three myosin filaments and every myosin filament is surrounded by six actin filaments. Though this arrangement is common to vertebrate striated muscle, other arrangements are found among the invertebrates. For example, in insect muscle (Huxley and Hanson, 1957) each actin is related to two myosins and each myosin to six actins, and in some other insect muscles (Toselli, 1965) each myosin is related to 12 actins and the actin filaments at the corners of the hexagonally arranged 12 are related to three myosins and the others are related to only two. The myosin filaments of annelid we have studied are surrounded by 18 actins and these actins are shared by two myosins (Fig. 5.9). In general it can be said that the pattern is basically hexagonal except in the Z band, where it is tetragonal.

There are two interpretations of the Z band structure (Fig. 5.12). Knappeis and Carlsen (1962) believe that each actin filament ends by attachment to four Z filaments and that each one of these attaches to a different actin filament from the sequential sarcomere. The Z filaments thus outline a regular pyramid with a tetragonal base. On the other hand, Franzini-Armstrong and Porter (1964b) concluded that the Z disc is a membranous structure drawn up into peaks by its alternate attachment to actin filaments in the contiguous sarcomeres. They agree with Knappeis and Carlsen that the densities in the Z band which they interpret as edges or folds in the membrane are tetragonally arranged. They assert that the appearance of a thin straight line running the length of the Z band in well-oriented longitudinal sections is evidence for the membranous character of the disc.

Several years ago Huxley and Hanson (1954) proposed a model to explain the sequence of events during contraction and relaxation of striated muscle. This model is now widely known as the "sliding filament" concept. According to this view, contraction is a consequence of the actin filaments sliding over the myosin filaments, gradually diminishing the width of the I band as the Z substance is brought closer to the ends of the myosin filaments and at the same time reducing the width of the H band as the ends of the actin filaments from opposite ends of the sarcomere approach each other. The lengths of the myofilaments do not change during contraction (Page and Huxley, 1963). Projections from the myosin filament represent bonding sites for the action which are made and broken repeatedly during contraction. The energy for this bonding is believed to be derived from the high energy phosphate bond of ATP which is split by the action of myosin adenosine triphosphatase. It will be recognized at once that a hierarchical arrangement of affinities is required along the length of the myosin filament to satisfy the requirements of this model. Thus far, no way has been found to demonstrate this sequence.

The "sliding filament" concept has been challenged numerous times. Although a variety of interpretations have been suggested they have in common the proposal that sarcomere shortening is brought about by intrafilamentous, or intramolecular, contraction with the relationship between actin and myosin filaments remaining fixed. Some, such as Gilev (1962), have proposed that both systems are operative. He saw the initial contraction (down to 74% of rest length) as a sliding of filaments and the remainder (down to 58% of rest length) as explained by contraction of both A and I filaments. Others do not concede any sliding of the filaments during contraction (Carlsen, Knappeis, and Buchthal, 1961; de Villafranca and Marschaus, 1963; Podolsky, 1962). They call attention to such experiments as those of Tunik and Holtzer (1961), where the localization of fluorescent antibodies suggested an outward movement of myosin during contraction. This and similar observations can only be explained as incompatible with the sliding filament hypothesis or as the consequence of variation during contraction of the exposed reactive sites on myosin. Szent-Györgyi and Johnson (1965) believe that these observations support their concept of muscle contraction. Actin filaments pass through the H band before attaching to the myosin. Upon contraction, the myosin migrates outward along the H band filament, thus pulling the actin from the opposite half of the sarcomere into the A band. Sjöstrand has been one of the most active electron microscopists convinced that the filaments shorten during contraction. In a recent report (1964), he interprets increased density at the A–I junction in incipient contraction, as contraction bands. If this is a correct interpretation it provides the first strong evidence against the sliding filament concept. Sjöstrand proposes that the ends of the A filaments fray, exposing reactive sites previously covered. These react with the I filaments causing them to collapse inward, thus pulling the Z band into contiguity with the A band. The displacement of the actin filaments into the A band is a consequence of the readjustments which occur during relaxation.

It is not possible at this time to say with certainty that one or another of the interpretations of the morphological events during contraction is correct. It must be said, however, that Huxley's concept of sliding filaments has withstood numerous challenges and has recently received renewed support from the studies of Stephens (1965). This investigator has disrupted different parts of single sarcomeres with accurately focused ultraviolet microbeams and concludes from the effects of this treatment on contraction that the sliding of filaments is the only permissible interpretation.

A few striated muscle cells have been studied with the electron microscope during the process of differentiation (Hay, 1963). Heuson-Stiennon (1964), Firket (1963), and Waddington and Perry (1963) have reported that the basophilia of myoblasts is attributable to a large accumulation of free ribosomes in the cytoplasm before the appearance of any myofilaments. The ribosomes then aggregate in polysome clusters of characteristic configuration with approximately ten particles held together by a thin filament. Later, the ribosomes appear strung on a thicker filament, 110 Å in diameter, which extends considerably beyond the polysome. Heuson-Stiennon interprets these figures as nascent myosin filaments already partly loosened from the polysomes which form them. The aggregation of filaments into sarcomeres is even less well understood. Fine filaments concentrate on each side of an elongate dense body in the cytoplasm. This complex then takes up the appropriate position for the next I and Z bands in the forming sarcomere and the myosin filaments fill in the gap. In hypertrophied adult cardiac muscle, however, Richter and Kellner (1963) report that growth is not only by addition of new myofibrils but by addition of new filaments around the periphery of the old fibrils.

In skeletal muscle the transverse dimension of a sarcomere is relatively constant from one sarcomere to the next in line. Thus the consequence of end-to-end formation of sarcomeres is the production of uniform cylindrical structures running the full length of the myofiber — the myofibrils. In cardiac muscle, however, myofibrils of constant diameter are rarely seen. Fusion of adjacent myofibrils and subsequent redistribution of the myofilaments into quite different fibrils (Fig. 5.1) repeated several times along the length of the myofiber is the rule. So extensive is the process of fibril fusion that in some planes of section the transverse dimension of the sarcomeres may approximate the width of the cell itself.

At the ends of a skeletal myofiber the myofilaments take origin from the plasmalemma as though it were a Z disc. This observation has been used by Franzini-Armstrong and Porter (1964b) to substantiate their understanding of the Z band as a membranous structure. Because cardiac muscle is cellular instead of syncytial the irregular myofibrils are interrupted much more frequently by the plasmalemma and therefore are very much shorter than those in skeletal muscle. At the region of attachment of the myofilaments there is an elaborate convolution of the sarcolemma so that peglike interdigitations are formed with the membrane of the next cell in line. These areas of modified membrane constitute the intercalated discs (Fig. 5.10). In some animals these are "step-wise"; that is, they interrupt different myofibrils at different Z band levels. In others, such as certain birds, most of the discs transect all the myofibrils at the same Z band level. At the interfibrillar parts of the disc there is a condensation of dense material adjacent to the inner surface of the sarcolemma and the actin filaments appear to insert there. The structure is evidently a type of desmosome (*zonula adhaerens*), a modification for firm attachment of cells. The sarcolemma is so convoluted that the actin filaments are most frequently inserted into the disc at a low angle, suggesting that the attachments are best adapted to resist shear forces. In the intersarcoplasmic parts of the disc the modification of the plasma membrane is more akin to the *zonula occludens* or tight junctions of the epithelial cells and like it may be modified by partial fusion of contiguous membranes to favor ionic continuity from one cell to the next (Loewenstein and Kanno, 1964; Barr, Dewey, and Berger, 1965). The basement membrane which surrounds the myofibers is excluded from the intercellular gap at the intercalated discs. Desmosome-like structures are seen also in some hearts holding cells together side-to-side at some of the Z band levels (Fig. 5.6).

With relatively few exceptions the myofibrils of all striated muscles are surrounded by a profuse and complex system of membrane-bounded tubules and vesicles. These are known collectively as the sarcoplasmic reticulum and probably are continuous with the elements of the reticulum found at the poles of the nuclei and beneath the sarcolemma (Fig. 5.4). The sarcoplasmic reticulum (SR) is made up of two parts (Figs. 5.11, 5.17). One is known as the "L," longitudinal or sarcotubular system. It consists of tubules whose orientation is parallel to the myofilaments, hence longitudinal relative to the myofiber (Figs. 5.13, 5.14, 5.15). In the cells where they are most abundant the tubules are convoluted and frequently anastomotic, particularly over the H and I bands. At the A–I junction in higher vertebrates and at the Z band in lower vertebrates the L tubules meet the other part of the SR, the "T," transverse or intermediate tubules (Figs. 5.11, 5.12, 5.13). These tubules completely surround the circumference of the myofibrils and are continuous from one fibril to the next, transversely across the skeletal muscle cell. Where the L and T systems meet there is a vesicular expansion of the L tubules (Figs. 5.11, 5.12,

Fig. 5.7. — This is a sarcomere from canary cardiac muscle. The myosin filaments (*My*), with their lateral projections, and the actin filaments (*Ac*) can be seen. A, H, M, I, N, and Z bands are evident. ×42,000.

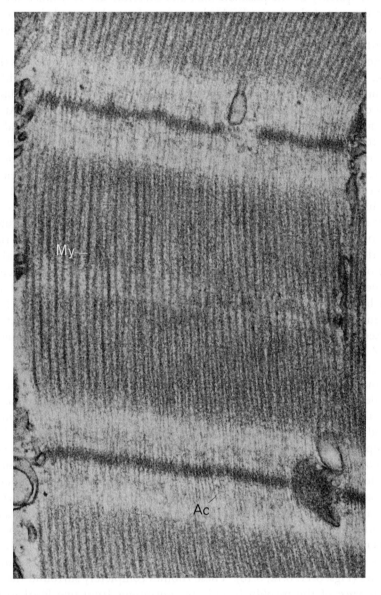

Fig. 5.8. — This is a transverse section of hummingbird cardiac muscle at the level of the A–I junction to show the relationship between the actin and myosin filaments. ×57,000.

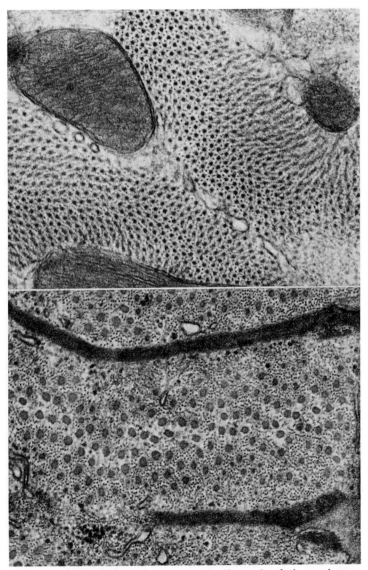

Fig. 5.9. — This is a section of the body-wall muscle of the earthworm, *Enchytraeus fragmentosus.* Two dense Z bands are evident even though this is a transverse section, because the array of filaments is staggered. Although the array is less regular than in vertebrate striated muscle, the disposition of 18 thin filaments around one thick filament can be seen in the central part of the figure. ×58,000.

Fig. 5.10. — The full extent of an intercalated disc is seen in this longitudinal section of canary cardiac muscle. In every case the disc intersects the myofibrils at the Z band level. ×44,000.

Fig. 5.11. — The distribution of triads at the Z band level and the relative uniformity of myofibril diameter is shown in this longitudinal section of the tail muscle of the fish, *Mollienesia* sp. Mitochondria are absent from the interfibrillar spaces. × 19,000.

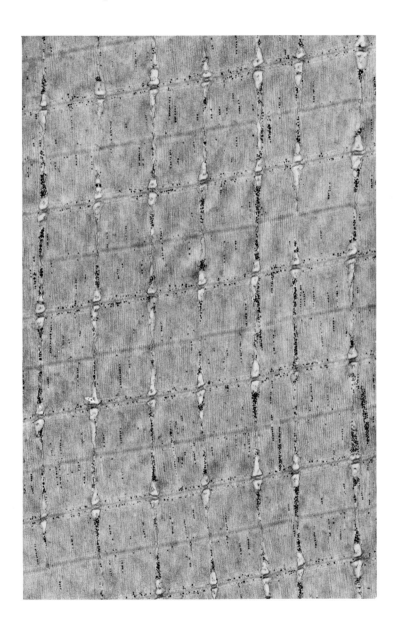

Fig. 5.12. — Like Figure 5.11, this is a section of a Black Molly tail. The central T tubule (*T*) and the lateral expansions of the L tubules (*L*) can be seen to make up a triad. The details of Z band structure and the distribution of particulate glycogen (*G*) are shown. ×51,000.

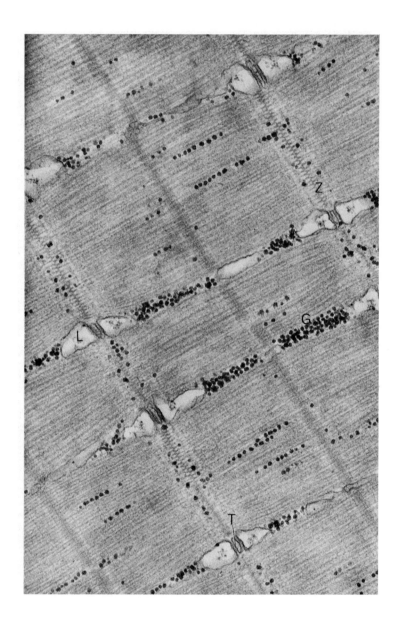

Fig. 5.13. — This grazing section of a myofibril gives an *en face* view of the sarcoplasmic reticulum of the Black Molly tail muscle. The tubular nature of the T system and the great extent of the expanded portion of the L system are evident. Notice also that the L tubules are more anastomotic over the H band. ×52,000.

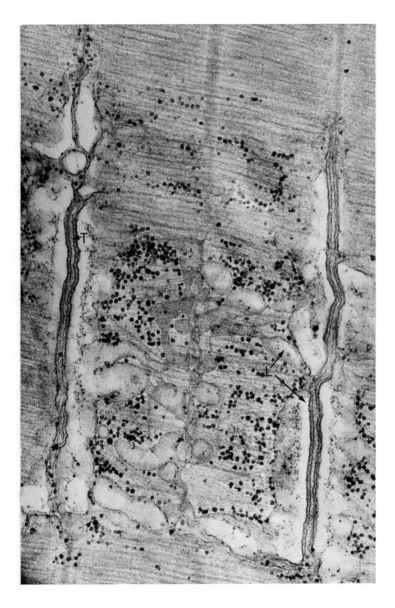

Fig. 5.14. — The triads of the extraocular muscle of this lizard, *Anolis carolinensis* are located just inside the A–I junction. The tubules over the A and Z bands are very abundant in this fast muscle. Notice also that the I band is much broader than in the Black Molly tail muscle. ×28,000.

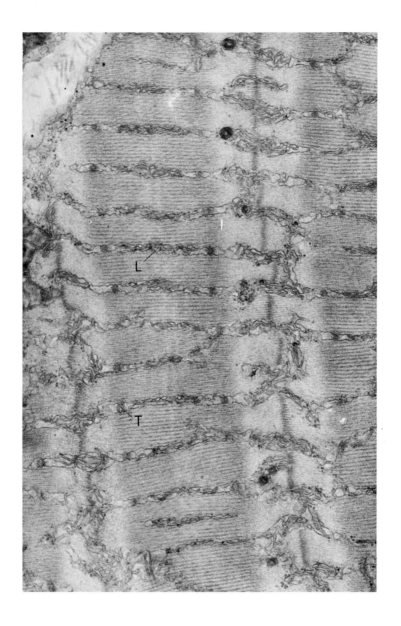

Fig. 5.15. — No identifiable T tubules are evident in this section of turtle cardiac muscle. Although this is a relatively slow heart muscle, it has a considerable amount of sarcoplasmic reticulum in comparison to other hearts. However, the contrast with the skeletal muscles, in organization and abundance of the reticulum, is striking. ×28,000.

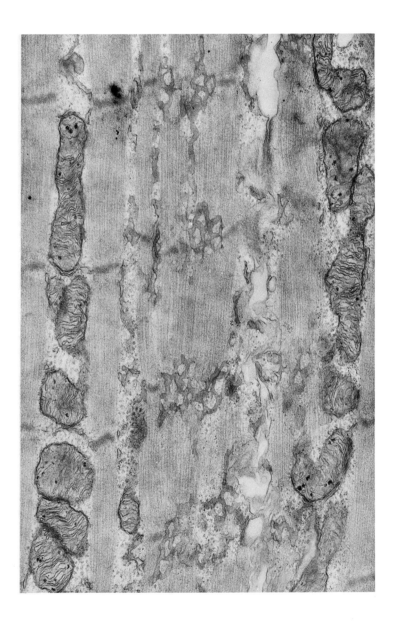

Fig. 5.16. — Notice the apparent formation of triads *(Tr)* in this edge-on view of the sarcoplasmic reticulum in the very fast cardiac muscle of the hummingbird. ×28,000.

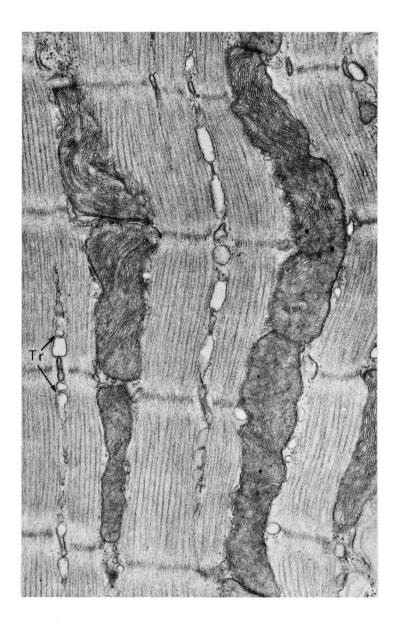

Fig. 5.17. — Continuity of the lumen of a T tubule with the extracellular space by fusion of its membrane with the sarcolemma, is indicated by the arrow. Elsewhere, the most prominent feature of this section of *Anolis* extraocular muscle is the continuous nature of the expanded portion of the L system and its unidentified dense content. The relative delicacy of the parts of this cell can be appreciated by comparing the magnification of this micrograph with the preceding one. $\times$ 78,000.

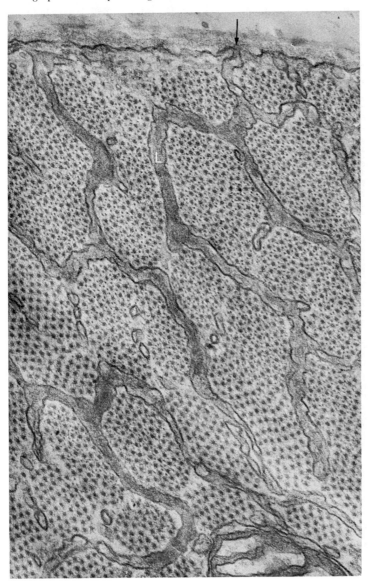

Fig. 5.18. — This micrograph, from a section of hummingbird heart, illustrates on the right an ordinary cardiac myofiber and on the left a Purkinje fiber of the conducting system. Notice the abundant sarcoplasm and prominent Golgi complex (*GC*) of the latter. ×9,000.

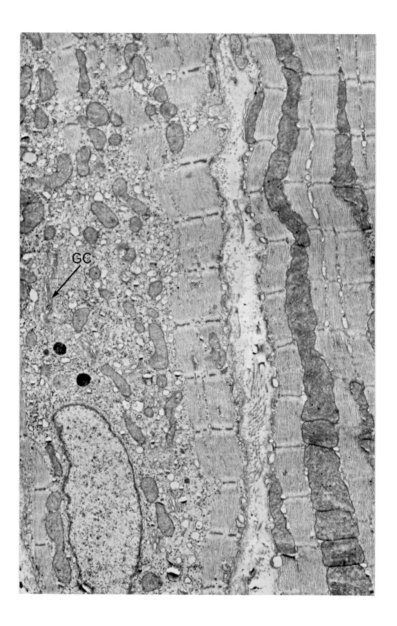

5.13). It is these three elements — the two expanded parts of the L system and the T tubule between — which are called the triad. In cardiac muscle, triads are rarely, if ever, seen; and although both systems appear to be present, they are more difficult to distinguish, less abundant, and much less regularly organized (Figs. 5.6, 5.15, 5.16). Triads are sometimes replaced by dyads (Fig. 5.5) which are associations between meandering T tubules and elements of the L system. The relationship is reminiscent, on a small scale, of the *en passant* synapse of the nervous system. The triad of vertebrate skeletal muscle causes a total interruption of the L system at the end of each sarcomere. This seems not to be the rule in cardiac muscle (see Figs. 5.16 and 5.18 for possible exceptions) nor in several of the invertebrate muscles studied (Fahrenbach, 1963, 1964).

Explanation of the function of such an elaborately differentiated organelle and explanation of the differences in its organization in various striated muscles (especially vertebrate cardiac and skeletal) have concerned many investigators in the last ten years. It has been suggested that the SR might be involved in the transmission of the stimulus from the sarcolemma to the deeper lying myofibrils, and a specific proposal to this effect was published by Peachey and Porter (1959). In many cases the distances are so great that the probability of synchronous contraction of all the myofibrils of a single large myofiber seemed unlikely. If contraction were not synchronous, then the shear forces set up could be expected to destroy the cell. Hill (1948) had shown earlier that diffusion of an activator substance through the sarcoplasm would not be fast enough to account for synchrony. Then, Huxley and Taylor (1958) and Huxley and Straub (1958) showed that local contractions could be obtained by application of a weak current with a microelectrode touching the sarcolemma. If the muscle cell had its triad at the A–I junction (Fig. 5.14) then only stimulation over the A–I junction would produce a contraction, but if the triad were at the Z line (Fig. 5.11) then stimulation there was effective. The fact that the T system is tubular and not vesicular as had been thought at first (Fig. 5.13), and that these tubules extended through the sarcoplasm to the sarcolemma even when several microns distant, was shown to particularly good advantage by Revel (1962) in the cricothyroid muscle of the bat. These and related reports supported the view that the T system was involved in impulse conduction. However, efforts to demonstrate continuity of these tubules with the sarcolemma were for a long time unsuccessful. This, in spite of the fact that Smith (1961a) had shown that the appearance of the T tubule membrane is like the plasma membrane and unlike the membrane of the tubules of the L system. Continuity of the T system with the plasmalemma was established for insect muscle by D. S. Smith (1961a, 1961b, 1962) and for some other invertebrates by Fahrenbach

(1963, 1964) and by Reger (1962). Two reports of such continuities in vertebrate cardiac muscle (Nelson and Benson, 1963; Simpson and Oertelis, 1962) are ambiguous because of fixation problems and the difficulty of interpreting the plane of section and the effects of full contraction on the published images. In spite of these difficulties the continuity of the T tubule lumen with extracellular space by fusion of its membrane with the plasmalemma has been demonstrated for vertebrate muscle by Franzini-Armstrong and Porter (1964a) using the Black Molly (Fig. 5.17).

Kilarski (1964) made a simlar observation in another fish, and Fawcett (1965) has seen it in the cat heart. Huxley, Page, and Wilkie (1963) previously saw this continuity in frog sartorius muscle which had been exposed to hypertonic Ringer's solution. This treatment caused shrinkage of all parts of the cell except the T tubules which were greatly swollen. Furthermore, Endo (1964) has recently reported the passage of a dye to which the sarcolemma is impermeable, from the extracellular space into the sarcoplasmic reticulum, and H. E. Huxley (1964) has shown that it will pass from extracellular space into the T tubules only. The last two observations were made on frog muscle. This concept of T system function is further supported by the relative paucity or complete absence of SR from muscle cells whose myofibrils are very close to the sarcolemma (Smith, 1962; Fahrenbach, 1963; Peachey, 1961).

It has been shown also that the T system tubules are selectively permeable to chloride ion and that together with the sarcolemma they form a current loop (Girardier *et al.*, 1963). Furthermore, Constantin, Franzini-Armstrong, and Podolsky (1965) and Pease, Jenden, and Howell (1965) found that calcium is concentrated in the lateral expansions of the L system. If these observations are considered together with the studies of Weber, Herz, and Reiss (1963) on the previously reported relaxing effect of isolated sarcoplasmic reticulum, an intriguing hypothesis emerges. Weber concluded that the L tubules regulate critically the sarcoplasmic calcium concentration around a threshold value which when relatively high activates a myosin adenosine triphosphatase, and when relatively low causes its inactivation. It is tempting to think that variation of the permeability of the T system may be coupled with the regulatory action of the L tubules to bring about contraction and relaxation of sarcomeres.

In slow skeletal muscles of both vertebrates (Hess, 1965; Peachey and Huxley, 1962) and invertebrates (Smith, 1962; Fahrenbach, 1963) both elements of the SR are greatly reduced, and this would be expected if the hypothesis were correct. In cardiac muscle, however, the situation is otherwise. In these cells the specific association between the two elements of the SR is greatly reduced and the T system is less abundant than in skeletal muscle, but the L system remains abundant (Figs. 5.6, 5.15). This may be because the L system is involved in glycogen metabolism as was suggested by Andersson-Cedergren and Muscatello (1963) or, what is perhaps more likely, it may be because cardiac innervation only regulates the speed of contraction and does not initiate it. With the contraction initiated intrinsically the need for an elaborate T system may be obviated. The fact that there is relatively little variation in the amount of SR in fast and slow cardiac muscle (Figs. 5.1, 5.5, 5.18), except at the extremes, may be a reflection of the relatively smaller range of twitch velocities available to these cells as compared to skeletal cells. Cell to cell transmission of the impulse may be as Fawcett (1965) has suggested by way of the *fasciae occludens* which are known to provide ionic continuity in epithelial cells (Loewenstein and Kanno, 1964).

Because of the necessary brevity of this report, I have omitted consideration of the important contributions to electron microscopic histochemistry of muscle enzymes. I seek solace in the fact that as reported by Essner, Novikoff, and Quintana (1965), there is still considerable disagreement in published conclusions. I would like, however, to allude to the interesting but as yet difficult-to-interpret finding of Karnovsky (1964) that acetylcholinesterase is found in the A band and L tubules in cardiac muscle. Since the effect of acetylcholine on the permeability of cell membranes to ions is recognized, the significance of the presence of this enzyme, and presumably its substrate, at the site where ion movements may be most critical, is an exciting subject for conjecture. Also of great interest is the emerging fact that the SR is chemically dissectible into localized regions carrying specific functions (A. F. Huxley, 1964).

Finally, I hope I have sufficiently indicated the real progress made in the last decade in understanding striated muscle morphology. May I remind the reader also that for some contractile cells — oligocendrocytes, endothelial cells, myoendothelial cells, myoepithelial cells, musculoepithelial cells, the many different forms of smooth muscle and the protozoa — progress in understanding contraction has not been so rapid and it may be very hazardous to generalize to all of them from the events in striated muscle.

ACKNOWLEDGMENT

The author's research reported in this publication was supported wholly by Public Health Service Research Grant No. GM 06934, from the Division of General Medical Sciences.

References

Andersson-Cedergren, E., and U. Muscatello. 1963. The participation of the sarcotubular system in glycogen metabolism. *J. Ultrastruc. Res.* 8:391.

Barr, L., M. M. Dewey, and W. Berger. 1965. Propagation of action potentials and the structure of the nexus in cardiac muscle. *J. Gen. Physiol.* 48:797.

Carlsen, F., G. G. Knappeis, and F. Buchthal. 1961. Ultrastructure of the resting and contracted striated muscle fiber at different degrees of stretch. *J. Biophys. Biochem. Cytol.* 11:95.

Constantin, L. L., C. Franzini-Armstrong, and J. Podolsky. 1965. Localization of calcium-accumulating structures in striated muscle fibers. *Science* 147:158.

De Villafranca, G. W., and C. E. Marschaus. 1963. Contraction of the A band. *J. Ultrastruc. Res.* 9:156.

Endo, M. 1964. Entry of a dye into the sarcotubular system of muscle. *Nature* 202:1115.

Essner, E., B. Novikoff, and N. Quintana. 1965. Nucleoside phosphatase activities in rat cardiac muscle. *J. Cell Biol.* 25:201.

Fahrenbach, W. H. 1963. The sarcoplasmic reticulum of striated muscle of a cyclopoid copepod. *J. Cell Biol.* 17:629.

———. 1964. A new configuration for the sarcoplasmic reticulum. *J. Cell Biol.* 22:477.

Fawcett, D. W. 1965. Sarcolemmal invaginations and cell to cell contacts of cardiac muscle. *Anat. Rec.* 151:487.

Fernandez-Moran, H., T. Oda, P. V. Blair, and D. E. Green. 1964. A macromolecular repeating unit of mitochondrial structure and function. *J. Cell Biol.* 22:63.

Firket, H. 1963. Étude de l'ultrastructure de bourgeons musculaires en régénération pendant la myogénèse. *J. Microscopie* 2:639.

Franzini-Armstrong, C., and K. R. Porter. 1964a. Sarcolemmal invaginations constituting the T system in the fish muscle fibers. *J. Cell Biol.* 22:675.

———. 1964b. The Z disc of skeletal muscle fibrils. *Z. Zellforsch.* 61:661.

Gilev, V. P. 1962. A study of myofibril sarcomere structure during contraction. *J. Cell Biol.* 12:135.

Girardier, L., J. P. Reuben, P. W. Brandt, and H. Grundfest. 1963. Evidence for Anion-Permselection membrane in crayfish muscle fibers and its possible role in excitation-contraction coupling. *J. Gen. Physiol.* 47:189.

Hay, E. D. 1963. The fine structure of differentiating muscle in the salamander tail. *Z. Zellforsch.* 59:6.

Hess, A. 1965. The sarcoplasmic reticulum, the T system and the motor terminals of slow and twitch muscle fibers of the garter snake. *Anat. Rec.* 151:360.

Heuson-Stiennon, J. A. 1964. Intervention de polysomes dans la synthèse des myofilaments du muscle embryonnaire du rat. *J. Microscopie* 3:229.

Hill, A. V. 1948. On the time required for diffusion and its relation to processes in muscle. *Proc. Roy. Soc.* (London), B, 135:446.

Huxley, A. F. 1964. Muscle. *Annu. Rev. Physiol.* 26:131.

Huxley, A. F., and R. W. Straub. 1958. Local activation and interfibrillar structures in striated muscle. *J. Physiol. 143:*40.

Huxley, A. F., and R. E. Taylor. 1958. Local activation of striated muscle fibers. *J. Physiol. 144:*426.

Huxley, H. E. 1964. Evidence for continuity between the central elements of the triads and extracellular space in frog sartorius muscle. *Nature 202:*1067.

Huxley, H. E., and J. Hanson. 1954. Changes in the cross-striations of muscle during contraction and stretch and their structural interpretation. *Nature 173:*973.

———. 1957. Preliminary observations on the structure of insect flight muscle, p. 202. In *Proc. Stockholm Conference on Electron Microscopy.* Academic Press, New York.

Huxley, H. E., S. Page, and D. R. Wilkie. 1963. An electron microscopic study of muscle in hypertonic solutions. *J. Physiol. 169:*325.

Jamieson, J. D., and G. E. Palade. 1964. Specific granules in atrial muscle cells. *J. Cell Biol. 23:*151.

Karnovsky, J. J. 1964. The localization of cholinesterase activity in rat cardiac muscle by electron microscopy. *J. Cell Biol. 23:*217.

Kilarski, W. M. 1964. Observations on the T system in striated muscles of the swim-bladder of the burbot (Latalata L.), p. 79. *In* A. L. Houwink and B. J. Spit (eds), *Third European Regional Conference on Electron Microscopy.* Delft, Netherlands.

Knappeis, G. G., and F. Carlsen. 1962. The ultrastructure of the Z disc in skeletal muscle. *J. Cell Biol. 13:*323.

Loewenstein, W., and Y. Kanno. 1964. Studies on an epithelial (gland) cell function. *J. Cell Biol. 22:*565.

Nelson, D. A., and E. S. Benson. 1963. On the structural continuities of the transverse tubular system of rabbit and human myocardial cells. *J. Cell Biol. 16:*297.

Page, S. G., and H. E. Huxley. 1963. Filament lengths in striated muscle. *J. Cell Biol. 19:*369.

Palade, G. E. 1961. Secretory granules in the atrial myocardium. *Anat. Rec. 139:*262.

Peachey, L. D. 1961. Structure of the longitudinal body muscles of amphioxus. *J. Biophys. Biochem. Cytol. 10(suppl. 4):*159.

Peachey, L. D., and A. F. Huxley. 1962. Structural identification of twitch and slow striated muscle fibers of the frog. *J. Cell Biol. 13:*177.

Peachey, L. D., and K. R. Porter. 1959. Intracellular impulse conduction in muscle cells. *Science 129:*721.

Pease, D. C., D. J. Jenden, and J. N. Howell. 1965. Calcium uptake in glycerol-extracted rabbit psoas muscle fibers. II. Electron microscopic localization of uptake sites. *J. Cell. Comp. Physiol. 65:*141.

Podolsky, R. J. 1962. Mechanochemical basis of muscle contraction. *Fed. Proc. 21:*964.

Reger, J. F. 1962. The fine structure of triads from swimmerette muscle of A.

salinus. *In* Sidney Breese (ed.), *Electron Microscopy* (5th Int. Congr. Electron Microscopy), *2:*TT-4.

Revel, J. P. 1962. The sarcoplasmic reticulum of the bat cricothyroid muscle. *J. Cell Biol. 12:*511.

Rhodin, J. A. G., P. del Missier, and L. C. Reid. 1961. The structure of the specialized impulse conducting system of the steer heart. *Circulation 24:*349.

Richter, G. W., and A. Kellner. 1963. Hypertrophy of the human heart at the level of fine structure. *J. Cell Biol. 18:*195.

Simpson, R. O., and S. J. Oertelis. 1962. The fine structure of sheep myocardial cells; sarcolemmal invaginations and the transverse tubular systems. *J. Cell Biol. 12:*91.

Sjöstrand, F. S. 1963. A new ultrastructural element of the membranes in mitochondria and of some cytoplasmic membranes. *J. Ultrastruc. Res. 9:*340.

———. 1964. Ultrastructural changes in skeletal muscle myofibrils in connection with contraction. *Nature 201:*45.

Slautterback, D. B. 1965. Mitochondria in cardiac muscle cells of the canary and some other animals. *J. Cell Biol. 24:*1.

Smith, D. S. 1961*a.* The structure of insect fibrillar flight muscle. A study made with special reference to the membrane systems of the fiber. *J. Biophys. Biochem. Cytol. 10:*123.

———. 1961*b.* The organization of the flight muscle in a dragonfly, *Aeshna* sp. (Odanata). *J. Biophys. Biochem. Cytol. 11:*119.

———. 1962. The sarcoplasmic reticulum of insect muscle. *In* Sidney Breese (ed.), *Electron Microscopy* (5th Int. Congr. Electron Microscopy), *2:*TT-3.

Stephens, R. E. 1965. Analysis of muscle contraction by ultraviolet microbeam disruption of sarcomere structure. *J. Cell Biol. 25:*129.

Szent-Györgyi, A. G., and W. H. Johnson. 1964. An alternative theory for contraction of striated muscles, p. 485. *In* J. Gergely (ed.), *Biochemistry of Muscle Contraction.* Little, Brown & Co., Boston.

Toselli, P. A. 1965. The fine structure of the fully developed intersegmental abdominal muscles of *Rhodnius prolixus. Anat. Rec. 151:*427.

Trautwein, W., and K. Uchizono. 1963. Electron microscopic and electrophysiologic study of the pacemaker in the sino-atrial node of the rabbit heart. *Z. Zellforsch. 61:*96.

Tunik, B., and H. Holtzer. 1961. The distribution of muscle antigens in contracted myofibrils determined by fluorescein-labeled antibodies. *J. Cell Biol. 11:*67.

Waddington, C. H., and M. M. Perry. 1963. Helical arrangement of ribosomes in differentiating muscle cells. *Exp. Cell Res. 30:*599.

Weber, A., R. Herz, and I. Reiss. 1963. On the mechanism of the relaxing effect of fragmented sarcoplasmic reticulum. *J. Gen. Physiol. 46:*679.

Chapter 6

Summary and Discussion of Part I

PANEL MEMBERS: W. G. HOEKSTRA, *Chairman*
J. R. BENDALL
R. E. DAVIES
R. G. KAUFFMAN
R. N. SAYRE

Hoekstra: Part I has considered muscle development as affected by age, exercise, and restraint; control of metabolic pathways in muscle; and the ultrastructure of muscle.

Muscle is generally considered to be a nutritionally desirable food. In Chapter 3, Dr. Helander described many compositional changes occurring in muscle with age, use, and disuse. These changes have been implicated in regard to properties of muscle which affect its use as a food. Dr. Helander pointed out that muscle with too much connective tissue or too many fibrils (too large fibers) is often undesirable. This, however, does not adequately explain the effect of age, preslaughter treatment, or carcass-handling on muscle tenderness. As will be shown in later chapters, the nature of the connective tissue in muscle changes markedly with age. Also, antemortem handling of the animal, as well as postmortem carcass-handling, is of great importance in determining muscle quality.

Numerous items mentioned by Dr. Helander have not, to my knowledge, received much attention previously in the study of muscle quality. Included here are such changes as the amount of intracellular vs. extracellular space and the effect of muscle disuse. What effect does short-term, quite abrupt, and essentially complete muscle immobilization have on muscle quality? The so-called "full-feeding" program for a period before slaughter usually results in the deposition of fat in the muscle. Numerous recent experiments have cast doubt on the significance of fat in this regard. How much of the improvement in muscle quality is instead related to the confinement of the animals? Moreover, does level of feeding cause some change in muscle composition or structure other than in fat?

In Chapter 4, Dr. Lardy outlined some of the mechanisms of regulation of energy-yielding processes in muscle. That such regulation is of great importance to the use of muscle as a food has been well documented and will receive attention in later chapters. Particularly in the porcine animal, too rapid a rate of postmortem glycolysis is very deleterious to muscle quality and causes a loss of water and development of undesirable texture and pale color. Regulation of glycolytic rate in muscle postmortem is not well understood at present. It may or may not involve some of the same controlling factors as does in vivo regulation of the muscle.

In Chapter 5, Dr. Slautterback described some of the fascinating advances in our knowledge of muscle through the use of electron microscopy. Mechanistic theories of muscle contraction have been formulated largely from these observations; and, although still somewhat controversial, the final explanation must be commensurate, to some extent, with what one sees in muscle with the electron microscope. Theories on the control of muscle contraction and relaxation have recently been aided immensely by electron microscopic observation of the sarcotubular system in muscle. However, the location of specific chemical components of muscle within certain ultrastructural units of the muscle is still insufficiently conclusive and far from complete.

Another point made by Dr. Slautterback is that muscle is much more than just a collection of filaments of contractile proteins with cross banding. Collagenous tissues and mucopolysaccharides, as well as a number of types of seemingly insignificant cells and subcellular structures such as lysosomes, may be of great importance in muscle metabolism and in the use of muscle as a food.

DISCUSSION

Sayre: How does lengthening of the myofibrils take place in postfetal growing muscle?

Slautterback: Postfetal growth occurs largely by addition of sarcoblasts to the ends of the myofibers.

Sayre: Is there any information on how the actin and myosin filaments become arranged in position?

Slautterback: There is very little evidence as to how this occurs. The following sequence probably occurs: myosin and fine filaments are randomly scattered in the cytoplasm. The filaments become larger and longer and settle into position in the incipient A band region. In some muscles the Z band does not appear to take up its position before the A filaments become oriented. After the myosin filaments become oriented, the actin filaments, with their Z bands, fall into place.

Bendall: It is very difficult to see how the number of sarcomeres increases during postnatal growth; yet they appear to do so in bullocks, up to the age of two years. In the mouse, on the contrary, the numbers only increase postnatally until the animal is able to stand, so that further lengthening of the muscle must then occur either by adding new actin or myosin molecules to the already existing filaments in each sarcomere, or by stretching the sarcomeres and widening their H zones.

G. A. Goll: How confident are you that there is no increase in muscle cell numbers during adolescence?

Helander: This is a generally accepted theory and I refer you specifically to Cowdry's (3d ed., 1952) text on aging. However, most information relating to this subject is quite old and a reconfirmation would be in order.

Bendall: We have recently studied the question of the decrease in fiber numbers during maturation of bovine animals and find a very significant decrease of about one-third in the number of fibers between the ages of 18 months and two years, in both the longissimus dorsi and semitendinosus muscles. This result is surprising, since bovine animals of this age are certainly not mature. Similar results were obtained by Goldspink (1964), whose studies of the effect of controlled exercise on the biceps brachii of the mouse show that the muscle fibers enlarge as exercise increases, by increasing the numbers of the constituent myofibrils. The process is quantized in this muscle, the so-called small phase fibers growing into large phase fibers without the appearance of fibers of intermediate size.

Kauffman: Could muscle cells undergo unlimited hypertrophy or mitosis if the genetic control center were altered?

Helander: Even if there were a drug that would promote the hypertrophy of a muscle cell, I do not think that this hypertrophy would be unlimited. A cell must be provided with oxygen right into its most central part, and an excessively large cell would have circulatory difficulties.

Kauffman: What is the histological or biochemical explanation for the development of "muscle tone" resulting from increased exercise, and what is its significance, if any, in controlling and explaining muscle hypertrophy during physical exercise?

Slautterback: I do not know the answer to this question, but in view of Richter and Kellner's (1963) study of hypertrophied heart muscle, I presume that one aspect of the development of muscle tone is the addition of newly formed myofilaments to the periphery of old myofibrils and the formation of new myofibrils.

Davies: Dr. E. E. Gordon (unpublished, University of Chicago) has recently suggested that very short isometric or near isometric contractions cause an increase in the number of the myofilaments, whereas prolonged repetitive lightly loaded isotonic contractions cause hypertrophy of the sarcoplasmic reticulum.

Bendall: Could Dr. Helander give the evidence for the statement that atrophied muscle fibers will not regenerate? Surely this depends on the degree of atrophy.

Helander: It is a matter of definition. If we interpret atrophy to mean total degeneration then no regeneration will occur. However, if during different stages of hypertrophy the muscle fiber is partly damaged, regeneration may occur (Helander, 1958).

Wierbicki: Is it possible to increase the amount of myofibrillar proteins in porcine muscles by exercise?

Helander: It is possible to increase the amount of myofibrillar proteins in animals by physical exercise. The time needed to achieve a certain increase will depend on several factors: the type and daily duration of physical exercise, the state of the skeletal muscles prior to training, the general physical performance of the animal at the beginning of the exercise period, the age of the animals, etc. (Helander, 1961, 1962*a*, 1962*b*).

Mommaerts: The soluble muscle protein increases in immobilized muscle. Is the increase due to enzymes resulting from a decrease in metabolic rate or activity? Or is there synthesis of other kinds of protein?

Helander: To my knowledge, this point has not been established.

Sayre: How do the membranes of the sarcolemma and the transverse tubular system differ from the membranes of the longitudinal sarcotubular system?

Slautterback: Frequently, membranes of T tubules and sarcolemma appear thicker than those of L tubules. Also, as indicated earlier, reports of difficulty in demonstrating the unit-membrane structure in L tubule membranes may indicate either a different response of the membranes to preservation procedures or the absence of unit-membrane structure in L tubule membranes. In either case, the T and L system membranes are evidently different.

Davies: Does the collagenous mesh remain intact after death? Is it destroyed by boiling the muscle?

Slautterback: Ito (1962) has reported that the collagen associated with a variety of secretory epithelia shows little or no change after remaining at room temperature for several days after death. I have no information on the ultrastructure consequences of boiling muscle.

Kauffman: Is it conceivable that the permeability of the various connective tissue membranes, structurally supporting other muscle proteins, and of those membranes supporting the capillary walls within striated muscle tissue, is directly responsible for the rates and quantities of lipid (primarily neutral triglycerides) deposited within striated muscles?

Helander: Changes in tissue permeability do occur with advancing age, and the accumulation of fat in a muscle may be directly associated with this fact.

Bendall: As bovine animals age, the fat seems to be deposited predominantly in the perimysial layers. We have very little evidence that it is deposited around the capillaries.

Kauffman: Is it appropriate to suggest that the lymphatic system may be important in the biochemical changes which occur in striated muscles during aging and exercise?

Helander: Very little is known about the role of the lymphatic system in muscle and the changes it shows with age.

Bendall: Our results with bovine muscle show that the percentage of collagen content at one month of age is about twice that at six months. From six months up to two years the collagen content remains virtually constant at the lower value. This applies to seven different muscles of vastly differing collagen contents.

Allen: Is it probable that highly marbled (high extracellular fat content) muscles come from animals tending to be arteriosclerotic?

Helander: One would not suspect that the marbling of the muscles of large laboratory animals is due to arteriosclerosis. I would refer you for further information to Helander, 1959, 1960*a*, 1960*b*, 1960*c*.

Kauffman: Can information obtained from the study of cardiac muscle be applied to striated skeletal muscle, with little or no reservations? If not, what are the limitations and why?

Slautterback: In general, one cannot with certainty transfer information obtained on one cell type directly to another cell type without confirming evidence. Of course, one may draw useful inferences where confirming evidence is difficult or impossible to obtain.

Mommaerts: Muscles may predominantly metabolize lipids under aerobic conditions. Anaerobically they use carbohydrates exclusively and in times of intensive metabolism they utilize glycogen. Dr. Lardy discussed glucose entry as a rate-limiting factor in muscle metabolism. It would seem that under conditions of intensive metabolism this should present no problem because the muscles use either lipids or glycogen. Glucose entry, therefore, becomes important during the restitution, when the glycogen stores are being reaccumulated. Would Dr. Lardy comment further on various types of metabolism which may occur in muscle?

Lardy: When glucose or carbohydrate is restricted in the diet the muscle is capable of using relatively large amounts of fat. This is demonstrable in several ways: artery and vein glucose differences, respiration quotient of the muscle, etc. Under these circumstances ketone bodies and neutral fat are burned. Glucose permeability is important for regulating glycolysis in resting muscle. Work is known to be a condition that induces permeability of the muscle to glucose.

Kauffman: Do lipids accumulate in muscle tissues (and other depot sites) as the result of an attempt by the circulatory system to remove them from the blood because of their interference with efficient circulation or is this a functional mechanism for the conservation of excess energy?

Lardy: The lipids in adipose tissue and presumably those that accumulate between muscles are largely synthesized by the cells that retain them.

Kauffman: What evidence is there that lipids stored in muscle tissue may be metabolized within the muscle to supply a direct source of energy in muscle contraction, etc.?

Lardy: Probably relatively little neutral fat is stored in muscle cells where large amounts of fat are burned during muscular work. Muscle cells burn fatty acids brought to them by the blood. I have no idea whether any fatty acids released from fat-depositing cells in a muscle mass can be carried more or less directly to the working fibers.

Allen: Considerable emphasis has been given to the importance of the quantity of intramuscular fat in the muscles of large laboratory animals. This emphasis has resulted in selection for animals with the ability to acquire large quantities of intramuscular fat. It is, in fact, not unusual to find two to five times more fat in muscles from these animals than in muscles of most small laboratory animals. Would you comment on whether or not it is possible that this selection has been for enzymes and cofactors necessary in fat synthesis within the muscle itself?

Lardy: It is likely that the fat deposited is synthesized in the muscle, but also likely that it is not synthesized in myofibrils. Animals that have been selected through many generations for intramuscular fat probably have more fat-synthesizing cells, and if one were to measure the total muscle mass for fat-synthesizing enzymes, the values would probably be higher than for a comparable sample of lean muscle, but only because of the difference in the distribution of cell types.

De Fremery: Is the citric acid inhibition of the phosphofructokinase reaction due to chelation of an essential mineral, or does it have some other specific action?

Lardy: Phosphofructokinase is a magnesium-requiring enzyme, and for this reason it could be inhibited by citrate if magnesium were present in limiting amounts. Those who have reported inhibition of this enzyme by citrate claim that the results are not due to metal chelation. Mr. Verner Paetkau is now examining this question in our laboratory, using pure phosphofructokinase.

Davies: I would like to comment on an aspect of muscle ultrastructure which helps to explain how the myosin filaments are held in hexagonal

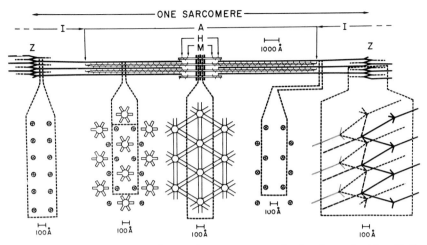

Fig. 6.1. — Molecular anatomy of part of one sarcomere of striated muscle. After H. E. Huxley, 1965.

array (Huxley, 1965). Figure 6.1, based on Dr. H. E. Huxley's work, shows that at the M region there are hexagonal links between the thick filaments. Besides helping to hold the sarcomeres together, the links explain part of the thickening in the M region. The links tend to get lost during the fixation and heavy metal staining procedures that are used in normal electron microscopy. The figure also shows the 216 cross links per thick filament with the hexagonal screw axis of symmetry.

Hoekstra: Is anything known of the chemical nature of the cross links in the M region?

Davies: They are a material which can be shown with a variety of electron stains. The ordinary cross links are the heads of heavy meromyosin. Their nature is quite unknown.

Schram: The ratio of actin to myosin filaments may be as high as 18:1 in certain specialized structures. It is difficult for me to see how the sliding filament theory can be made to operate with this sort of geometry.

Davies: I find no problem in seeing how the sliding filament mechanism could work under these circumstances. The thick filaments are considerably thicker in invertebrate muscles, and yet a large number of them can lie peripherally in an orbit around each of these (much thicker) thick filaments in the specialized muscles. All that an actin has to do is to make contact with one or more of the cross bridges on the thick filaments at one end and then connect the other end of the actin (through the Z line in the organized muscles that have Z lines) with one or more cross bridges on another thick filament. This gives a tension-bearing unit from one tendon right through to the other tendon through many thousands of thick and thin filaments.

Schram: If we are talking about a myosin filament which is, say, twice or three times the diameter of the standard this still gives us a circumference which is barely adequate to carry the cross links which are suggested. How is it that in the case of 12 filaments the myosin filament is not larger but is about the same size; that is, 140–160 Å?

Davies: The most important factor is the number of equivalents of heavy meromyosin or places where the actual link between the actin and myosin occurs. Just because you see 18 filaments does not mean that there are 18 at all points. Twelve have been reported in ordinary vertebrate muscle where there is a double overlap. In a fully contracted muscle the actin filaments not only slide into the A band but also overlap with a double overlap in the middle and penetrate right through the H zone. Under these conditions and slightly to the side of the real M zone one can see 12 actins around each myosin. Only six of these make contact with the myosin while the remaining six are from the other side.

Slautterback: Nevertheless, in many muscles there are still 12, and not as a result of double overlap.

Davies: When you look at the X-ray diagrams, certainly for the paramyosin, you can see a very large number of the contact sites (the equivalent to the cross bridges), and they are entirely sufficient for this number of actions. Also, the thick filaments are tremendously long and the actins can also be interwoven over each other.

References

Cowdry, E. V. 1952. *Problems of Aging: Biochemical and Medical Aspects* (3d ed.). Williams & Wilkins Co., Baltimore.

Goldspink, G. 1964. Increase in length of skeletal muscle during normal growth. *Nature 204*:1095.

Helander, E. 1958. Adaptive muscular allomorphism. *Nature 182*:1035.

———. 1959. Fat content of skeletal muscular tissue. *Acta Morphol. Neerlando-Scandinavica 2*:230.

———. 1960a. Muscular atrophy and fat content of muscle after unilateral lumbar sympathectomy. *Acta Morphol. Neerlando-Scandinavica 3*:48.

———. 1960b. Fat content of muscular tissue after castration. *Acta Morphol. Neerlando-Scandinavica 3*:51.

———. 1960c. Muscular atrophy and lipomorphosis induced by immobilizing plaster casts. *Acta Morphol. Neerlando-Scandinavica 3*:92.

———. 1961. Influence of exercise and restricted activity on protein composition of skeletal muscle. *Biochem. J. 78*:478.

————. 1962. Myocardial protein composition and its relation to functional activity of varying degrees. *Cardiologia 41*:94.

Helander, E., and C. A. Thulin. 1962. Isometric tension and myofilamental cross-sectional area in striated muscle. *Amer. J. Physiol. 202*:824.

Huxley, H. E. 1965. Structural evidence concerning the mechanism of contraction in striated muscle, p. 3. *In* W. M. Paul, E. E. Daniel, C. M. Kay, and G. Monckton (eds.), *Muscle*. Pergamon Press, Oxford.

Ito, S. 1962. Light and electron microscopic study of membranous cytoplasmic organelles. In *The Interpretation of Ultrastructure* (Symp. Int. Soc. Cell Biol.) *1*:129.

Richter, G. W., and A. Kellner. 1963. Hypertrophy of the human heart at the level of fine structure. *J. Cell Biol. 18*:195.

PART II

Muscle Regulation and Its Response to Stress and Disease

Chapter 7

Regulation of Muscle Growth by Androgens

C. D. KOCHAKIAN

The growth of mammals now is known to be regulated by the function of several endocrine organs. Each organ seems to play a specific role. The anterior pituitary, by the secretion of growth hormone, is responsible for general over-all growth of not only the body but also the major internal organs. The removal of the anterior pituitary in the immature animal markedly decelerates growth; and extracts of the anterior pituitary not only restore growth but can produce giantism (Evans, Simpson, and Li, 1948). Thyroidectomy also interrupts growth, but internal secretions of the thyroid cannot substitute for that of the growth hormone of the anterior pituitary (Scow, 1959). In addition to these two endocrine organs, the testis also plays an important role in the growth and development of the body (muscles). The hormones of this endocrine organ impart the extra growth which is characteristic of the difference in muscular development between males and females. This report will be concerned with the nature of the induction of growth of the skeletal muscles by androgens from the whole animal to the molecular level.

NITROGEN BALANCE STUDIES [1]

Dog

True growth occurs when tissue protein is increased. This phenomenon is best demonstrated in the total animal by the nitrogen balance technic. The formation of new protein is reflected by a positive nitrogen balance. This type of study was utilized in the discovery of the protein anabolic action of the androgens (Kochakian, 1935, 1946, 1950a, 1964; Kochakian and Murlin, 1935). A positive nitrogen balance in castrated dogs was produced within 24 hr by the administration of an extract of male urine. Continuation of the injections produced a further decrease in the urinary

1. This subject and the one discussed next (composition of change in body weight) have been reviewed in detail in Kochakian, 1946, 1950a, and 1964.

nitrogen excretion to a minimal level where it was maintained. Cessation of the injections produced a short period of negative nitrogen balance. The changes in total urinary nitrogen were accompanied by parallel changes in the urea. The fecal nitrogen excretion was not affected. The body weight of the dogs showed changes in parallel with the changes in nitrogen balance. The body weight initially increased and reached a maximum where it was maintained. When the injections were stopped, a decrease in body weight occurred. The normal male dog was unresponsive.

The protein anabolic effect of the androgens was accompanied by an increased utilization of fat as indicated by RQ determinations, but no major change in the basal metabolic rate occurred (Kochakian, 1935, 1946).

Effects identical to those of the urinary androgenic extracts were induced not only in the dog (Kochakian and Murlin, 1936; Kochakian, 1937, 1964) but also in man (Kenyon *et al.*, 1938) with crystalline androgenic preparation as soon as it became available.

Rat

The studies in the dog were extended to the rat in order to be able to make a more detailed analysis of the protein anabolic effect of the androgens (Kochakian, 1950a, 1964). The administration of testosterone propionate produced a decrease in urinary nitrogen excretion within 24 hr (Fig. 7.1). Continuation of the injections produced a further decrease in urinary nitrogen excretion to a minimal level within two to three days, where it was maintained for several days and then gradually returned to the basal level in spite of the continued injections. On interruption of the injections a short period of extra excretion of nitrogen occurred. Thus, a new phenomenon was observed and was designated as the "wearing-off effect." The animal, however, does not become refractory to the androgen. The experiment can be repeated apparently indefinitely in the same animal. The "wearing-off effect" also has been observed in the dog (Kochakian, 1964) and in man (Kochakian, 1946), but occurs much later. Several other androgens produced the same pattern of response at different dose levels (Kochakian, 1950b).

The anabolic action of the androgens is not mediated through any of the other endocrine organs (Kochakian, 1950, 1964). In some instances, however, the phenomenon is partially modified by the presence or absence of a specific endocrine organ. The normal rat was less responsive and required a higher dose of androgen. The body weight of the depancreatized dog increased in an amount greater than could be accounted for by the decrease in urinary nitrogen excretion. The extra increase apparently was due to a synthesis of fat from glucose. The calculation of the decrease in urinary glucose to fat gave a value in excellent agreement with the extra increase

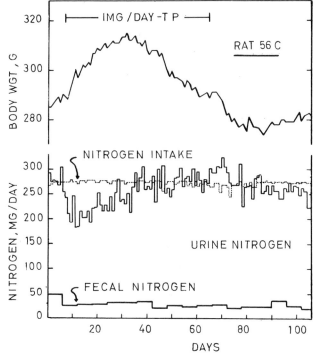

Fig. 7.1.—The effect of testosterone propionate (*TP*) on the body weight and nitrogen balance of the castrated rat. From Kochakian, 1950*b*.

in body weight. The hypophysectomized rat exhibited the same pattern of response as the non-hypophysectomized rat in urinary nitrogen excretion, but the body weight response was modified (Fig. 7.2). The decrease in body weight from the induced maximum did not occur with continued injection of the androgen.

Since growth hormone seems to be the regulating hormone for general growth, a comparison of the anabolic property of this hormone with that of testosterone propionate was made. The administration of growth hormone to the hypophysectomized rat produced a pattern of response identical with that of the androgen, including the "wearing-off effect" on urinary nitrogen excretion (Fig. 7.3). The effect on urinary nitrogen excretion and body weight, however, was greater than that produced by the androgen. The administration of growth hormone to the non-hypophysectomized castrated rat at maximal dose level (Fig. 7.4) produced a response in nitrogen excretion and change in body weight practically identical to that of the androgen with one exception. The decrease in body weight on con-

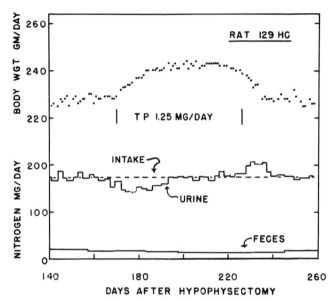

Fig. 7.2. — The effect of testosterone propionate (*TP*) on the body weight and nitrogen excretion of the hypophysectomized castrated (*HC*) rat. From Kochakian, 1950*b*.

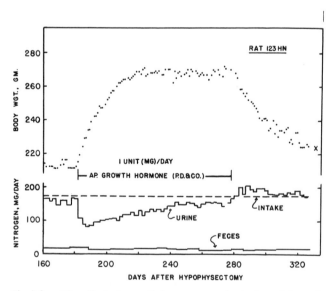

Fig. 7.3. — The effect of growth hormone on the body weight and nitrogen excretion of the hypophysectomized rat. From Kochakian, 1950*b*.

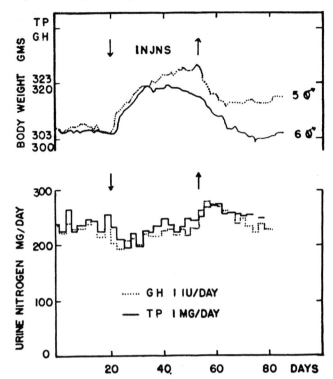

Fig. 7.4. — Comparison of the effect of testosterone propionate (*TP*) and growth hormone (*GH*) on the nitrogen excretion of castrated rats. From Kochakian, 1950*b*.

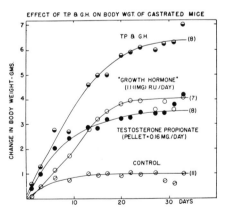

Fig. 7.5. — The effect of testosterone propionate (*TP*) and growth hormone (*GH*) on the body weight of adult castrated mice. From Kochakian and Stettner, 1948.

tinued injection of the hormones did not occur with the growth hormone. The simultaneous administration of growth hormone and testosterone propionate to the castrated rat resulted in a summation of their effects on nitrogen balance and increase in body weight (Kochakian, 1960).

The removal of the anterior pituitary of young adult rats produced not only a loss in body weight but also a marked negative nitrogen balance and a gradual decrease in the level of food intake to conform with the reduced caloric requirement (Kochakian, 1950c). The removal of the testes, on the other hand, had only a small transitory effect on nitrogen balance and body weight.

COMPOSITION OF CHANGE IN BODY WEIGHT

Mice

The administration of androgens to castrated adult mice resulted in an increase in body weight (Kochakian and Stettner, 1948; Kochakian, 1949). The increase was progressive to a maximal level where it was maintained (Fig. 7.5). Growth hormone produced practically an identical response. The simultaneous administration of the two hormones at their respective maximal effective doses produced an exact summation of their effects on body weight. Separate groups of mice were analyzed after 10, 20, and 34 days of treatment. The increase in body weight was due to a progressive accretion of protein accompanied by the essential water (Fig. 7.6). The body fat was decreased. Growth hormone appeared to be more effective than the androgen in the utilization of body fat. These changes were progressive with duration of hormonal treatment. The effect on protein accretion summated when the two hormones were administered simultaneously, but a summation effect on fat catabolism was not as apparent. The changes in fat metabolism occurred in the carcass. The tissues which increased in weight demonstrated an increase not only in protein and accompanying water but also in fat. The induced protein synthesis occurred primarily in the carcass (Fig. 7.7). Protein synthesis was induced in the liver by both hormones. The androgen in addition stimulated growth of the accessory sex organs and the kidneys. Growth hormone had no detectable effect on the accessory sex organs but had a small effect in the kidney. The simultaneous administration of the hormones produced a summation of their respective effects in the various tissues.

It is apparent from these and the nitrogen balance studies that these two hormones have separate and nonconflicting roles in regulating metabolism.[2]

2. One of the characteristics of a rat treated with growth hormone is an appearance of roundness. This is due to a lack of muscle tone. The abdominal wall bulges, and when the animals are picked up, the lack of tone is readily apparent. The androgen-treated animal does not present this appearance and has excellent muscular tone.

Rats

Studies in the rat illustrate the importance of dose and duration of treatment with androgen as well as the influence of the age of the animal. It was early recognized that castration retarded the rate of growth (Rubinstein, Abarbanel, and Kurland, 1939) and that physiological doses of androgens would increase (Rubinstein and Solomon, 1941; Edgren, 1963) while larger doses would inhibit the rate of growth of young rats (Rubinstein, Kurland, and Goodwin, 1939). The growth inhibitory effect of testosterone propionate also was apparent in male but not in female mice

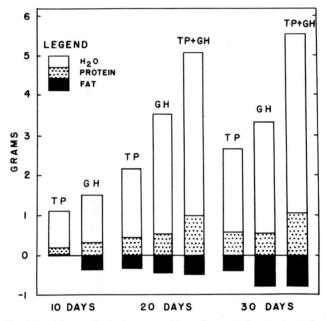

Fig. 7.6. — Change in body composition of castrated mice treated with testosterone propionate (*TP*) and growth hormone (*GH*). From Kochakian and Stettner, 1948.

(Kochakian, 1940). The failure of Scow and Hagan (1957) to observe any changes after castration and testosterone propionate administration is puzzling and may be due to the wide variations in the body weights of the rats. The inhibitory effect is more readily apparent in the normal than in the castrated rat (Kochakian, 1964). Testosterone propionate produced a progressive increase in body weight (Fig. 7.8), but as the dose of the androgen was increased above 1.0 mg per day the maximum increase in body weight became progressively less and was followed by an increasingly greater decrease in body weight with continued injection of the androgen.

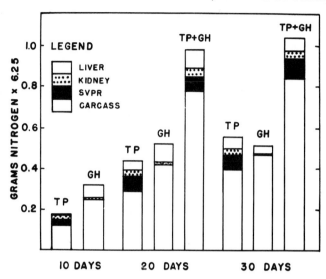

Fig. 7.7. — The sites of increase in protein content of mice treated
with testosterone propionate (*TP*) and growth hormone (*GH*).
SVPR = seminal vesicles and prostates. From Kochakian and Stettner, 1948.

On cessation of androgen treatment the body weights increased. The rate
of increase was greatest in the rats which received the highest dose of the
androgen. These changes in body weight were accompanied by parallel
changes in food intake (appetite). Thus, the intake of food increased during
the initial period of growth, then decreased, and on cessation of injections
increased. The normal adult rat responded in a similar fashion except that
the increase in body weight was less and the decrease became apparent
with a lower dose of the androgen (Fig. 7.9). The changes in body weight
again were reflected in the food intake. In one series of studies in normal
rats, nitrogen balance and the composition of the rats were determined.
The androgen produced a definite positive nitrogen balance (Table 7.1).
Analysis of the rats showed a marked decrease in fat which was restored
during the postinjection period. The changes in amount of fat occurred
in the carcass and were calorically equivalent to the changes in food intake (Table 7.2).

Prolonged treatment with androgen at a high dose in young adult
castrated rats not only decreased the rate of growth after the initial spurt
(Fig. 7.10) but also utilized the androgen-induced accretion of protein in
the carcass (Table 7.3) for further growth of the accessory sex organs and
kidneys with a further catabolism of carcass fat (Table 7.4). The initial
spurt in growth was increasingly less apparent in younger animals (Kochakian, Robertson, and Bartlett, 1950).

CASTRATE RATS

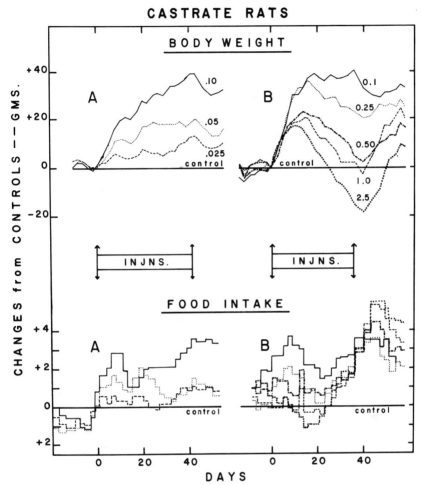

Fig. 7.8. — Changes in body weight and food intake in castrated rats injected with various doses of testosterone propionate. Changes are from control rats which during injection period gained 107 g in series *A*, and 77 g in series *B*. Average body weights at beginning of injection were, for series *A*, 254–260 g per group; and, for series *B*, 274–294 g per group. Series *A* contained ten rats per group; and series *B*, five to seven rats per group. Dose of testosterone propionate (mg/day) is indicated beside body weight curves of respective groups. From Kochakian and Endahl, 1959.

WEIGHT OF SKELETAL MUSCLE

Rat

Since the hormones induce an increase in carcass protein, it was assumed that the protein of the skeletal muscles was increased. The rate of growth of muscles in the rat after castration decreased in parallel with the decrease

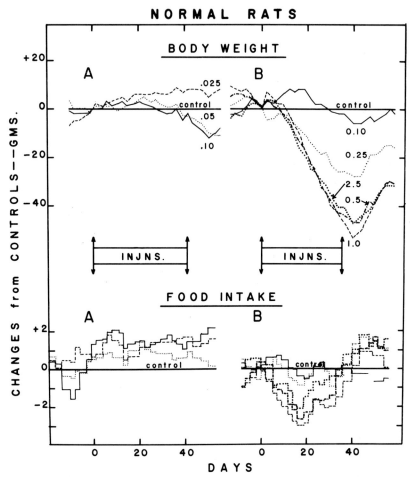

Fig. 7.9. — Changes in body weight and food intake in normal rats injected with various doses of testosterone propionate. Changes are from control rats which during injection period gained 107 g in series *A*, and 90 g in series *B*. Average body weights at beginning of injection were, for series *A*, 301–315 g per group; and, for series *B*, 276–283 g per group. Series *A* contained ten rats per group; and series *B*, five to eight rats per group. Dose of testosterone propionate (mg / day) is indicated beside body weight curves of respective groups. From Kochakian and Endahl, 1959.

in rate of growth of the animal[3] (see Fig. 7.11; also Kochakian, Tillotson, and Endahl, 1956*a*). Proportionate decreases were obtained in the nitro-

3. The muscles of the perineal complex of the rat (Wainman and Shipounoff, 1941) and mouse (Kochakian, 1959), however, show a dependence in testicular secretion similar to that of the accessory sex organs. One of these muscles, the so-called levator ani, which appears to be in fact the dorsal bulbocavernosus (Hayes, 1965), has been proposed (Eisenberg and Gordan, 1950; Hershberger *et al.*, 1953) and used extensively (see Kochakian,

gen (protein) content. Administration of testosterone propionate reversed the effects of castration in a uniform fashion. Korner and Young (1955a) noted that 17-methyl-androstene-3β,17β-diol at 1 mg per day for 35 days increased the body weight of rats with an isometric increase in several skeletal muscles, but the acromiotrapezius grew faster and the digastric and soleus slower than the body weight. The protein content changed in parallel with the weight. The effects were observed in 14-week-old normal

TABLE 7.1

Effect of testosterone propionate (TP, 2.5 mg/day) on the nitrogen balance of normal male adult rats fed ad libitum

| Period | Days | Mg of nitrogen retained per period | | | | | |
| | | Experiment 1 | | | Experiment 2 | | |
		Control	TP	Diff.	Control	TP	Diff.
Basal	7	730	775	+45	844	860	+16
Injection	28	2,785	1,975	−810	3,449	2,443	−1,006
Postinjection	21	....	....	....	1,980	1,873	−107
				−765			−1,097

Source: C. D. Kochakian and J. A. Webster, "Effect of testosterone propionate on the appetite, body weight and composition of the normal rat," *Endocrinology 63(1958):737.*

TABLE 7.2

Comparison of the caloric changes in body fat and food intake produced by testosterone propionate in adult normal rats

Period	Body fat		Food intake	
Injection	−24.9 g	−227 cal	−62 g	−248 cal
Postinjection	+27.5 g	+250 cal	+64 g	+256 cal

Source: C. D. Kochakian and J. A. Webster, "Effect of testosterone propionate on the appetite, body weight and composition of the normal rat," *Endocrinology 63(1958):737.*

female and 12-week-old normal male rats. The age of the male rats was very critical. Slightly older or younger animals gained less weight. Hypophysectomized female rats of the same age also responded to the steroid with an increase in body weight and an isometric increase in the several muscles. The administration of testosterone propionate to rats hypophysectomized or thyroidectomized at 25 days of age also produced an increase in body weight but no significant increase in weight and protein content of the thigh muscles (Scow, 1952).

1964; Edgren, 1963) as an indicator of the anabolic effect of steroids. On the basis of the comparison of the response of this muscle to that of the seminal vesicles or the prostates, a large number of steroids has been proposed as possessing preferentially anabolic activity. Unfortunately, clinical trials have not completely supported the laboratory deductions (see Edgren, 1963; Hayes, 1965).

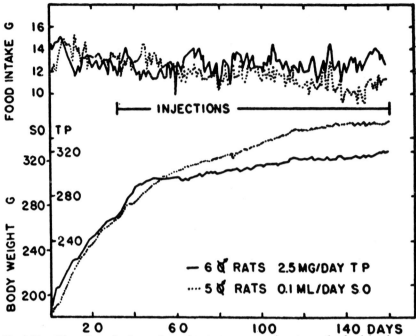

Fig. 7.10. — The effect of a large dose of testosterone propionate on the food intake and body weight of the castrated rat. From Kochakian, Robertson, and Bartlett, 1950.

TABLE 7.3

Changes in composition of castrated "fat" rats produced by testosterone propionate at 1 mg/day for 13 days, expressed in grams

Body portion	Wt	H$_2$O	Protein	Fat	Rest
Carcass and gut	9.90	18.70	3.82	−13.49	0.87
Sem. ves., pros.	2.24	1.80	0.38	0.04	0.02
Liver	1.03	0.70	0.17	−0.01	0.17
Kidney	0.45	0.32	0.09	0.01	0.03
TOTAL	13.62	21.52	4.46	−13.45	1.09

Note: Values are the differences between the changes in the control and androgen-treated rats during the 125 days (see Fig. 7.10).

Source: C. D. Kochakian, E. Robertson, and M. N. Bartlett, "Sites and nature of protein anabolism stimulated by testosterone propionate in the rat," *Amer. J. Physiol. 163(1950):332.*

Guinea pig

Weight. — In contrast to the rat, certain skeletal muscles of the guinea pig show marked dependency on androgens for their full development.[4] Papanicolaou and Falk (1938) first observed a great difference in the size

4. Limited observations on specific muscles of other species have been reported (see Kochakian, Hill, and Costa, 1964).

TABLE 7.4

Effect of 125 days of injections of testosterone propionate on the composition of gain in body weight of castrated rats fed ad libitum, expressed in grams

Composition	Carcass	Liver	Kidney	Sem. ves. and pros.	Total
Weight	−34.30	+1.00	+1.30	+7.52	−24.48
Water	−1.00	+0.54	+0.99	+5.41	+5.94
Protein	−2.92	+0.33	+0.67	+3.65	+1.73
Fat	−30.60	−0.13	+0.05	+0.19	−30.49

Source: C. D. Kochakian, E. Robertson, and M. N. Bartlett, "Sites and nature of protein anabolism stimulated by testosterone propionate in the rat," *Amer. J. Physiol. 163(1950):332.*

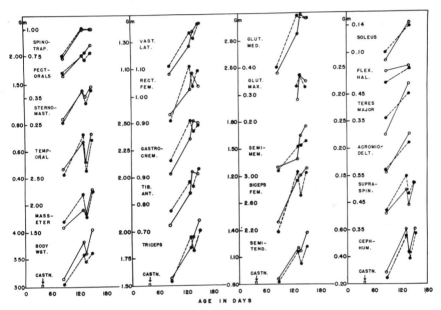

Fig. 7.11. — Comparison between muscle weights of normal and castrated rats at different ages (castration at 36–40 days of age). Normal: O—O; castrated: ●—●. From Kochakian, Tillotson, and Endahl, 1956.

of the temporal muscle of the male and female guinea pig and noted that administration of testosterone propionate increased the size of the muscle in the female. This observation was confirmed (see Fig. 7.12; also Kochakian, Humm, and Bartlett, 1948; Scow and Roe, 1953) and extended in a detailed study of 47 other muscles and the heart.

Castration did not initially alter the growth rate of young male guinea pigs, but after about ten weeks the rate of growth was progressively retarded (see Fig. 7.13; also Kochakian *et al.*, 1956*b*). Older animals, however, showed a rapid decrease in body weight. The rate of growth of all of

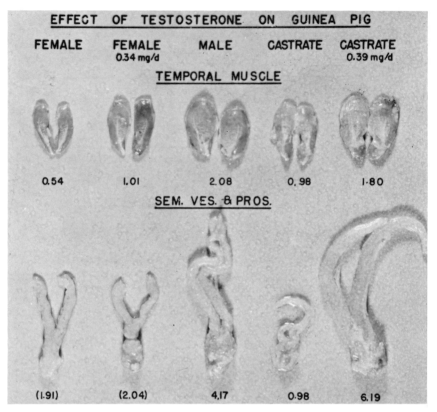

Fig. 7.12. — Comparison of the size of the temporal muscle of the male and female adult
guinea pig and the effect of testosterone propionate. Castration was performed at 400 g
body weight. Two pellets of testosterone propionate (15 ± 1 mg each) were implanted
subcutaneously at the time of castration. Autopsy was 54 days later. Total testosterone
propionate absorbed was 13–14 mg. The weights of the tissues in grams are presented
below each tissue. From Kochakian and Tillotson, 1956.

the skeletal muscles was decreased, but to markedly varying degrees (Fig.
7.14). The greatest decrease occurred in the head muscles, with a progressive decrease in the other muscles from head to rear. The same effect was
noted in the guinea pigs castrated at the older age. The retractor penis
muscle (Fig. 7.13) was more responsive than the most responsive skeletal
muscle and was similar to those of the perineal complex (see Fig. 7.14;
also Wainman and Shipounoff, 1941; Kochakian, 1959). The administration of testosterone (Fig. 7.15) at an adequate dose level restored the decrease in weight of the respective muscles (Kochakian and Tillotson, 1957).
The effect of testosterone was compared with that of several other steroids
(Table 7.5). Androstan-17β-ol, 3-one proved to be the most effective steroid

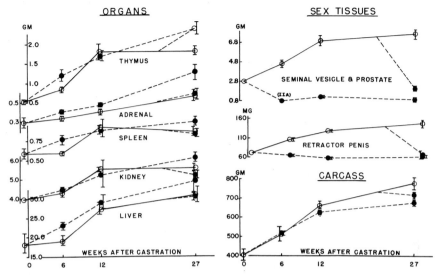

Fig. 7.13. — The effect of castration on the carcass, sex tissues, and organs of the male guinea pig. Castration was performed at three to four months of age, 534 (457–573) g average body weight. The solid lines represent the normal; and the broken lines, the castrated guinea pigs. The standard errors of the mean values are indicated by the perpendicular lines. From Kochakian *et al.*, 1956*b*.

on all of the most responsive muscles. Introduction of a methyl group in the 17 position decreased the effectiveness of each of the steroids. Further alterations in the steroid molecule produced progressive decreases in efficacy. The degree of efficacy, moreover, did not change in parallel with that of the accessory sex organs (Table 7.6).

Growth hormone also stimulated growth in the temporal muscles (Kochakian and Robertson, 1950). This probably is an expression of its general effect on growth of all tissues. The accessory sex organs also were stimulated to grow. The response in the tissues, however, was less than those observed after androgen administration.

Composition. — The weight changes after castration and administration of the androgens were accompanied by proportionate changes in protein, water, and nonprotein nitrogen constituents (Kochakian *et al.*, 1948; Kochakian *et al.*, 1956*b*; Kochakian and Tillotson, 1957) in the individual muscles. Furthermore, the amino acid composition was not changed by androgen administration and was the same in the several muscles which were analyzed (Kochakian, Hill, and Costa, 1964).

The myosins, collagen, and sarcoplasm of the temporal muscle decreased after castration and were restored to normal by testosterone (Scow and Hagan, 1955). The myoglobin, however, was unchanged and im-

Fig. 7.14. — The effect of castration on the weight of the muscles of the guinea pig. The muscles from both the left and the right sides were removed. The values, however, are one-half the averages of both muscles except for the diaphragm and retractor penis (see Fig. 7.13 for further details).

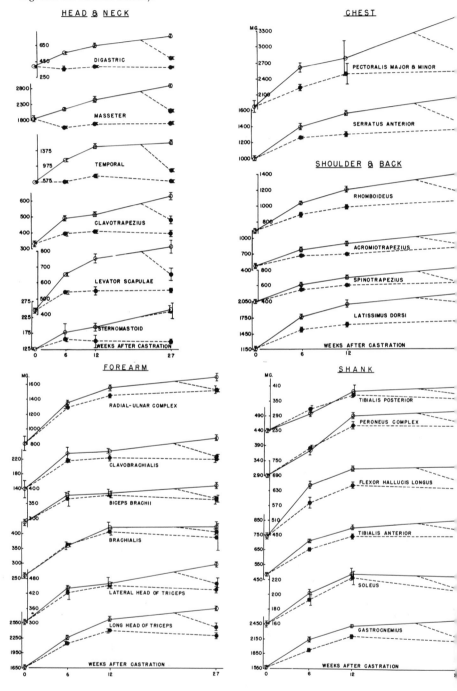

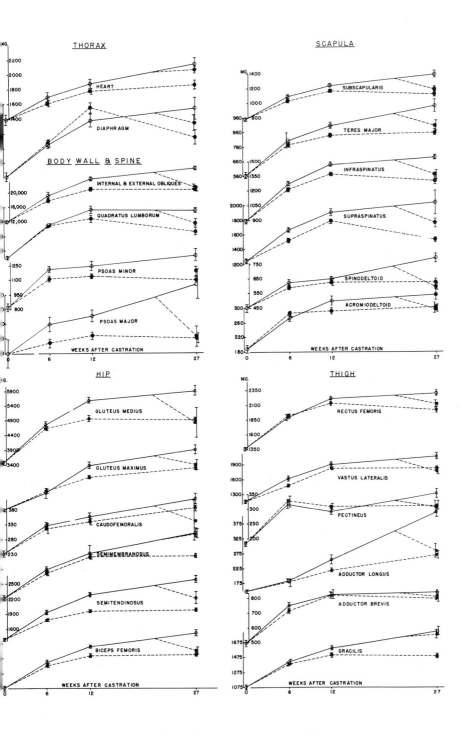

Fig. 7.15. — The response of the individual muscles of the castrated male guinea pig to testosterone stimulation. The values are the averages of two separate experiments at approximately same dose level (5.9 and 5.4 mg / 21 days of testosterone); 8 and 7 animals per group. The difference from the average for the first experiment is indicated by the horizontal solid line; and for the second experiment, by the broken line. The third experiment (×) was at fivefold increase in dose (28.4 mg / 21 days). The normal values (O—O) are the average of 12 guinea pigs. The values for the castrated control guinea pigs (the zero line) are the averages of 30 animals. From Kochakian and Tillotson, 1957.

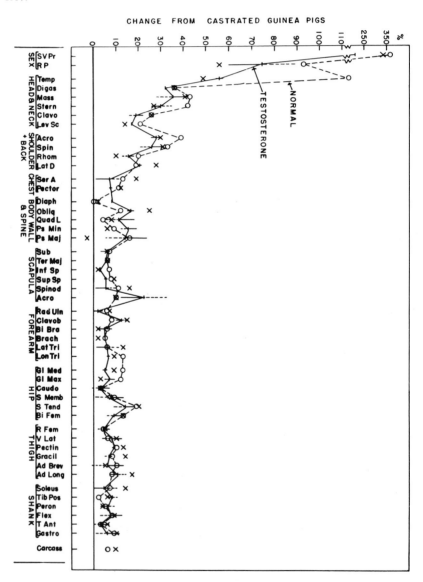

TABLE 7.5

Relative myotrophic and androgenic potencies of several C_{19} steroids. The respective values are compared to those of testosterone set at 100.

Steroids	Sem. ves. and pros.	Digastric	Masseter	Clavo-trapezius	Temporal	Sterno-mastoid	Retractor penis
Androstan-17β-ol,3-one	150	380	320	280	230	190	150
Testosterone	100	100	100	100	100	100	100
Methylandrostan-17β-ol,3-one	100	140	120	80	90	100	80
Androstane-3α,17β-diol	50	60	70	280	70	90	30
Methyltestosterone	50	60	50	40	30	20	100
Methylandrostane-3α,17β-diol	16	30	20	9	20	. . .	4
Androstene-3,17-dione	17	10	10	. . .	10	3	20
Androstane-3,17-dione	16	20	10	20	10	8	8
Dehydroepiandrosterone	15	10	4	20	10	3	4
Epiandrosterone	5	10	6	. . .	4	. . .	30

Source: C. D. Kochakian, "Protein anabolic property of androgens," *Alabama J. Med. Sci. 1(1964)*:24.

TABLE 7.6

Ratio of myotrophic to androgenic (seminal vesicles and prostates) activity of several C_{19} steroids. The respective values are compared to those of testosterone set at 1.0.

Steroids	Digastric	Masseter	Clavo-trapezius	Temporal	Sterno-mastoid	Retractor penis
Androstan-17β-ol,3-one	2.5	2.1	1.9	1.5	1.3	1.0
Androstane-3α,17β-diol	1.2	1.4	5.7	1.4	1.8	0.6
Methylandrostan-17β-ol,3-one	1.4	1.2	0.8	0.9	1.0	0.8
Methylandrostane-3α,17β-diol	1.8	1.2	0.6	1.3	. . .	0.3
Testosterone	1.0	1.0	1.0	1.0	1.0	1.0
Methyltestosterone	1.2	1.0	0.7	0.5	0.4	1.9
Androstane-3,17-dione	1.3	0.8	1.4	1.3	0.5	0.5
Epiandrosterone	2.6	1.2	. . .	0.8	. . .	5.8
Androstene-3,17-dione	0.8	0.8	. . .	0.6	0.2	1.3
Dehydroepiandrosterone	0.7	0.3	1.5	0.7	0.2	0.3

Source: C. D. Kochakian, "Protein anabolic property of androgens," *Alabama J. Med. Sci. 1(1964)*:24.

parted a characteristic redness to the muscle of the castrated animal. Histological examination of the muscles demonstrated a decrease in the diameter of the fibrils after castration and a restoration in size by androgen.

Comparison of the effect of fasting. — The removal of food for nine days produced a rapid and similar loss (approximately 30%) in body weight in normal, castrated, and testosterone-treated guinea pigs (Kochakian, Tillotson, and Austin, 1957). The individual muscles of the normal animals lost weight to approximately the same degree (Fig. 7.16). A similar effect was noted in the castrated animals except that only a small fur-

Fig. 7.16. — The effect of castration, inanition, and testosterone on the weight of the individual muscles of the young adult male guinea pig. The weights of the muscles of the normal animals are presented with the specific muscle. From Kochakian, Tillotson, and Austin, 1957.

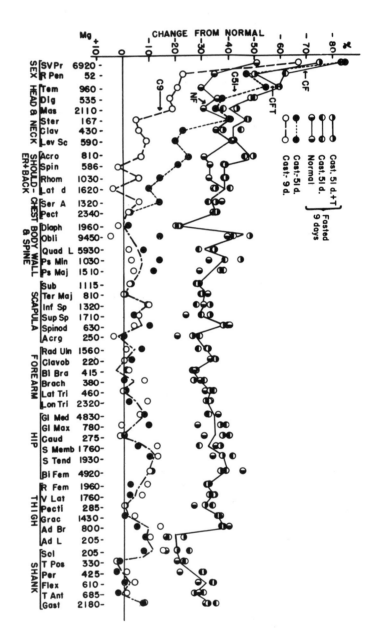

ther decrease occurred in those muscles which had already decreased greatly as a result of castration. The administration of testosterone as a subcutaneously implanted 15 mg pellet produced an increase in weight of only the accessory sex tissues. The injection of 10 mg per day of testosterone propionate during the fast, however, increased the weight and protein content of many of the muscles (Table 7.5). Thus, the androgen is able to stimulate a mobilization of amino acids and other essential constituents from other tissues to build specialized tissues — an effect similar to that observed on prolonged administration of androgen to rats fed *ad libitum*.

NUCLEIC ACIDS

The RNA and DNA concentration or amount showed no correlation with the dependency of the muscle on androgen (see Table 7.7; also, Kochakian, Hill, and Harrison, 1964).

TABLE 7.7
Nucleic acid content of muscles of the male guinea pig

Muscle	Weight mg	RNA		DNA		RNA/DNA
		mg	mg/g	mg	mg/g	
5 months (approx.) of age [a]						
Masseter	5,190	6.42	1.25	4.82	0.94	1.33
Temporal	1,690	1.72	1.04	0.77	0.46	2.24
Gastrocnemius	4,370	4.19	0.96	2.31	0.53	1.81
10 months (approx.) of age [b]						
Masseter	6,730	7.86	1.18	4.46	0.67	1.76
Temporal	2,450	2.39	0.97	0.75	0.31	3.18
Gastrocnemius	5,420	5.76	1.02	2.21	0.40	2.60
Oblique			0.93		0.30	3.10

[a] Average body weight of 15 guinea pigs was 790 (695–890) g.
[b] Average body weight of 8 guinea pigs was 1,010 (910–1,190) g.
Source: C. D. Kochakian, J. Hill, and D. G. Harrison, "Regulation of nucleic acids of muscles of accessory sex organs of guinea pigs by androgens," *Endocrinology 74(1964)*:635.

The highest concentration of both nucleic acids occurred in the masseter muscle. Three other muscles showed essentially the same concentrations in spite of their wide difference in responsiveness to androgen. Furthermore, the RNA increased in direct proportion with the increase in weight of the muscles in the older animals. The DNA, on the other hand, had already attained the maximum level when the animals were five months of age.

Castration produced the expected small decrease in weight of the gastrocnemius and oblique muscles, and no detectable change in either RNA or DNA was observed. The rate of growth of the temporal and masseter muscles, on the other hand, was markedly decreased, with a concomitant decrease in RNA (Table 7.8). Prolongation of the period of castration, moreover, indicated that these two muscles continued to grow but at a much slower rate than those of the normal animal. The RNA increased in direct proportion with the increase in weight. This RNA,

TABLE 7.8
Effect of castration and age on the nucleic acids of the muscles of the male guinea pig

Guinea pigs	Temporal			Masseter		
	Weight, mg	RNA, mg	DNA, mg	Weight, mg	RNA, mg	DNA, mg
	At castration [a]					
Normal	625	0.86	0.42	3,028	4.59	3.06
	35–55 days after castration [b]					
Normal	1,690	1.72	0.77	5,190	6.42	4.82
Castrated	600	0.64	0.52	3,190	4.28	3.91
	223–230 days after castration [c]					
Normal	2,450	2.39	0.75	6,730	7.86	4.46
Castrated	930	0.95	0.67	4,040	5.36	4.91

[a] Average body weight of 5 normal guinea pigs was 517 (489–537) g. This was the weight at castration; the age was approximately three months.

[b] Average body weight of 15 normal guinea pigs was 790 (695–980) g, and of 20 castrated animals was 680 (480–901) g.

[c] Average body weight of 8 normal guinea pigs was 1,010 (910–1,190) g, and of 12 castrated animals was 970 (680–1,250) g.

Source: C. D. Kochakian, J. Hill, and D. G. Harrison, "Regulation of nucleic acids of muscles of accessory sex organs of guinea pigs by androgens," *Endocrinology 74(1964):*635.

however, did not seem to be related to the growth stimulatory effect of the androgens. The administration of testosterone at various periods of time after castration produced remarkably identical absolute increases in the temporal muscles in spite of the great differences in both weight and RNA content of the muscle of the castrated animals at the different ages (Table 7.9).

It was of particular interest that the DNA had not reached its maximum level in these muscles[5] at the age of castration, i.e., three months (Table 7.8) and that castration decreased the rate of formation of the full complement of DNA (and presumably nuclei).

5. The DNA of the skeletal muscles of the rat also continue to increase until at least 95 days of age (Enesco and LeBlond, 1962).

TABLE 7.9

Effect of duration of castration on the weight and testosterone responsiveness of the temporal muscles of the guinea pig

Duration of castration, in days	Temporal muscle		
	Castrate, mg	Testosterone, mg	Difference, mg
35	530	750	220
86	800	1,030	230
220	930	1,150	220

Note: Castration was performed at 420–700 g body weight. There were at least six animals per group. Two pellets of 15 ± 1 mg each were implanted 12 to 15 days before autopsy. The masseter muscle responded in the same manner as the temporal muscles.

Testosterone induced an early rapid increase in the RNA content of both muscles (Figs. 7.17, 7.18). Prolongation of androgen stimulation resulted in the expected progressive increase in muscle weight without a continued increase in rate of RNA formation; consequently the high concentration of RNA was decreased to that of the normal values. Thus, an increase in RNA preceded the increase in weight of muscle, presumably to provide the RNA's essential for protein biosynthesis. The total DNA was not changed.

PROTEIN BIOSYNTHESIS

In vivo

The incorporation of glycine-2-^{14}C administered four hours before autopsy into the protein of the temporal muscle was slightly decreased by castration and increased to above twice normal by the administration of testosterone (Table 7.10). A similar effect was noted in a more detailed

TABLE 7.10

Effect of castration and testosterone [a] administration on the rate of incorporation of glycine-2-14C into the protein of guinea pig temporal muscles [b]

Animal group	Body wt, g	Temporal muscle	
		mg	count / min per 10 mg protein [c]
Normal	815	1,820	41
Castrate [d]	840	640	34
Castrate [d] + T	783	990	96

[a] Two pellets of testosterone were implanted subcutaneously 38 or 48 days after castration and 14 days before autopsy, 7.7 mg absorbed.

[b] 50 μc glycine-2-^{14}C was injected ip four hours before autopsy.

[c] The incorporation of radioactivity into the nucleic acids changed in a comparable manner.

[d] Body weight at castration was 468–538 g. Three guinea pigs per group.

Fig. 7.17. — The effect of castration and testosterone administration on the weight and nucleic acids of the temporal muscles of male guinea pigs. Castration was performed at 420–730 g body weight (approximately three months of age). Experiments were initiated approximately seven months later. Testosterone was implanted subcutaneously as two cylindrical pellets of about 15 mg each. There were six guinea pigs per period. The testosterone absorbed for the respective periods was 3.2, 6.6, 13.7, and 17.7 mg. The following were average values for 12 castrated guinea pigs: body wt., 970 (680–1,250) g; temporal muscles, 930 (720–1,250) mg; DNA, 0.72 (0.64–0.87) mg / g; and RNA, 1.02 (0.93–1.30) mg / g. Body weight of eight normal animals was 1,010 (910–1,190) g, and that of testosterone-treated animals was 980 (830–1,100) g, 991 (860–1,100) g, 956 (740–1,170) g, and 1,010 (870–1,190) g, respectively. Ranges in values are expressed by vertical lines. Most variation is a reflection of range in body weight. From Kochakian, Hill, and Harrison, 1964.

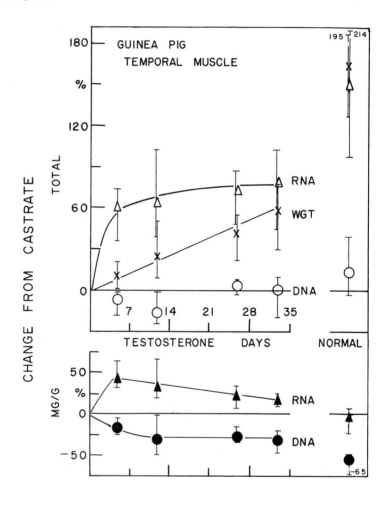

Fig. 7.18. — The effect of castration and testosterone administration on the weight and nucleic acids of the masseter muscles of male guinea pigs (see legend of Fig. 7.17 for details). The following were average values of the masseter muscles for the 12 castrated guinea pigs: wt., 4,040 (3,200–4,980) mg; DNA, 1.22 (1.06–1.28) mg/g; RNA, 1.33 (1.20–1.54) mg/g. From Kochakian, Hill, and Harrison, 1964.

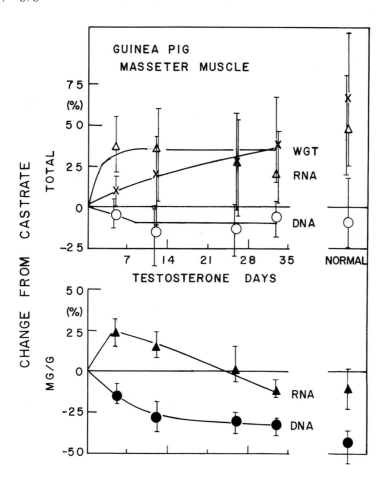

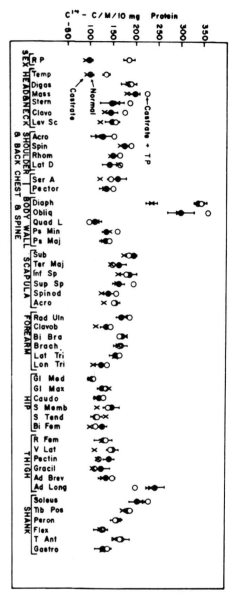

Fig. 7.19. — Comparison of the ability of normal, castrated, and testosterone propionate treated guinea pigs to incorporate ¹⁴C into the protein of their muscles after administration of glycine-2-¹⁴C twelve hours prior to autopsy. The guinea pigs were 510 (490–540) g body weight at castration. The injections were begun three weeks later and continued daily for three weeks. The standard errors of the mean values for the normal (●) guinea pigs are indicated by the horizontal lines; those for the castrated (×) and treated (○) are indicated only when statistically significant difference was obtained. From Costa, Kochakian, and Hill, 1962.

study (Costa, Kochakian, and Hill, 1962) in which the glycine was injected 12 hours prior to autopsy (Fig. 7.19). Castration significantly decreased the rate of incorporation (specific activity) in only one muscle, the diaphragm. The administration of testosterone restored the rate of incorporation of the amino acid into the diaphragm and increased that of the retractor penis and temporal muscle above normal. None of the other 45 muscles was detectably affected by either castration or androgen administration. The changes in the rate of incorporation were reflections of not only glycine but also its metabolite serine. The radioactivity in the other metabolites, aspartic and glutamic acid, was present in trace amounts.

In vitro

The rapid development of knowledge concerning the mechanism of protein biosynthesis has permitted the extension of the studies in vivo to cell-free systems. The first step in protein biosynthesis — amino acid activation (Kochakian *et al.*, 1961) — decreased in activity in direct proportion with the decrease in weight of the temporal muscle after castration (Fig. 7.20). The administration of androgens reversed the effect of castration (Fig. 7.21). The degree of activation of the individual amino acids varied, but the response to castration and androgen was the same. The rate of

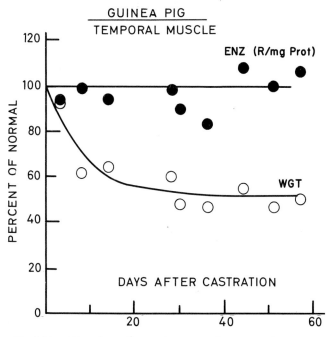

Fig. 7.20. — The effect of castration on ATP-P-32P exchange and weight of temporal muscles of male guinea pigs. Castration was performed at 750–900 g body weight. Average values for 23 normal guinea pigs were as follows: temporal muscles, $1,940 \pm 41$ mg; enzyme activity 10.9 ± 0.4 mμmoles P-32P Ex / min per mg protein (blank $= 1.6 \pm 0.1$). From Kochakian, Tanaka, and Hill, 1961.

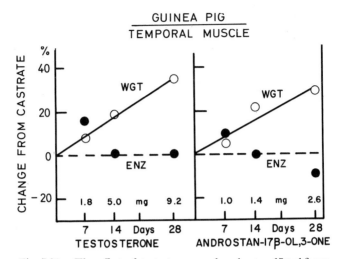

Fig. 7.21. — The effect of testosterone and androstan-17β-ol,3-one on ATP-P-32P exchange and weight of temporal muscles of the castrated male guinea pig. Male guinea pigs were castrated at 660–810 g body weight for two equal and separate series of experiments. One pellet (15 ± 1 mg) of testosterone and two of androstan-17β-ol,3-one were implanted subcutaneously in the guinea pigs 35 days after castration. Two groups of two castrated and three treated guinea pigs were studied simultaneously at each time interval. Average values of temporal muscles for the 12 castrated controls: weight, 1,076 ± 70 mg; and enzyme, 10.6 ± 0.25 mμmoles 32P Ex / min per mg protein (blank = 1.60 ± 0.13). From Kochakian, Tanaka, and Hill, 1961.

incorporation of leucine-U-14C into protein (perchloric acid precipitable material) was decreased by castration and increased to above normal by testosterone administration (Table 7.11). Phenylalanine not only demonstrated a similar effect, but when poly U was added to the incorporating system the rate of incorporation was tremendously increased. Further-

TABLE 7.11

Comparison of the rate of incorporation of amino acids into protein by a microsomal-"pH5" preparation from the temporal muscles of normal, castrated, and testosterone-treated guinea pigs

	Normal	Castrated	Testosterone
Amino acid	count / min per mg		
Leucine-U-14C	126	83	124
Phenylalanine-U-14C	58	36	78
Phenylalanine +poly U	890	800	1,510

Note: The guinea pigs were castrated at 560 (500–660) g body weight. Two pellets of testosterone, 15±1 mg each, were implanted subcutaneously after 64 and 83 days. Autopsy was 14 days later. The muscles were minced with scissors and homogenized for 30 sec in ice-cold medium with a motor-driven Teflon pestle fitted in a glass tube. The homogenate was centrifuged at 12,000 × g for 10 min, and the pellet was rehomogenized for 15 sec. The combined supernatant (postmitochondrial) fraction was made to 10 ml/g and the microsomal material separated from the soluble fraction by centrifugation at 105,000 × g. The microsomal fraction was resuspended in medium at 1 ml/g of muscle. The soluble fraction was adjusted to pH 5.2 with 1 N acetic acid, chilled for 20 to 30 min, and centrifuged at 12,000 × g for 20 min. The sediment was resuspended in medium at 1 ml/g of muscle. The medium contained 0.25 M sucrose, 0.0075 M $MgAc_2$, 0.100 M KCl, 0.035 M Tris-HCL (pH 7.8), and 0.006 M mercaptoethanol. The reaction mixture contained 1 μmole ATP Na_2, 0.2 μmole GTP, 20 μmoles phosphocreatine, 40 μg phosphocreatine kinase (Sigma), 0.4 μc L-amino acid, 0.3 ml of microsomes, and 0.3 ml of "$pH5$" material. All of the reactants were dissolved in the medium except the amino acids, which were in 0.1 ml of water. The final volume was 1 ml. The incubation period was 30 min at 37 C. The specific activities of the amino acids (Schwarz) were L-leucine-U-^{14}C, 240 mc/mole; and L-phenylalanine-U-^{14}C, 165 mc/mmole.

more, the difference between the normal and castrated guinea pigs was no longer detectable, but the effect of androgen was still very evident. Similar results with phenylalanine were obtained with the postmitochondrial fraction. Leucine-U-^{14}C was incorporated at an insignificant rate. These results are comparable to the studies in vivo.

Concentrated cell-free preparations of rat thigh muscles also incorporated amino acids at a lower rate after castration. Androgen administration restored the rate of incorporation to normal (Breuer and Florini, 1965).

SUMMARY

The androgens stimulate an increase in body weight, with a concomitant synthesis of protein in the skeletal muscles accompanied by a decrease in body fat. This property of the androgens is not mediated through any of the other endocrine organs. The endocrine status, as well as the age of the animal and the dose and duration of treatment in certain instances, modifies the action of the androgens. Furthermore, the response of the skeletal muscles is uniform in the rat, but in the guinea pig the individual muscles vary markedly in responsiveness. The changes in weight produced by the androgen do not alter the composition of the muscles. The androgens induce the synthesis of protein by the regulation of the ribonucleic acids and the protein biosynthesis system at the microsomal level.

ACKNOWLEDGMENTS

The investigations of the author reported in this paper were supported by the Committee on Scientific Research of the American Medical Association; Ciba

Pharmaceutical Products, Inc.; Josiah Macy, Jr., Foundation; Committee on Endocrinology of the National Research Council; Committee on Growth of the National Research Council; American Cancer Society; Atomic Energy Commission; and the National Institutes of Health.

References

Breuer, C. D., and J. R. Florini. 1965. Amino acid incorporation into protein by cell-free systems from rat skeletal muscle. IV. Effects of animal age, androgens and anabolic agents on activity of muscle ribosomes. *Biochemistry* 4:1544.

Costa, G., C.D. Kochakian, and J. Hill. 1962. Effect of testosterone propionate on the incorporation of glycine-2-C^{14} in guinea pig tissues. *J. Endocrinol.* 70:175.

Edgren, R. A. 1963. A comparative study of the anabolic and androgenic effects of various steroids. *Acta Endocrinol.* 44(suppl.):87.

Eisenberg, E., and G. S. Gordan. 1950. The levator ani muscle of the rat as an index of myotrophic activity of steroidal hormones. *J. Pharmacol. Exp. Therap.* 99:38.

Enesco, M., and C. P. LeBlond. 1962. Increase in cell number as a factor in the growth of the organs and tissues of the young male rat. *J. Embryol. Exp. Morphol.* 10:530.

Evans, H. M., M. E. Simpson, and C. H. Li. 1948. Gigantism produced in normal rats by injection of pituitary growth hormone: body growth and organ changes. *Growth* 12:15.

Hayes, K. J. 1965. The so-called "Levator ani" of the rat. *Acta Endocrinol.* 48:337.

Hershberger, L. G., E. G. Shipley, and R. K. Meyer. 1953. Myotrophic activity of 19-nortestosterone and other steroids determined by modified Levator ani muscle methods. *Proc. Soc. Exp. Biol. Med.* 83:175.

Kenyon, A. T., I. Sandiford, A. H. Bryan, K. Knowlton, and F. C. Koch. 1938. The effect of testosterone propionate on nitrogen, electrolyte, water and energy metabolism in Eunuchoidism. *Endocrinology* 23:135.

Kochakian, C. D. 1935. Effect of male hormone on protein metabolism of castrate dogs. *Proc. Soc. Exp. Biol. Med.* 32:1064.

————. 1937. Testosterone and testosterone acetate and the protein and energy metabolism of castrate dogs. *Endocrinology* 21:750.

————. 1940. The tolerance of male and female mice respectively to estrogens and androgens. *Endocrinology* 26:54.

————. 1946. The protein anabolic effect of steroid hormones. *Vitamins and Hormones* 4:255.

————. 1949. Renotrophic-androgenic and somatotrophic properties of further steroids. *Amer. J. Physiol.* 158:51.

————. 1950a. The mechanism of the protein anabolic action of testosterone propionate, p. 113. *In* E. S. Gordon (ed.), *Symposium on Steroid Hormone.* Univ. of Wis.

————. 1950*b*. Comparison of protein anabolic property of various androgens in the castrated rat. *Amer. J. Physiol. 160:*53.

————. 1950*c*. Comparison of protein anabolic properties of testosterone propionate and growth hormone in the rat. *Amer. J. Physiol. 160:*66.

————. 1959. Mechanisms of androgen actions. *Lab. Invest. 8:*538.

————. 1960. Summation of protein anabolic effects of testosterone propionate and growth hormone. *Proc. Soc. Exp. Biol. Med. 103:*196.

————. 1964. Protein anabolic property of androgens. *Ala. J. Med. Sci. 1:*24.

Kochakian, C. D., and B. R. Endahl. 1959. Changes in body weight of normal and castrated rats by different doses of testosterone propionate. *Proc. Soc. Exp. Biol. Med. 100:*520.

Kochakian, C. D., J. Hill, and G. Costa. 1964. Amino acid composition of the proteins of the muscles and organs of the normal, castrated and testosterone treated guinea pig. *Acta Endocrinol. 45:*613.

Kochakian, C. D., J. Hill, and D. G. Harrison. 1964. Regulation of nucleic acids of muscles of accessory sex organs of guinea pigs by androgens. *Endocrinology 74:*635.

Kochakian, C. D., J. H. Humm, and M. N. Bartlett. 1948. Effect of steroids on the body weight, temporal muscle and organs of the guinea pig. *Amer. J. Physiol. 155:*242.

Kochakian, C. D., and J. R. Murlin. 1935. The effect of male hormone on the protein and energy metabolism of castrate dogs. *J. Nutr. 10:*437.

————. 1936. The relationship of the synthetic male hormone, androstendion, to the protein and energy metabolism of castrate dogs, and the protein metabolism of a normal dog. *Amer. J. Physiol. 117:*642.

Kochakian, C. D., and E. Robertson. 1950. Effect of growth hormone on temporal muscle of the guinea pig. *Proc. Soc. Exp. Biol. Med. 73:*388.

Kochakian, C. D., E. Robertson, and M. N. Bartlett. 1950. Sites and nature of protein anabolism stimulated by testosterone propionate in the rat. *Amer. J. Physiol. 163:*332.

Kochakian, C. D., and C. E. Stettner. 1948. Effect of testosterone propionate and growth hormone on the weights and composition of body and organs of the mouse. *Amer. J. Physiol. 155:*255.

Kochakian, C. D., R. Tanaka, and J. Hill. 1961. Regulation of amino acid activating enzymes of guinea pig tissues by androgens. *Amer. J. Physiol. 201:*1068.

Kochakian, C. D., and C. Tillotson. 1956. Hormonal regulation of muscle development, p. 63. *In* E. T. Engle and G. Pincus (eds.), *Hormones and the Aging Process.* Academic Press, New York.

————. 1957. Influence of several C[19] steroids on the growth of individual muscles of the guinea pig. *Endocrinology 60:*607.

Kochakian, C. D., C. Tillotson, and J. Austin. 1957. A comparison of the effect of inanition, castration, and testosterone on the muscles of the male guinea pig. *Endocrinology 60:*144.

Kochakian, C. D., C. Tillotson, J. Austin, E. Dougherty, V. Haag, and R. Coalson. 1956 [Kochakian *et al.*, 1956*b*]. The effect of castration on the weight and composition of the muscles of the guinea pig. *Endocrinology 58:*315.

Kochakian, C. D., C. Tillotson, and G. L. Endahl. 1956 [Kochakian *et al.*, 1956*a*]. Castration and the growth of muscles in the rat. *Endocrinology 58:*225.

Korner, A., and F. G. Young. 1955*a*. The influence of methyl androstenediol on the body weight and carcass composition of the rat. *J. Endocrinol. 13:*78.

———. 1955*b*. Effect of methyl androstenediol on the weight and protein content of muscles of the rat. *J. Endocrinol. 13:*84.

Papanicolaou, G. V., and E. A. Falk. 1938. General muscular hypertrophy induced by androgenic hormone. *Science 87:*238.

Rubinstein, H. S., A. R. Abarbanel, and A. A. Kurland. 1939. The effect of castration on body weight and length of the male albino rat. *Endocrinology 25:*397.

Rubinstein, H. S., A. A. Kurland, and M. Goodwin. 1939. The somatic growth depressing effect of testosterone propionate. *Endocrinology 25:*724.

Rubinstein, H. S., and M. C. Solomon. 1941. The growth stimulating effect of small doses of testosterone propionate in the castrate albino rat. *Endocrinology 28:*229.

Scow, R. O. 1952. Effect of testosterone on muscle and other tissues and on carcass composition in hypophysectomized thyroidectomized and gonadectomized male rats. *Endocrinology 51:*42.

———. 1959. Effect of growth hormone and thyroxine on growth and chemical composition of muscle, bone and other tissues in thyroidectomized-hypophysectomized rats. *Amer. J. Physiol. 196:*859.

Scow, R. O., and S. N. Hagan. 1955. Effect of testosterone propionate on myosin, collagen and other protein fractions of striated muscles of gonadectomized male guinea pigs. *Amer. J. Physiol. 180:*31.

———. 1957. Effect of testosterone propionate on myosin, collagen and other protein fractions in striated muscle of gonadectomized rats. *Endocrinology 60:*273.

Scow, R. O., and J. H. Roe. 1953. Effect of testosterone propionate on weight and myoglobin content of striated muscles in gonadectomized guinea pigs. *Amer. J. Physiol. 173:*22.

Wainman, P., and G. C. Shipounoff. 1941. The effects of castration and testosterone propionate on the striated perineal musculature in the rat. *Endocrinology 29:*975.

Chapter 8

The Histological Reaction
of Muscle to Disease

M. H. BROOKE

The histological changes in abnormal muscle are well recognized, have been described on innumerable occasions, and are a source of constant and acrimonious debate.

The anterior horn cell in the spinal cord, together with its axon and the muscle fiber it supplies, acts as a functional unit, the so-called motor unit. Although it acts as a unit, it is not involved in disease processes as a unit. In some of the diseases which this chapter will discuss, the brunt of the illness is borne by the neural part of the motor unit, whereas in others the muscle suffers primarily and without the involvement of the motor neuron. Both types of involvement, however, produce anatomical changes in the muscle fibers. Because of this, pathologists have differentiated the changes occurring in muscle in primary muscle disease — "myopathic changes" — from those occurring as a secondary phenomenon due to the damaged motor nerve supply — "neurogenic changes." The description of these changes and the attempts to correlate them with the underlying neurogenic or myopathic disease have taken a great deal of time and effort. Studies on animals to ascertain the effect of experimental denervation are bedeviled by the high incidence of infestation in laboratory colonies, infestations which may themselves give rise to a myopathy. Moreover, each species behaves differently under the stress of disease, and changes which are established in the rabbit, for example, are not necessarily true of the rat.

In attempting to study disease syndromes as a means of shedding light on the problem we are in an even more precarious position. We may decide that poliomyelitis is a classical example of neurogenic disease since anterior horn cells are selectively destroyed. This, however, presupposes that the poliomyelitis virus does not directly involve muscle, a supposition

113

which may be difficult to substantiate. It only requires the statement that the findings on biopsy do not show evidence of primary muscle involvement for the argument to complete its fallacious circle. On the other hand if we were able to collect muscle biopsies from a large series of poliomyelitis patients and examine them at length we would be able to describe the changes seen in poliomyelitis and avoid stepping into the controversy. Such is the aim of this article, and although it is as impossible to describe muscle pathology without using the words "neurogenic" or "myopathic" as it is to describe a spiral staircase without using one's hands, the statements here should be interpreted in the light of the preceding remarks.

Most of this article will deal with the histological changes which are present in abnormal muscle; a summary of the details of preparation of the tissue and the techniques of staining can be found elsewhere (Engel and Brooke, 1966).

NORMAL MUSCLE

Normal muscle comprises large numbers of muscle fibers which are collected into fascicles. The fascicles are separated by connective tissue, and in this space lie the small blood vessels and nerve bundles of the muscle. The individual fibers are of fairly uniform size; and although the actual values depend upon the species, the age, and the activity of the animal, they conform to a random distribution curve with a well-marked mean (see Chart 8.1). Each fiber is made up of many myofibrils separated by the intermyofibrillar network, the latter consisting of mitochondria, sarcoplasmic reticulum, lipid droplets, glycogen granules, and the aqueous sarcoplasm. The sarcolemmal nuclei are flattened and elongated and lie at the periphery of the fiber under the investing sarcolemmal membrane. The myofibrils, of course, constitute the actual contractile elements, and their obvious cross striation may be seen in longitudinal section. The accompanying photographs are illustrative of normal muscle (Figs. 8.1 through 8.6).

Histochemical studies of muscle enable us to obtain additional information on the cytology of normal muscle. It has been known since the nineteenth century that there were two types of muscle fiber (Knoll, 1891). Because of their physiological properties these have been described as slow and fast fibers. Histologically, "red" muscle fibers have been differentiated from "white"; and on histochemical grounds, fibers which develop a pronounced reaction in media designed to demonstrate the oxidative enzymes (such as succinic dehydrogenase and reduced diphosphopyridine nucleotide — tetrazolium reductase) but which are not well demonstrated with the reaction for myosin adenosine triphosphatase are termed Type I fibers. Type II fibers possess exactly the reverse properties

Chart 8.1. — Histograms of muscle fiber diameters in biopsies of normal human muscle and in patients with amyotrophic lateral sclerosis and muscular dystrophy. The cross-sectional diameters of the fibers are plotted against the number of fibers.

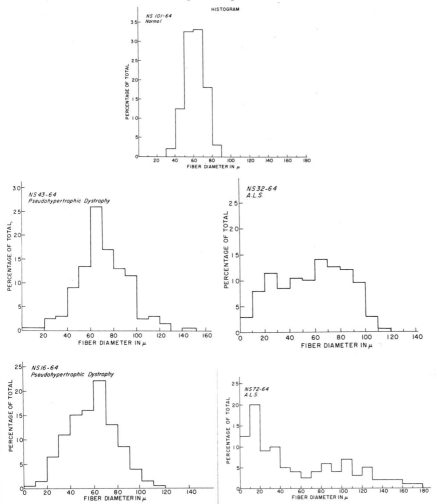

(Engel, 1962). Although the soleus muscle of many animals is physiologically a slow muscle in which the vast majority of fibers are red and are Type I, it is not yet proven that the terms "slow," "red," and "Type I" can be used synonymously. I shall refer to Type I and Type II fibers since most of my studies have involved histochemical reactions. It is possible, but unproven, that under certain circumstances a fiber may change its histochemical characteristics from one type to another; physiologically, certain muscles may change their characteristic reactions following various pro-

Fig. 8.1. — Normal human muscle. The nuclei are situated at the periphery of the fiber and are darkly stained and elongated. The myofibrillar cross striations are visible. (F, HVG, × 219.)

Fig. 8.2. — Normal human muscle. In this photograph of a longitudinal section the paired dots *(arrow)* in the I band near the A–I junction correspond to the location of the mitochondria on electron microscopy. (FS, CS, NBT, × 1300.)

Fig. 8.3. — Normal human muscle. The dark fibers and light fibers are visible on this preparation. The fine intermyofibrillar network is to be noted. The nuclei occupy a peripheral position in the fiber. In this and other cryostat sections the contour of the fibers is different from that which is seen in fixed and paraffin-embedded preparations. (CS, Tri, × 140.)

Fig. 8.4. — Normal rabbit muscle. With this stain the intermyofibrillar network (composed of the sarcoplasmic reticulum and the mitochondria) is seen. The individual components cannot be distinguished, but the network pattern is clearly seen. (FS, CS, NBT, × 1300.)

Fig. 8.5. — Normal human muscle. The histochemical reaction for TPNH-Tetrazolium reductase results in a dark stain of the Type I fibers. The Type II fibers are only lightly stained (compare with Fig. 8.6). (CS, TPNH-TR, × 114.)

Fig. 8.6. — Normal human muscle. This is a serial section to that shown in Fig. 8.5, but the histochemical technique used is designed to demonstrate the myofibrillar adenosine triphosphatase. The dark fibers are Type II fibers, and comparison with Fig. 8.5 shows that the staining pattern is the reverse of the TPNH-TR reaction (compare the group of fibers around the arrow). A blood vessel is seen in the cleft between the fascicles in both photographs. (CS, adenosine triphosphatase, × 114.)

(See page 126 for key to abbreviations.)

cedures (Ewell and Zaimis, 1954; Bach, 1948). In most normal human muscles there is a random distribution of approximately equal numbers of Type I and Type II fibers, and a mosaic pattern is seen in reactions which differentiate the two types (Figs. 8.5, 8.6).

The histochemical reactions for the oxidative enzymes are particularly useful in demonstrating the mitochondria, or the sarcoplasmic reticulum, or both, whereas the adenosine triphosphatase reaction of Padykula and Herman (1955) is limited to the myofibrillar A bands and can be employed to identify myofibrils.

THE ABNORMAL REACTIONS OF MUSCLE

Muscle is quite limited in the way in which it may react to disease stress; in fact, there are only four common ways in which the fibers themselves may change, at least as seen under the microscope. These are hypertrophy, atrophy, degeneration, and regeneration, to which must be added the cellular and proliferative reactions of the noncontractile components of muscle tissue.

Hypertrophy

Although not all forms of work are equally effective, activity of muscle is responsible for hypertrophy. Repeated short periods of maximum effort

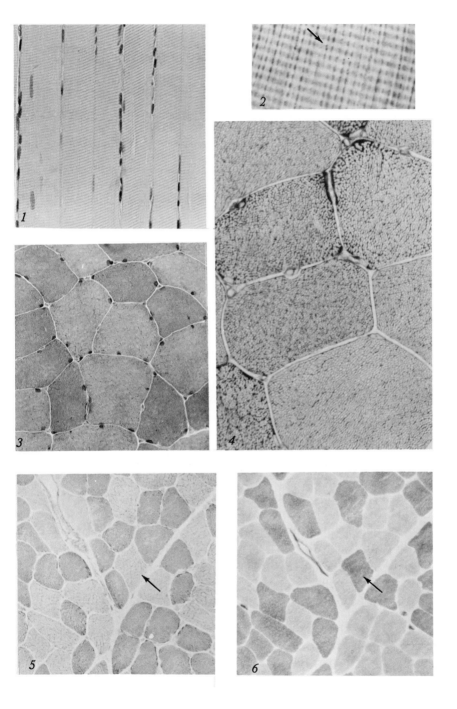

Figs. 8.7, 8.8, and 8.9. — Tigroid nuclei. These nuclei, with a very characteristic staining appearance, may appear in clumps or in chains. Occasionally they may be very large and assume bizarre shapes. (B, HVG, × 569.)

Fig. 8.10. — Tigroid nuclei. (× 437.)

Fig. 8.11. — Type II atrophy. In this histochemical reaction for adenosine triphosphatase the Type II fibers are dark. It can be seen from the photographs that all of the small atrophic fibers are Type II. (CS, adenosine triphosphatase, × 136.)

Fig. 8.12. — "End stage" muscle. With severe disease the muscle becomes replaced by fibrous and fatty tissue as in this photograph. Only clumps of dark pyknotic nuclei and some myofibrillar fragments remain as evidence of the fact that this was muscle tissue. (F, HVG, × 57.)

Fig. 8.13. — Small angular fiber. The small fibers seen in atrophy adopt an angular configuration. They are also very dark with the histochemical reactions for the oxidative enzymes, as for example in this preparation with TPNH-TR. (CS, TPNH-TR, × 219.)

Fig. 8.14. — Small angular fibers; similar to Fig. 8.13.

(See page 126 for key to abbreviations.)

are known to increase muscle bulk up to 20% (Hettinger and Muller, 1953). Such hypertrophy is due to an increase in the size of the muscle fiber rather than a numerical increase of fibers. Experiments on animals have suggested that the increase in size is due to an increase in the "sarcoplasm" (i.e., intermyofibrillar substance) and possibly to an increase in the number of myofibrils in each fiber (Denny-Brown, 1961). This increase in size is accompanied by a tougher consistency of the muscle. The relationship between physiological hypertrophy and the giant fibers seen in some disease states is not clear, although it may be that these fibers are the result of an increased load which is thrown upon them as others drop out.

Atrophy

The term "atrophy," which has had various uses among muscle pathologists, has now come to signify a series of changes which are not easy to define. Muscle which is involved in a disease process may be the site of changes that provoke a great deal of reaction within the tissue, in the form of phagocytosis (inflammatory and other cellular reactions), fatty infiltration, or fibrosis which is early and marked. In such conditions the muscle fibers exhibit changes in many different directions. To use a picturesque oversimplification, in such conditions the disease appears "active." Atrophy, on the contrary, refers to a much more "passive" process, attended by gradual shrinkage of fibers and, at least in the early stages, not much reaction from the other tissue components. Such atrophy is classically found after section of the motor nerve, when it is referred to as neurogenic or denervation atrophy. It has long been recognized, however, that other types occur. The best-known is disuse atrophy, which results

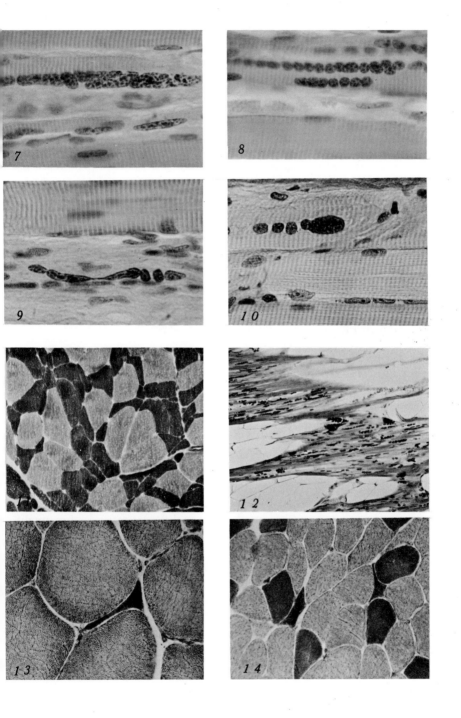

Fig. 8.15. — Simple necrosis. The muscle fiber in the center of the field has lost its normal staining characteristics and presents a pale unstained appearance. One area of the fiber in the upper right-hand corner also appears abnormal. (CS, Tri, × 96.)

Fig. 8.16. — Basophilic fibers. In this photograph there are several small fibers which appear dark when compared to their neighbors. The dark appearance is due to a bluish tint which they assume with the H and E stain. (B, H, and E, × 219.)

Fig. 8.17. — Phagocytosis. This longitudinal section shows a fiber which is similar to the one seen in Fig. 8.15 but which has become filled with phagocytes. (CS, Tri, × 101.)

Fig. 8.18. — Cellular reaction. A collection of small round cells in which can be seen two atrophic muscle fibers. (CS, Tri, × 110.)

Fig. 8.19. — Mitosis. A mitosis occurring in a region of active phagocytosis. Differentiation between sarcolemmal nuclei and the nuclei of phagocytes is difficult, and the consensus is that mitoses do not occur in sarcolemmal nuclei. (F, HVG, × 525.)

Fig. 8.20. — Cellular reaction. In this case the cellular reaction is seen in longitudinal section. The patient had a laryngeal carcinoma with a peripheral neuropathy. (CS, H, and E, × 61.)

Fig. 8.21. — Phagocytosis. The pale nuclei with prominent nucleoli are sarcolemmal nuclei; and the smaller, elongated, and slightly darker nuclei are probably those of phagocytes. Intermediate forms are present which are difficult to assign to either group. Note the mitosis in the center of the photograph. (Z, HVG, × 262.)

Fig. 8.22. — A perivascular cellular reaction. The small blood vessel can be seen in longitudinal as well as transverse section. This is from a muscle biopsy in a patient with scleroderma and Raynaud's phenomenon. (Z, HVG, × 262.)

(See page 126 for key to abbreviations.)

when muscle is rendered inactive by one of several means. More recently a third type of atrophy has been described and given the name of "Type II fiber atrophy" (Engel, 1966*a*, 1966*b*; Brooke and Engel, 1966; Engel, Brooke, and Nelson, 1966). The place of atrophy seen in cachexia is uncertain.

Neurogenic atrophy. — The changes which occur in muscle as the result of destruction of the motor nerve have been the object of investigation for a long time. In 1888, Krauss was commenting upon the "remarkably frequent" occurrence of such studies (Krauss, 1888). This enthusiasm has continued unabated and has involved many different muscles of many different species (Ricker and Ellenbeck, 1899; Langley and Hashimoto, 1918; Hines and Knowlton, 1933; Chor, Dolkart, and Davenport, 1937; Tower, 1935, 1939; Reid, 1941; Sunderlands and Ray, 1950; Willard and Grau, 1924). There may be differences from muscle to muscle and species to species but certain general statements may be made without arousing controversy. In experimental denervation one of the earliest changes occurs in the nuclei, which become plumper and move towards the center of the fiber. The cytoplasm becomes clearer and the nucleolus more heavily defined. After a variable length of time nuclei are found with heavy clumping of chromatin material. These have been called "tigroid" nuclei (Figs. 8.7–8.10). Concurrently, the muscle fibers decrease in size, and

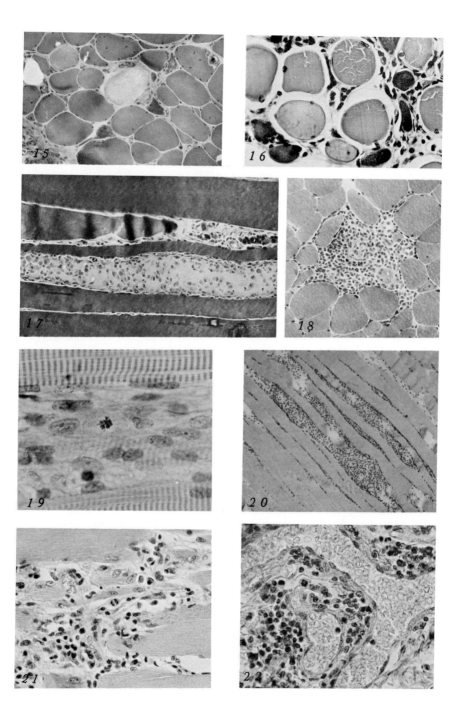

Fig. 8.23. — Atrophy occurring in large groups of fibers. Although all fascicles are affected both above and below the fibrous tissue band running across the photograph, the reduction in size is much greater in the upper group of fibers than in the lower. (CS, Tri, × 118.)

Fig. 8.24. — Atrophy occurring in small groups of fibers. Two small groups of atrophied fibers are indicated by the arrows. (CS, Tri, × 87.)

Fig. 8.25. — Target fibers. The characteristic three-zoned target fiber is seen in this histochemical reaction for adenosine triphosphatase. (CS, adenosine triphosphatase, × 109.)

Fig. 8.26. — Clumping of fiber types. The usual mosaic pattern is lacking, and in its place there are many fibers of the same type next to each other. (CS, DPNH-TR, × 55.)

Fig. 8.27. — Splitting of fibers. There is splitting of three (possibly four) fibers in this field. The fiber on the upper right has a connective tissue strand which extends part of the way across the fiber. The lighter fiber below appears to be split into four smaller fibers. (CS, Tri, × 122.)

Fig. 8.28. — Vesicular nuclei. These nuclei are easily recognized by their heavily staining nucleoli. (B, HVG, × 547.)

Fig. 8.29. — Vesicular nuclei. This photograph is similar to the previous one. Nuclei with multiple nucleoli may be seen in the lower left and upper right corners. (B, HVG, × 350.)

Fig. 8.30. — Ring fiber. In this example the central disc of transversely cut myofibrils is surrounded by a circumferential band of myofibrils cut longitudinally. (F, PTAH, × 420.)

(See page 126 for key to abbreviations.)

up to 80% of the weight of the muscle tissue may be lost. During such wasting the myofibrillar striations are relatively well preserved, and some striations may be discerned in a fiber which has been reduced to a small strand. A certain amount of fibrosis is seen, but this varies from species to species, and no general statement can be made, except that in severely wasted muscle much of the bulk may be replaced by fibrous tissue or fat (Fig. 8.12). The reduction in the size of the muscle fiber results in a closer approximation of the existing nuclei, giving the appearance of "nucleosis." Altschul has used this word to denote what he considered to be an increase in the nuclei of the fiber; such proliferation he considered to be due to a simple fission (Altschul, 1947). Actual nuclear counts, however, have shown that this increase is probably an apparent one only (Sunderlands and Ray, 1950; Willard and Grau, 1924). The changes described later, such as degeneration and phagocytosis, are remarkable for their absence, although certain authors claim that they play an important role (Tower, 1935, 1939). Tower states that degenerative changes were a characteristic feature in denervated cat muscle and that between the fourth and sixth months following denervation large groups of fibers were destroyed, but the infestation of her laboratory colony with trichina makes the results difficult to evaluate.

The foregoing remarks apply to complete nerve section. Most disease

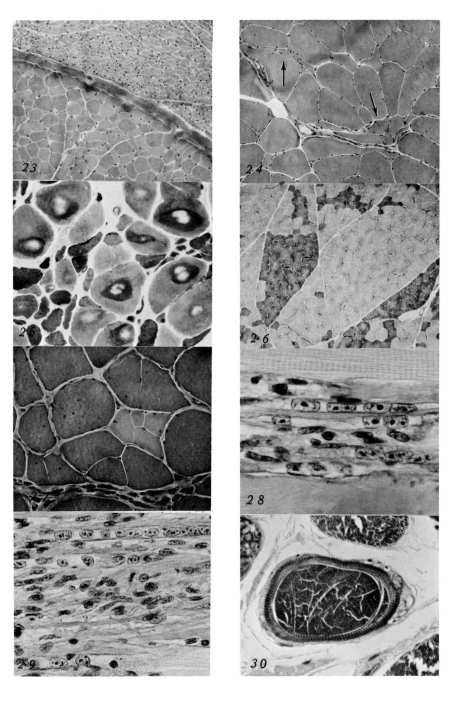

Fig. 8.31. — In many of the fibers the intermyofibrillar network is distorted: its precise and regular appearance is no longer seen. Notice the variability in fiber size. This is a biopsy from a patient with a progressive proximal myopathy. (CS, LDH, × 219.)

Figs. 8.32 and 8.33. — Abnormalities are also seen in the intermyofibrillar network with nonenzymatic reactions, in this case the modified trichrome. These fibers should be compared with those in Fig. 8.3. (CS, Tri, × 341.)

Fig. 8.34. — Internal nuclei seen in a case of myotonic dystrophy. The arrow indicates a clump of pyknotic nuclei next to an angulated fiber. (CS, Tri, × 87.)

(See page 126 for key to abbreviations.)

states do not affect all nerve fibers in a motor nerve simultaneously but rather selectively involve individual nerve fibers. As a consequence not all muscle fibers are involved in the atrophic process. Although this can be seen on the paraffin-embedded sections where atrophic fibers may be observed adjacent to normal ones, it is on fresh frozen cryostat sections that the findings are most pronounced. In this type of section, the abnormal atrophic fibers are similarly scattered throughout the muscle, but they assume a peculiar angular shape, being indented at their edges by the convex borders of adjacent fibers (Figs. 8.13, 8.14). It is possible that as the fiber loses bulk and becomes atrophic there is enough pressure within the muscle belly to cause such a distortion by mechanical compression. This might also explain the rarity of such angular fibers in a muscle in which the fibers are undergoing a uniform atrophy. Histochemical studies on human material have shown that as the fibers assume the small angular shape they no longer demonstrate the phosphorylase reaction (Engel, 1966a, 1966b). They also develop a very intense color with the reactions designed to demonstrate the oxidative enzymes. This latter fact may be due to an absence of all or part of the cytochrome chain in these fibers. Furthermore, in the atrophying fibers the neat and precise arrangement of the intermyofibrillar net is deranged.

Disuse atrophy. — Disuse atrophy has been produced experimentally in three different ways. Tower prevented any reflex or voluntary activity by sectioning the dorsal roots and transecting the spinal cord, thus leaving the actual motor neuron intact. This "isolated cord" technique was carried out in puppies (Tower, 1937). Eccles has performed similar experiments (Eccles, 1941). Several authors have investigated the effect of tenotomy on muscle, in order to prevent use of the muscle (Lipschuetz and Audova, 1921; Lange, 1929; Davenport and Ranson, 1930; Eccles, 1944; McMinn and Vrbová, 1964; Engel, Brooke, and Nelson, 1966). The third method, of immobilizing the limb in a cast, has been employed by Chor and Dolkart (1936) and by Ferguson, Vaughan, and Ward (1957, with a review of the literature). All methods employed produced a significant weight loss in the muscle. Values have varied from 20% to 55% of the

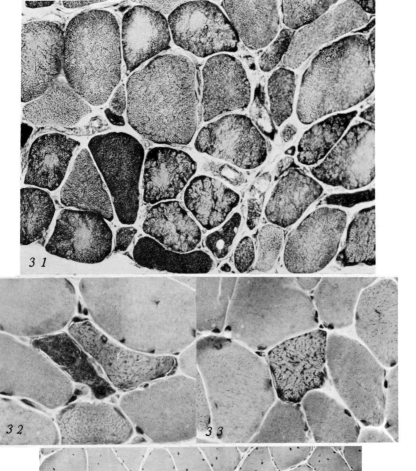

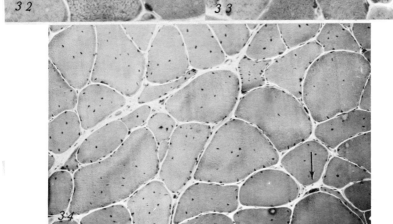

Key to abbreviations in figure legends

B	Fixed in Bouins solution
CS	Fresh frozen cryostat sectioned
DPNH-TR	Histochemical reaction for diphosphopyridine (reduced)–tetrazolium reductase
F	Fixed in Formol saline
FS	Fixed in cold Formol sucrose
H and E	Haematoxylin and eosin stain
HVG	Haematoxylin van Gieson's stain
LDH	Histochemical reaction for lactic dehydrogenase
NBT	Nitro blue tetrazolium
PTAH	Phosphotungstic acid haematoxylin
TPNH-TR	Histochemical reaction for triphosphopyridine (reduced)–tetrazolium reductase
Tri	Trichrome stain
Z	Zenkers

normal weight of the muscle. In general the histological changes in all methods are very similar. There is a reduction in fiber diameter similar to that seen in denervation atrophy, but not as severe. The nuclear changes, which are so prominent in denervation atrophy, are not reported. Davenport and Ranson (1930) have shown that, following section of the *tendo Achillis* in the cat, dark angular fibers are found between larger more rounded fibers. These angular fibers were dark with van Gieson's stain and with Sudan III and were thought to be "red" fibers. In the cat, tenotomy results in Type I fiber atrophy whereas denervation results in atrophy of Type II fibers (Engel, Brooke, and Nelson, 1966). The nuclear changes which are so pronounced in denervation are not seen in disuse atrophy. McMinn and Vrbová have shown that, in the rabbit, tenotomy of the soleus is accompanied by a marked cellular reaction with some fibro-fatty replacement. They suggest that denervation or cord transection protects the muscle against such degeneration, although according to their photographs, it does not seem to alter the actual reduction of fiber size (McMinn and Vrbová, 1964).

Other patterns of atrophy (Type II). — A rather unusual type of atrophy occurs which seems to be limited to one type of fiber. In the most easily recognized form it can be seen that all the fibers of one type are small and slightly angulated but possess the normal histochemical reactions (Engel,

1966a, 1966b). This atrophy is called Type II fiber atrophy, indicating the fiber type involved (Fig. 8.11). Type II atrophy is found in myasthenia (Engel and McFarlin, 1966), and is present in other disease syndromes (Engel, 1966a, 1966b; Engel and Brooke, 1966). Type I atrophy is discussed elsewhere (Brooke and Engel, 1966).

Cachectic atrophy. — In 12 patients with cachexia investigated by Marin and Denny-Brown there were changes of atrophy which produced a population of very small dark fibers together with fibers whose average diameter was not as markedly reduced (Marin and Denny-Brown, 1962). Whether this bore any relation to Type II atrophy is not possible to say in the absence of histochemical studies. A further difficulty is that 10 of the 12 patients had carcinoma, which may produce involvement of muscle even in the absence of cachexia.

Degeneration and regeneration

The changes of degeneration and regeneration often occur simultaneously, and the borderline between the two processes is ill-defined. A fiber undergoing degeneration may lose the well-defined myofibrillar cross striation and assume a more homogeneous appearance; this may be "waxy," "hyaline," or "granular" — adjectives which are all commonly used for various appearances of degeneration. There is often an alteration in the staining characteristics of the degenerating fiber, and the normal histochemical reaction may be lost. Such degeneration, without attendant cellular reaction, is conveniently termed "simple necrosis" (Fig. 8.15). Any degenerating tissue — and muscle is no exception — is invaded by histiocytes; the necrotic material undergoes phagocytosis, and fibers may become filled with these cells (Fig. 8.17). Other distortions of the muscle fibers are seen in degeneration, such as central necrosis in which the necrosis appears to be limited to the innermost part of the fiber. Vacuoles may appear in fibers under conditions of both experimental necrosis and disease.

Regeneration of muscle tissue occurs in one of two ways. In fibers which have been damaged, but in which the investing membranes remain intact, the empty tubes are used as the framework of the regenerating fiber; alternatively, regenerating muscle buds may develop from existing fibers and "invade" areas in which total destruction of muscle has occurred. In both types there is probably proliferation of the sarcolemmal nuclei by a process which has never been satisfactorily defined. The nuclei are pale and vesicular with from one to four heavily staining nucleoli. There is basophilia of the sarcoplasm of these fibers (Fig. 8.16) which is associated with the larger amounts of RNA.

There are some differences of opinion on the problem of degeneration and regeneration, and the chief bones of contention concern the presence of mitoses and the significance of basophilia. Although the majority of workers feel that basophilia occurs only in regenerating fibers, some investigators have stated that it may occur in degenerating fibers. A definite answer is difficult because the two processes occur simultaneously under most experimental conditions. The problems are fully discussed elsewhere (Adams *et al.*, 1962). Mitoses are seen in muscle which is undergoing degeneration as well as regeneration, but only in situations in which there is prominent phagocytosis. Although some investigators feel that mitoses occur in sarcolemmal nuclei, the great majority feel that mitoses when present in muscle tissue occur only during division of the histiocytes (**Fig. 8.19**). The enzyme histochemistry of degeneration and regeneration is not well known at an experimental level, and the changes which we believe represent degeneration will be noted under the discussion of the dystrophies below.

Cellular reactions

The reactions which are provoked in diseased muscle are those of fibrosis, which occurs between the individual fibers, of fatty infiltration or replacement, and of accumulations of various cell types. The phagocytes may be present not only within a muscle fiber but may spill out for some distance around it (Fig. 8.21). Other cellular reactions may be provoked, including the accumulation of small round cells within the muscle. Although these may be associated with necrotic fibers they may also appear around a medium-sized vessel and spread out for some distance (Figs. 8.18, 8.20, 8.22). Other cells, including polymorphonuclear leukocytes or eosinophils, may be found from time to time.

These, then, are the basic reactions of muscle to disease processes: hypertrophy, atrophy, degeneration and regeneration, and the various kinds of cellular reactions. The next section will discuss the production of these changes as seen in certain disease states. It is to be stressed that the list of diseases is extremely selective and each disease is chosen to represent an example of a particular type of change. For a more comprehensive list of diseases involving muscle, other references may be consulted (Engel and Brooke, 1966; Engel, 1966*a*, 1966*b*; Adams *et al.*, 1962; Greenfield *et al.*, 1957).

REACTION OF MUSCLE TO DISEASE

Upper motor neuron

That wasting of muscles may occur in limbs which are spastic as a result of various cerebral cortical or pyramidal tract lesions is well known. Recently Fenichel, Daroff, and Glaser (1964) have shown in four patients with cerebrovascular lesions that the wasted muscle possesses fibers that are somewhat smaller than average and that there are very small round fibers with some internal nuclei on fixed paraffin-embedded sections. In a patient with a residual spastic hemiparesis from a hemiplegia occurring in childhood, tests on fresh frozen section showed the fibers from the affected side to be smaller than from the normal side, with scattered small angular fibers which suggested an atrophic process (Engel, 1966a). The absence of nuclear changes suggested that this could be differentiated from denervation.

Anterior horn cell

The most prevalent disease affecting the anterior horn cells is probably amyotrophic lateral sclerosis, or motor neuron disease, in which both upper and lower motor neurons are the site of degeneration. The changes occurring in muscle are commonly ascribed to the degeneration of the lower motor neuron. The dominant change is that of denervation atrophy with reduction in fiber size; many of the fibers are small, angular, and very dark with the oxidative enzyme reactions (Fig. 8.13). The atrophied fibers have a tendency to occur in groups both small and large (Figs. 8.23, 8.24). The nuclear changes are marked and tigroid, and vesicular nuclei are prominent, the former occurring in clumps and short chains. Pyknotic nuclei are also found.

Of the various forms of abnormal nuclei, the tigroid variety is most often the dominant one in biopsies from patients with amyotrophic lateral sclerosis. In addition to the changes of atrophy, hypertrophy also occurs, as can be seen from the histograms in Chart 8.1. It is not certain whether the large fibers are undergoing hypertrophy as an extra load is placed upon them owing to the loss of function of the atrophying fibers, but it seems a reasonable hypothesis. Although the changes of atrophy and hypertrophy are always the most striking ones, other abnormalities are seen. The changes of degeneration may be present in a few fibers with the attendant phagocytosis. Basophilia of occasional fibers may point to attempted regeneration. Infiltrates of small round cells occurring around a necrotic fiber or around blood vessels may also be noted. Again it is emphasized that these changes are minor ones.

Histochemical studies may give additional findings. In reactions which differentiate Type I fibers from Type II, the normal mosaic pattern of the fiber types may be disturbed and large numbers of contiguous fibers may be of the same type. This gives the appearance of clumping of the different fiber types. Architecturally the fibers show several types of change. With atrophy, they lose the neat intermyofibrillar network pattern, which becomes obscured or coarsened. Target fibers and targetoid fibers, as described by Engel (1961), may be seen (Fig. 8.25). Target fibers are fibers with three concentric zones, the central one of which is unstained with the myofibrillar adenosine triphosphatase reaction and with the reactions for the oxidative enzymes; the myofibrillar striations in this central region are also lost. The PTAH stain, of paraffin-embedded material, stains this central region darkly. The intermediate zone is unstained with PTAH but develops a stronger than normal reaction with adenosine triphosphatase and the oxidative enzymes. The outermost zone appears normal.

Peripheral nerves

There does not seem to be any basic difference in the reactions of muscle to anterior horn cell disease and to peripheral nerve lesions, the changes in both being similar to those of experimental denervation. It is convenient to divide the peripheral neuropathies into three groups: (1) those due to metabolic or dietary abnormalities such as are seen with diabetes or chronic alcoholism — uncomplicated by the acute alcoholic myopathy as described by Ekbom et al. (1964); (2) those associated with the collagen vascular diseases or with carcinoma; and (3) those comprising the familial neuropathies such as peroneal muscular atrophy. Atrophy, occurring in scattered fibers, or as large or small groups, may be seen in all types; and vesicular, tigroid, and clumped pyknotic nuclei are prominent. Target fibers and small dark angulated fibers may be present in histochemical reactions, as in anterior horn cell disease. Clumping of the fiber types may also be seen (Fig. 8.26). Differences between the three categories are not absolute; rather there are differences in emphasis, which become apparent as a number of biopsies from one group is compared to the others. In the neuropathies associated with collagen vascular disease and with carcinoma, cellular reactions occur more frequently and are often around blood vessels as well as around necrotic fibers. Patients with peroneal muscular atrophy have more marked changes of degeneration and regeneration and of necrosis (Haase and Shy, 1960). Phagocytosis and internal nuclei are a more prominent part of the picture. The abnormal nuclei are as often vesicular as tigroid, which is not generally true of the other types. In short, this type of peripheral neuropathy exhibits changes which are in the direction of those seen in the progressive muscular dystrophies. Hypertrophy of the fibers is also more pronounced in this last group.

Neuromuscular junction

Myasthenia gravis, which is often stated to have little in the way of histological changes, has recently been the subject of several reports which indicate quite well-marked pathology (Engel and McFarlin, 1966; Fenichel and Shy, 1963).

Engel and McFarlin (1966) found that 50% of the biopsies reviewed showed Type II atrophy, and 60% showed changes of atrophy. There were no normal biopsies. The nuclear changes are probably similar to those seen in experimental denervation, with tigroid forms predominating. Cellular reactions, chiefly in the form of small round cell infiltrations around necrotic muscle fibers, are not uncommon.

Primary muscle involvement

In this group of diseases I have selected the hereditary muscular dystrophies of the pseudohypertrophic and the limb girdle varieties for discussion. Clinically and histologically, they present findings which are quite different from those of amyotrophic lateral sclerosis, and histologically the two varieties appear to be rather similar.

The variation in fiber size in this group is as great as or greater than that of amyotrophic lateral sclerosis, but the histogram (Chart 8.1) demonstrates the different pattern: the curve still tends to be "bell-shaped" but the spread is very much wider. The mean fiber diameter may be unchanged from the normal values. The small angular fibers characteristic of atrophy are lacking. Although small fibers are present, they do not have the appearance of having been compressed into the interstices between their larger neighbors which is seen in atrophy. Splitting of fibers is often seen, particularly in the large fibers which are divided into smaller ones by the development of connective tissue septa (Fig. 8.27). As opposed to the changes seen in amyotrophic lateral sclerosis, necrosis and phagocytosis are very common and are present in almost all biopsies. Cellular reactions are also prominent in this group of diseases, usually being associated with necrotic fibers. Fibrosis, occurring around the individual fibers, is also marked in the dystrophies, as opposed to the lack of such fibrosis in atrophy. The reaction of the nuclei is also slightly different from that seen in other muscle pathology. The most prominent abnormal form is the pale vesicular nucleus with one large prominent nucleolus or three to four smaller nucleoli; this, combined with a heavier staining rim, gives a characteristic appearance (Figs. 8.28, 8.29). Abnormal tigroid nuclei are only rarely present. The nuclei are also situated centrally within the fiber to a far greater extent in the dystrophic group than in those with amyotrophic lateral sclerosis. Alterations in the architecture of the individual fibers are prominent. Ring fibers, which are present in several types of muscle disease and in some normal muscles (Perry, Smith, and Wrenn, 1956; Berthrong and Griffith, 1961), may be seen in the progressive dystrophies (Fig. 8.30).

Histochemical studies show a variety of changes in the normal fiber architecture. The network may be granular or coarsened or may present bizarre distortions of its pattern (Figs. 8.31, 8.32, 8.33; and Engel, 1966*b*). None of these changes however appear to be specific to this group of muscular dystrophies.

Myotonic dystrophy does not present the same picture as the progressive dystrophies previously mentioned (Greenfield *et al.*, 1957; Brooke and Engel, 1966). The presence of small angular fibers, the presence of tigroid nuclei and pyknotic nuclear clumps, the plethora of internal nuclei, and the frequent occurrence of Type I atrophy serve to differentiate the disease from the dystrophic group discussed above (Fig. 8.34).

Other

There are a variety of bizarre and rather rare abnormalities which have been described in human muscle, such as nemaline myopathy and central core disease. These do not seem to be part of the general reaction of muscle to disease, and references to them may be found elsewhere (Shy and Magee, 1956; Shy *et al.*, 1956; Engel, Wanko, and Fenichel, 1964; Engel *et al.*, 1961).

SUMMARY

It is possible to describe the biopsy seen in particular diseases by describing the component reactions which are present. Atrophy may be simple atrophy, as is seen in disuse or tenotomy, or may be denervation atrophy which can be distinguished by the additional nuclear changes. Type II atrophy is a different form which is revealed only in histochemical studies. Distinct from the changes of atrophy are degeneration and regeneration, phagocytosis, and the cellular reactions. The concept of neurogenic and myopathic disease is perhaps outmoded, since the boundaries between the two categories are hazy even in the experimental animal. There is a spectrum of changes in the various diseases; and at the opposite ends of this spectrum are amyotrophic lateral sclerosis, which presents mainly the changes of denervation atrophy, and the group of muscular dystrophies which, with the important exception of myotonic dystrophy, show little in the way of atrophic changes. The nuclear changes in the dystrophic group show one important difference from all the others in that tigroid nuclei are not seen nearly so frequently. Since the significance of their presence is not known, their absence is even harder to interpret.

There are probably very few diseases which do not produce changes in muscle sooner or later. Histologically the etiology may be apparent, as for example in trichinosis or sarcoidosis when the characteristic lesions are seen. In the majority of diseases, however, we can only evaluate the process in terms of the reaction to the underlying disease which occurs in muscle. Occasionally these reactions may be specific for a disease entity such as nemaline myopathy or central core disease, but more often these reactions are nonspecific and are produced by more than one disease. This article is an attempt to summarize these nonspecific changes and to discuss the proportions in which they are present in a few selected diseases.

ACKNOWLEDGMENT

This work was supported by a special fellowship, 1 F 11 NB 1301-01 NSRB, from the National Institute of Neurological Diseases and Blindness, Public Health Service.

References

Adams, R., D. Denny-Brown, and C. M. Pearson. 1962. *Diseases of Muscle: A Study in Pathology* (2d ed.). Paul B. Hoeber, Inc., New York.

Altschul, R. 1947. On nuclear division in damaged skeletal muscles. *Rev. Can. Biol. 6:485.*

Bach, L. M. N. 1948. Conversion of red muscle to white muscle. *Proc. Soc. Exp. Biol. 67:268.*

Berthrong, M., and P. Griffith. 1961. Ring forms in skeletal muscle. *J. Pathol. Bacteriol. 82:287.*

Brooke, M. H., and W. K. Engel. 1966. The histologic diagnosis of neuromuscular diseases: a review of 79 biopsies. *Arch. Phys. Med. Rehab. 47:99.*

Chor, H., and R. E. Dolkart. 1936. A study of simple disuse atrophy in the monkey. *Amer. J. Physiol. 117:626.*

Chor, H., R. E. Dolkart, and H. A. Davenport. 1937. Chemical and histological changes in denervated skeletal muscle of the monkey and cat. *Amer. J. Physiol. 118:580.*

Davenport, H. K., and S. W. Ranson. 1930. Contracture resulting from tenotomy. *Arch. Surg. 21:995.*

Denny-Brown, D. 1961. Experimental studies pertaining to hypertrophy, regeneration and degeneration. *Res. Pub. Ass. Neurol. Ment. Dis. 38:147.*

Eccles, J. C. 1941. Disuse atrophy of skeletal muscle. *Med. J. Australia. 2:160.*

————. 1944. Investigations of muscle atrophy arising from disuse and tenotomy. *J. Physiol. 103:253.*

Ekbom, K., R. Hed, L. Kirstein, and K. Astrom. 1964. Muscular affections in chronic alcoholism. *Arch. Neurol. 10:449.*

Engel, W. K. 1961. Muscle target fibers: a newly recognized sign of denervation. *Nature 191:389.*

————. 1962. The essentiality of histo and cyto-chemical studies of skeletal muscle in the investigation of neuromuscular diseases. *Neurology 12:778.*

————. 1966a. Diseases of the neuromuscular junction and muscle. *In* C. Adams (ed.), *Histochemistry and Cytochemistry of the Nervous System.* Elsevier Press, Amsterdam. (In press.)

————. 1966*b*. (Guest editor). A symposium on "Current Concept of the Myopathies" in clinical orthopedics and related research. (In press.)

Engel, W. K., and M. H. Brooke. 1966. Muscle biopsy as a clinical diagnostic aid. *In* W. S. Fields (ed.), *Recent Advances in Neurological Diagnostic Methods.* Chas. C Thomas, Springfield, Ill. (In press.)

Engel, W. K., M. H. Brooke, and P. A. Nelson. 1966. Histochemical studies of denervated or tenotomized cat muscle. *Ann. N.Y. Acad. Sci.* (In press.)

Engel, W. K., J. B. Foster, B. P. Hughes, H. E. Huxley, and R. Mahler. 1961. Central core disease: an investigation of a rare muscle cell abnormality. *Brain* 84:167.

Engel, W. K., and D. E. McFarlin. 1966. Skeletal muscle pathology in myasthenia gravis. *Trans. N.Y. Acad. Sci.* (In press.)

Engel, W. K., T. Wanko, and G. M. Fenichel. 1964. Nemaline myopathy — a second case. *Arch. Neurol.* 11:22.

Ewell, P. A., and E. J. Zaimis. 1954. Changes at the neuromuscular junction of red and white muscle in the cat induced by disuse atrophy and hypertrophy. *J. Physiol.* 124:429.

Fenichel, G. M., R. B. Daroff, and G. H. Glaser. 1964. Hemiplegic atrophy: histologic and etiologic considerations. *Neurology* 14:883.

Fenichel, G. M., and G. M. Shy. 1963. Muscle biopsy experience in myasthenia gravis. *Arch. Neurol.* 9:237.

Ferguson, A. B., L. Vaughan, and L. Ward. 1957. A study of disuse atrophy of skeletal muscle in the rabbit. *J. Bone Joint Surg.* 39A:583.

Greenfield, J. G., G. M. Shy, E. C. Alvord, and L. Berg. 1957. *An Atlas of Muscle Pathology in Neuromuscular Diseases.* E. & S. Livingstone, Edinburgh.

Haase, G. R., and G. M. Shy. 1960. Pathological changes in muscle biopsies from patients with peroneal muscular atrophy. *Brain* 83:631.

Hettinger, T., and E. A. Muller. 1953. Muskel leistung und muskel training. *Arbeitsphysiologie* 15:111.

Hines, H. M., and G. C. Knowlton. 1933. Changes in the skeletal muscle of the rat following denervation. *Amer. J. Physiol.* 104:379.

Knoll, P. 1891. Uber protoplasma arme und protoplasmareiche Muskulatur. *Denkschrift Akad. Wiss. Wien, Math.-Nat. Kl.* 58:633.

Krauss, E. 1888. Beitraege zur Muskelpathologie. *Arch. Pathol. Anat. Physiol.* 113:315.

Lange, M. 1929. Die Bedeutung der Spannung fur die Muskelatrophie und Muskel regeneration. *Verhandl. Deutsch. Orthop. Ges.* 23:230.

Langley, J. N., and M. Hashimoto. 1918. Observations on the atrophy of denervated muscle. *J. Physiol.* 52:15.

Lipschuetz, A., and A. Audova. 1921. The comparative atrophy of the skeletal muscle after cutting the nerve and after cutting the tendon. *J. Physiol.* 55:300.

Marin, O. S., and D. Denny-Brown. 1962. Changes in skeletal muscle associated with cachexia. *Amer. J. Pathol.* 41:23.

McMinn, R. M. H., and G. Vrbová. 1964. The effect of tenotomy on the structure of fast and slow muscle in the rabbit. *Quart. J. Exp. Physiol.* 49:424.

Padykula, H. A., and E. Herman. 1955. The specificity of the histochemical method for adenosine triphosphatase. *J. Histochem. Cytochem. 3:*170.

Perry, R. E., A. G. Smith, and R. N. Wrenn. 1956. Ringbinding of skeletal muscle. *Arch. Pathol. 61:*450.

Reid, G. 1941. A comparison of the effects of disuse and denervation upon skeletal muscle. *Med. J. Australia 2:*165.

Ricker, G., and J. Ellenbeck. 1899. Beitraege zur Kenntniss der Veraenderungen des Muskels nach der Durchschneidung seines Nerven. *Arch. Pathol. Anat. Physiol. 158:*199.

Shy, G. M., W. K. Engel, J. E. Sommers, and T. Wanko. 1956. Nemaline myopathy: a new congenital myopathy. *Brain 79:*610.

Shy, G. M., and K. R. Magee. 1956. A new congenital nonprogressive myopathy. *Brain 79:*610.

Sunderlands, S., and L. J. Ray. 1950. Denervation changes in mammalian striated muscle. *J. Neurol. Neurosurg. Psychiat. 13:*159.

Tower, S. S. 1935. Atrophy and degeneration in skeletal muscle. *Amer. J. Anat. 56:*1.

———. 1937. Trophic control of non-nervous tissues by the nervous system: a study of muscle and bone innervated from an isolated and quiescent region of the spinal cord. *J. Comp. Neurol. 67:*241.

———. 1939. The reaction of muscle to denervation. *Physiol. Rev. 19:*1.

Willard, W. A., and E. C. Grau. 1924. Some histological changes in striated skeletal muscle following nerve section. *Anat. Rec. 27:*192.

Chapter 9

Metabolic Stresses Which Affect Muscle

R. A. LAWRIE

The issues involved in considering the metabolic stresses which affect muscle are, implicitly, physiological. They refer to muscle as a tissue integrated in the animal body, dependent on a blood supply and having nervous and hormonal connections with other tissues and organs. The behavior of muscle in isolation, to which different considerations must clearly apply, is the subject of other chapters of this book.

The importance of maintaining constant conditions within living cells was first realized about 100 years ago. "La fixité du milieu intérieur est la condition de la vie libre, indépendante," wrote Claude Bernard; subsequently, Schoenheimer (1942) has demonstrated that the equilibria essential to the integrity of living tissue depend on *dynamic* balances between catabolic and anabolic processes. It is clear that numerous metabolic equilibria in a complex organism must be coordinated physiologically if the organism as a whole is to resist adverse agencies. In the broadest definition, the disequilibria which these agencies tend to create can be referred to as "stress." The nature of the individual factors — "stressors" — which are capable of causing disturbance is varied. They may be associated with activity, temperature, humidity, atmospheric pressure, oxygen tension, nutrition, pathology (e.g., microbial or parasitic invasion, physical injury, metabolic disorientation), artificial injurious agents (e.g., drugs and toxins, ionizing radiation, electric shock), and psychology (e.g., temperament, fear, light, sound). The effects of only a selection of these can be mentioned in the present context.

HOMEOSTASIS AND THE HYPOTHALAMUS

Because the morphological and biochemical manifestations of stress are so diverse, observers had no reason to suppose that the various stressors were in any way related until the observations of Selye in 1936. He noted that animals exposed to such stressors as cold, fatigue, anoxia, inanition, and emotional excitement reacted by a discharge of hormones from the adrenal gland in a manner which was the same irrespective of the nature of the stressor. Maxima in the release of adrenaline from the adrenal medulla and of 17-hydroxycorticosterone and 11-deoxycorticosterone from the adrenal cortex arose — and in that order. These substances elicited numerous, but typical, responses in the animal which were collectively referred to as the "general adaptation syndrome." Although it is now known that not all stressors cause the release of 17-hydroxycorticosterone (e.g., severe heat: Hellman *et al.*, 1956), the views of Selye are still substantially accepted.

In the initial "alarm phase" of the general adaptation syndrome, adrenaline causes the passage of potassium from the muscles to the blood, and the breakdown of liver and muscle glycogens to glucose and lactic acid, respectively. Then, 17-hydroxycorticosterone tends to restore the glycogen balance by gluconeogenesis from protein; and 11-deoxycorticosterone tends to restore the potassium balance. The release of these hormones from the adrenal cortex arises from stimulation of the latter by adrenocorticotrophic hormone (ACTH) produced in the anterior pituitary (Selye, 1950).

The existence of both environmental and emotional stressors strongly indicated that the higher centers were involved in the general adaptation syndrome. Harris (1951) showed that the pituitary would not secrete ACTH by direct stimulation, but only by prior stimulation of the hypothalamus. Control by the nervous system of the release of ACTH, of thyroid-stimulating hormone (TSH), and of other hormones from the anterior pituitary is thought to depend on a chemical mediator (CRF, i.e., corticotrophin releasing factor) secreted by the hypothalamus and carried from the latter by blood vessels to the gland (Cross, 1964). According to present views (Page, 1958) this cannot be serotonin (5-hydroxytryptamine), although the hypothalamus contains a relatively high concentration of this substance (Bogdanski and Udenfriend, 1956) and injection of serotonin causes "sham" rage and other emotional upsets. (Moreover, the action of the hypothalamus can be inhibited by such drugs as reserpine, which exerts a general tranquilizing effect on the organism and exposes serotonin to inactivation by monoamine oxidase; see Brodie, Pletscher, and Shore, 1956.) The hypothalamus also contains high concentrations of noradrenaline and acetylcholine, the transmitter substances of the sympathetic and parasympathetic nerves, respectively (Grundfest, 1959). Enhanced excretion in the urine of ketosteroids (derived from adrenal cortex hormones), of 5-hydroxyindoleacetic acid (from serotonin; see Page, 1958), of 4-hydroxy-3-methoxy-mandelic and vanillic acids (both from adrenaline and noradrenaline; see Armstrong and McMillan, 1957; Smith and Bennett,

1958), and of N-methyl-3-O-methyladrenaline (from N-methyl-adrena-line; see Axelrod, 1960) parallel enhanced stress in the animal concerned.

The hypothalamus controls the posterior pituitary by direct nervous pathways through which it channels the antidiuretic, vasopressin, into the gland, from which it is released into the blood. Nervous pathways also connect the hypothalamus with the adrenal medulla and the pancreatic islets. In other words, the secretion of adrenaline and insulin is under hypothalamic control. Motor pathways from the hypothalamus include the nerve fibers which participate in the regulation of respiration, hunger and thirst sensations, shivering, piloerection, sweating, heart rate, gut mobility and secretion, widening of the bronchioles, and many other physiological phenomena; and yet other pathways from the hypothalamus, connecting with cerebral cortex, are responsible for maintaining wakefulness (Cross, 1964).

Such a multitude of functions explains the central importance of the hypothalamus in coordinating the dynamic equilibria already mentioned, in opposing stress and maintaining homeostasis, and in being highly responsive to environmental or internal change. It accords with this role that a large number of pathways run to the hypothalamus from the sensory nerves.[1] A feedback mechanism also operates in controlling the release of CRF from the hypothalamus: this is the level in the blood of glucocorti-coids (e.g., 17-hydroxycorticosterone) produced by the adrenal cortex in response to ACTH (Vogt, 1960).

Where stress can be accommodated by the hypothalamus-pituitary-ad-renal complex of reactions (i.e., the general adaptation syndrome), its repeated application will result in morphological and biochemical modi-fication which will be reflected in the continuing evolution and differen-tiation of biological systems. On the other hand, if a stressor is of great intensity or prolonged duration, the restoration of the normal optimum equilibrium may be impossible. Such may lead to so-called diseases of adaptation (Selye, 1946), or death. Even where the stressor is not excessive, there may be faulty adaptation in animals which are unusually susceptible to stressors, as when there is a deficiency of ACTH (Ludvigsen, 1957). What little is known about the effect of these circumstances on muscle will now be considered.

1. It is salutary to consider how great must be the amplification between the incoming signal caused by the stressor and its effect. Thus, 140 mg of liver glycogen are deposited in response to 1 mg 17-hydroxycorticosterone. The latter forms after stimulation of the adrenal cortex by 0.025 mg of ACTH; and this quantity of ACTH is secreted in response to ca. 0.0025 mg CRF from the hypothalamus (Saffran, 1962). If it be supposed that a similar relation holds between the incoming stimulus and the reaction of the hypothala-mus, it will be clear that nerve signals can be expected to produce changes which, in purely chemical terms, are 500,000 to 1,000,000 times greater in magnitude than those associated with the incoming signals themselves.

STRESS AND MUSCULAR ACTIVITY

Development and implications of oxygen debt

Muscular tissue is primarily designed to contract, thereby effecting movement, relative to one another, of those members of an organism to which the ends of the muscle are attached; and, additionally, in the case of striated muscles, with which we are principally concerned, movement of the organism as a whole in relation to its environment. In that it tends to disturb the dynamic equilibrium of the resting condition, muscular activity is a stressor. The development and differentiation of the 300 or so anatomically distinct units which mammalian musculature comprises reflects the diverse ways in which the tissue has been modified in an endeavor to resist stress and maintain its equilibrium while accommodating activity. The general biochemical features of contraction will not be discussed here (see Baldwin, 1963). Some points are relevant, however.

During contraction restoration of the ATP initially hydrolyzed will depend, in the first instance, on the Lohmann reaction, whereby phosphocreatine (CP) rephosphorylates the ADP and produces creatine (C):

$$ADP + CP \leftrightharpoons ATP + C$$

The restoration of CP from C clearly requires ATP. This is concomitantly produced during catabolism of muscle glycogen, either by anaerobic glycolysis, when it is converted to lactic acid, or by aerobic conversion to carbon dioxide and water. Normally, in the living animal, the blood brings oxygen from the lungs and glucose from the liver so adequately that the resting situation is quickly restored. Should the stimulus to contract continue, however, and the need for ATP increase, more oxygen and glucose can be supplied through an increase in blood flow to the muscle. If the severity of the stimulus increases yet further, so that the capacity of the muscle to gain ATP by respiration is exceeded, lactic acid production affords a swift, if inefficient and temporary, means of rephosphorylating ADP, until the falling pH causes fatigue and enforces a period of restorative inactivity (to repay "oxygen debt").

The muscles of an animal killed after activity but before the restorative period will be relatively deficient in glycogen, and may have a high ultimate pH. Because the isoelectric point of many muscles proteins is ca. 5.5, there will be a high water-binding capacity, and the tissue will be sticky to the touch. The eating quality of the meat may be impaired, since flavor diminishes in intensity and tenderness becomes excessive as pH rises (Bouton, Howard, and Lawrie, 1957).[2] Such muscles occurring in pigs

2. The high pH will also lead to a greater release of H_2S from cysteine and cystine on heating, and this causes greater staining if the meat is canned (Johnson and Vickery, 1964).

can produce "glazy bacon" if the meat is cured; and in this animal even a walk of a quarter of a mile can significantly deplete glycogen reserves (Callow, 1935). There is also a higher water *content* in the muscles (Lawrie, Pomeroy, and Cuthbertson, 1963) possibly because the stress of activity increases the intracellular content of intermediary metabolites and, thereby, the osmotic pressure, thus drawing fluid from the vascular spaces.

It is rare for cattle to be exhausted by preslaughter exercise (Hall, Latscher, and Mackintosh, 1944) even after fasting (Table 9.1; and Howard and Lawrie, 1956a). Insulin tetany, however, by preventing the replenishment of muscle glycogen from liver glucose and by inducing violent spasms in the muscle (because of the low blood sugar concentration) can cause a very high ultimate *p*H in this species (Table 9.1; and Hall *et al.*, 1944; Howard and Lawrie, 1956a), together with the phenomenon of "dark-cutting" beef. The latter arises through the effect of the high *p*H in shifting the absorption of the muscle pigments to the red end of the spec-

TABLE 9.1
Typical effects of various stressors on ultimate pH in two muscles

Stressor	Ultimate *p*H	
	Psoas	L. dorsi
Ox		
Rest with food; or 28 days without food	5.50	5.50
Heavy exercise preslaughter, with food; or 14 days without food	5.55	5.50
Heavy exercise preslaughter, with food, excitement in transit	6.20	5.70
Rest with food, inherent excitability or tuberculin shock	6.35	6.45
Rest with food, subsequent exposure to low temp.; or rest with food, adrenaline (sc) 24 hr preslaughter; or rest without food, insulin tetany	7.00	6.75
Pig		
Rest with food	5.50	5.50
Rest without food one day	5.75	5.65
Mild exercise preslaughter, excitement in transit	6.00	5.75
Rest with food, periodic electric shock	6.40	5.90
Rest with food, adrenaline (sc) 24 hr preslaughter	7.15	6.50
Rabbit		
Rest with food, and with or without cortisone 28 hr preslaughter	5.70	5.70
Rest, 3 days without food	6.40	5.90
Rest with food, reserpine 21 hr preslaughter	5.80	5.80
Rest with food, adrenaline (sc) 4 hr preslaughter	6.50	6.50
Rest with food, adrenaline 4 hr preslaughter and cortisone 28 hr preslaughter	6.00	5.80
Rest with food, tremorine injection	6.40	6.20
Rest with food, adrenaline 4 hr preslaughter and reserpine 21 hr preslaughter	7.10	6.75

trum and increasing the cytochrome oxidase activity (Lawrie, 1952). A high activity of this enzyme, combined with the swollen structure caused by the high pH, depletes the oxygen available to form bright-red oxymyoglobin at the surface of the meat, thus permitting the purplish-red color of reduced myoglobin to predominate (Lawrie, 1958). The high ultimate pH of dark-cutting beef, when it occurs naturally, is not caused, of course, by insulin tetany.

Accommodation of oxygen debt

Much muscle differentiation involves devices to withstand the stress of low oxygen tension. Muscles which operate in short bursts of activity, where they require energy from ATP quickly, but can shortly enter a restorative resting phase, have (1) myoglobin-poor, glycogen-loaded, broad fibers; (2) high stores of CP or of glycogen, or both, and a high content of phosphorylase; (3) a high capacity for splitting ATP; and (4) little capacity for respiratory activity, as represented by cytochrome oxidase and other Krebs cycle enzymes (Lawrie, 1953a, 1953b; Dubowitz and Pearse, 1960). The sarcoplasmic reticulum is well developed to expedite reaction speed (Fawcett and Revel, 1961). Such a muscle is the psoas of the rabbit (Table 9.2).

TABLE 9.2
Ratios of energy factors between various muscles

Factor	Rabbit		Horse			
	Psoas		L. dorsi	Psoas	Diaphragm	Heart
Adenosine triphosphatase activity	10 :		5 :	3 :	3 :	1
Phosphocreatine store	33 :		19 :	10 :	3 :	1
Glycogen store	1 :		2.5 :	1.5 :	1.2 :	2.5
Cytochrome oxidase activity	1 :		12 :	45 :	55 :	130
Myoglobin	1 :		24 :	35 :	30 :	16

Source: R. A. Lawrie, "The activity of the cytochrome system in muscle and its relation to myoglobin," *Biochem. J.* 55(1953):298; "The relation of energy-rich phosphate in muscle to myoglobin and to cytochrome oxidase activity," *Biochem. J.* 55(1953):305; "Residual glycogen at high ultimate pH in horse muscle," *Biochim. Biophys. Acta* 17(1955):282.

On the other hand, muscles which are more or less constantly in action (e.g., diaphragm) or those which have to develop slow steady power (e.g., the psoas of the horse) must be supplied with oxygen virtually continuously. In muscles of this type, which are referred to as "red" muscles, as opposed to the "white" muscles described in the previous paragraph, (1) the fibers are narrow, surrounded by capillaries (Romanul, 1964), and have an auxiliary oxygen reserve (elaborated as the pigment oxymyoglobin); (2) stores of CP and glycogen tend to be low; (3) the capacity for splitting ATP is relatively low, and there is little phosphorylase; and (4) the respiratory capacity is high (Lawrie, 1953a, 1953b; Dubowitz and Pearse, 1960). There is thus little provision for anaerobic glycolysis. Starch gel electrophoresis of extracts of "red" muscle shows that many of the proteins corresponding to the enzymes of the glycolytic pathway are present in low concentration only (R. K. Scopes, unpublished).

The heart is exceptional in having a considerable glycogen store as well as a high respiratory activity (Table 9.2). Indeed, in the fetus and newborn animal, where the oxygen supply is barely adequate, resistance to anoxia depends on anaerobic glycolysis, and more than 3% of glycogen may be present in heart muscle (Dawes, Mott, and Shelley, 1959). Again, considering its very high respiratory activity, heart muscle has very little myoglobin. This is presumably because its blood supply is so lavish that an auxiliary oxygen store is not so essential. Nevertheless, it is of interest that such myoglobin as the heart does have changes in phase with cytochrome activity, as it does in the skeletal muscles. This can be illustrated by the changes in rapidly growing and adult horses (Table 9.3).

TABLE 9.3

Yearly increase in cytochrome oxidase activity and myoglobin concentration of muscles in young and in adult horses, expressed as percentage of average adult values

Muscle	Cytochrome oxidase	Myoglobin
	0–2 years	
Heart	+37.0	+38.9
Diaphragm	+38.4	+40.1
Psoas	+37.9	+42.8
L. dorsi	+40.0	+37.3
	2–12 years	
Heart	−2.1	+0.7
Diaphragm	+0.7	+3.6
Psoas	+0.6	+2.1
L. dorsi	−3.3	+1.5

Source: R. A. Lawrie, "The activity of the cytochrome system in muscle and its relation to myoglobin," *Biochem. J. 55(1953)*:298.

The small, but definite, increase in the myoglobin content of muscle in animals after they reach physiological maturity and when cytochrome oxidase has reached a maximum may reflect an increased difficulty of oxygen exchange in the tissues of older animals, and may be symptomatic of a general increase in stress susceptibility with age. If so, this effect has not been taken into account so far in handling meat animals.

It is significant that a "red" muscle may alter its character to give more rapid, but weaker, contractions when its insertions are surgically altered to those of a neighboring "white" muscle. Moreover, the myoglobin content falls (Bach, 1948). Atrophy of a muscle through disuse, or hypertrophy through increased usage, are accompanied by decreases and increases, respectively, in myoglobin concentration (Jewell and Zaimis, 1959). An increase of myoglobin is one of the responses of a muscle to the stress of increased activity, as in training (Lawrie, 1953c), where the stressor is neither of sudden incidence nor excessive. Another response is the building up of glycogen reserves (Mitchell and Hamilton, 1933; Bate-Smith, 1948). A third is a hypertrophy of the muscle fibers, which depends on an increase in the number of constituent myofibrils (Denny-Brown, 1961) and occurs where the training involves near-maximal effort. A particularly striking effect of continuing activity (whether due to training in the individual or to selection for power over several generations) is shown by the differences in myoglobin concentrations in the muscles of horses (Table 9.4). That the myoglobin increment should be especially

TABLE 9.4
Myoglobin concentrations in horse muscles, expressed in percentage of wet weight

Muscle	Normal (draught)	Active (hunter)	Very active (thoroughbred)
Heart	0.29	0.40	0.43
Diaphragm	0.76	0.81	0.87
Psoas	0.82	0.81	0.88
L. dorsi	0.46	0.76	0.77

    Source: R. A. Lawrie, "Some observations on factors affecting myoglobin concentrations in muscle," *J. Agr. Sci. 40(1950):356.*

marked in the longissimus dorsi is significant, for although this muscle would be under relatively little stress in normal locomotion when the back is level, its use would be especially great in galloping, when the back is strongly flexed at each forward movement (Lawrie, 1950).

    For a tissue designed for activity, disuse constitutes a stressor whether induced by lack of exercise, immobilization, or section of the tendons or nerves. Immobilization is reflected initially by an increase in the water content of muscle, corresponding to a decrease in protein; later the water content falls (Fischer and Ramsay, 1946). Denervation atrophy is associated with progressive lessening of fiber diameter (Denny-Brown, 1961). It is significant that while "white" muscles are relatively unaffected by disuse induced by section of the tendons, "red" muscles atrophy — but only if the impulses from the nervous system continue (McMinn and

Vrbová, 1962). Denervation *accelerates* degeneration, however, if the muscles are subsequently injured (Denny-Brown, 1961).

It seems that not only the total quantity of muscle glycogen, but also its chemical nature, is important in resisting the stress of activity. Thus, in the levator palpebrae of the eye of the horse and in the sternocephalicus of the ox, there are substantial quantities of glycogen of a type which resists conversion to lactic acid during postmortem glycolysis (Lawrie, 1955, and unpublished data) and in vitro, when isolated and subjected to the action of phosphorylase b (Briskey and Lawrie, 1961). The residual glycogen in the sternocephalicus has a significantly shorter external chain length than that which is converted to lactic acid (Lawrie, Manners, and Wright, 1959). It is conceivable that the phenomenon reflects differentiation for precision of movement rather than for speed or duration of muscle activity and that it may involve an unknown stressor against which a particular glycogen molecule is useful. (In this general context, it may be significant that muscular dystrophies not infrequently involve the ocular muscles first of all; see Henson, 1960.)

The stress of low oxygen tension is considerable in diving mammals such as seals and whales (Irving, 1939; Scholander, 1940) and in animals at high altitude (Poel, 1949). Both these environmental circumstances are reflected by the elaboration of a relatively large store of oxygen bound to myoglobin. In the sperm whale, in which the dives may be lengthy, the concentration of myoglobin may reach 5% to 8% of the wet weight of the muscle (Sharp and Marsh, 1953; Robinson, 1939). Although the intrinsic rate of oxygen consumption in whale muscle is low compared with that in other mammals, and it can be calculated that the store of oxymyoglobin in whale psoas, for example, would last 20 times as long as that in horse psoas under comparable conditions (Lawrie, 1953a), the oxygen reserves are unlikely to be adequate for a long dive (Ishikawa, 1961). It would appear that in a diving mammal the oxygen is preferentially diverted to the brain and heart muscle by a shunt device; and the skeletal muscles, notwithstanding their high myoglobin content, may have to operate anaerobically and incur an "oxygen debt," to be discharged on surfacing (Irving, 1939). Indeed there can then be a massive flush of lactic acid into the blood stream from the muscles. It may be that it is against the stress of a high concentration of lactic acid during diving that the muscle of the whale is provided with exceptionally great quantities of the buffers carnosine and anserine (Davey, 1960).

TEMPERATURE STRESS

Bernard (1876) demonstrated that, on exposure to cold, animals produced heat both by visible muscular activity (shivering) and by some other chemical processes. Shivering is the first compensatory reaction, in a nonacclimated animal, to a low environmental temperature. Reserves of glycogen in both liver and muscle are depleted by shivering, and the muscles of animals slaughtered in this condition may have an ultimate pH above the normal 5.5. Indeed, acute exposure to a cold environment is one of the few naturally occurring circumstances that can be inferred to produce a high ultimate pH in cattle (Hall *et. al.*, 1944; Lawrie, 1958, and unpublished data), which is manifested as dark-cutting beef. The condition can be artificially produced in pigs by exposing them suddenly to a temperature of 0 C for 30 min before slaughter (Sayre *et al.*, 1961). Even when a high ultimate pH results, however, about 50% of the increase in metabolism is probably due to a centrally stimulated nonshivering thermogenesis (Davis *et al.*, 1960), mediated by the release of noradrenaline from the adrenergic nerve endings (Leduc, 1961).

If exposure continues, other changes occur, their nature depending both on the severity of the cold stress and on the cold-resisting mechanisms in the animal. Eventually, even if the animal has been able to maintain normal temperature, continuing cold may exhaust glycogen reserves completely and death will follow. On the other hand, the animal may become acclimated, in which case shivering stops, glycogen reserves are restored (Burton and Bronk, 1937), and nonshivering thermogenesis predominates. It is presently believed that, as with shivering itself, the muscles are primarily responsible for such heat production, which is associated with an increased activity of cytochrome oxidase (Jansky, 1963), possibly due to the oxidation of fatty acids (Hannon, Evonuk, and Larson, 1963). In this process a greater than normal percentage of the respiration is dissociated from the phosphorylation of ADP and is used more directly to produce heat (Beyer, 1963). It is significant that to animals in a cold environment administration of the tranquilizer reserpine, which releases stored noradrenaline and exposes it to destruction by monoamine oxidase (Leduc, 1961), should prejudice survival. As cold acclimation continues, the concentration in muscle of such enzymes as glutamic/oxaloacetic and glutamic/pyruvic transaminases increases. These are particularly useful in gluconeogenesis (Hannon, 1963). If acclimation to cold proceeds over several generations, further changes are found in the musculature. Thus Barnett and Widdowson (1965) have shown that the muscles of mice bred for two generations at -3 C tended to have less fat and nitrogen but more water than those of controls at 21 C; whereas after 24 generations at -3 C, the muscles had more fat and less water than those of the controls. In unacclimated animals, exposure to cold can elicit an attack of certain types of muscular dystrophy (Conn *et al.*, 1957).

Although many homeothermic animals die on prolonged exposure to cold, others have solved the problem of surviving prolonged cold by hibernating in winter. These have developed physiological adjustments which enable them to dispense with the high internal temperature they maintain when fully active; the metabolic rate is lowered, and the muscles (by which basal metabolic rate is largely determined; see Drabkin, 1950) respire at a very low level of intensity. In preparation for hibernation fats become desaturated, so that their melting point is lowered (Fawcett and Lyman, 1954). Nonhibernating homeotherms can survive cooling well below normal body temperature by being anaesthetized to prevent shivering (Smith, 1958). In this artificial hypothermia, the concentrations of ACTH, adrenal corticoids, adrenaline, and noradrenaline in their respective centers are depressed, and an insensitivity to insulin is shown by failure of this hormone to prevent hyperglycemia if the animal shivers (Smith, 1958).

High temperature is also a stressor. Heat tetany of the musculature is particularly frequent when the wet bulb temperature is above 41 C (Iampietro, 1963). It is thus of particular interest that the keeping of pigs for 30–60 min preslaughter at an environmental temperature of 42–45 C should be associated with rapid postmortem glycolysis, with the production of "pale, soft, exudative" musculature, and with decreased solubility of sarcoplasmic and myofibrillar proteins in comparison with controls (Kastenschmidt, Briskey, and Hoekstra, 1964). Some such effects on the muscle proteins would be expected from the combination of low pH and high temperature resulting from a fast rate of pH fall postmortem (Briskey and Wismer-Pedersen, 1961a; Bendall and Wismer-Pedersen, 1962). It is also possible that preslaughter temperature damage to specific enzyme-proteins of the glycolytic pathway may automatically predispose the musculature to an accelerated glycolysis. As studied in vitro, all temperatures above 20 C cause increasing loss of solubility in the sarcoplasmic proteins of muscle, especially at pH levels near their isoelectric point; but there is a striking loss of solubility at all pH levels as the temperature is raised between 37 C and 45 C (Fig. 9.1). I shall return to this question later.

NUTRITIONAL STRESS

Both deficiencies and excesses of nutrients can be stressors of muscle. Muscular tissue acts as a labile reserve of protein, and when protein is deficient in the diet, muscle is preferentially called upon (after the liver) to supply amino acids for the synthesis of proteins for more essential purposes (Addis, Poo, and Lew, 1936), such as to produce antibodies in febrile illness. Where there is a combined deficiency of protein and calories there is first of all a lowering in the level of protein, fat, and potassium, and an increase in the content of sodium and water (Widdowson, Dickerson, and McCance, 1960), the muscle becoming edematous and pale, as in

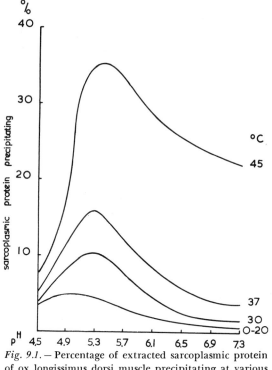

Fig. 9.1. — Percentage of extracted sarcoplasmic protein of ox longissimus dorsi muscle precipitating at various *p*H and temperature levels in vitro. After Scopes, 1964*a*.

kwashiorkor (Platt, Heard, and Stewart, 1964). Subsequently, the muscle wastes greatly in bulk. In general, wastage of enzyme proteins is more rapid than that of the structural elements, but cytochrome oxidase is exceptional in being preferentially retained (Gallagher, 1964), although its reduction in "red" muscle is more marked than in "white" (Tasker and Tulpule, 1964). Those muscles which lose weight most rapidly in inanition are those which respond most to growth-stimulating hormone (Greenbaum and Young, 1953); the masseter and soleus appear to be less readily depleted of nitrogen in such conditions. In nonruminants, particularly, specific deficiencies of methionine, leucine, or isoleucine have a greater effect in accelerating the wastage of muscle than those of histidine, tryptophan, lysine, or threonine (Gallagher, 1964).

Over a relatively short period, inanition depletes the glycogen reserves of muscle (Bernard, 1877). The importance of this factor in relation to the meat from domestic species was recognized by Callow (1938), who showed that fasting for 48 hr caused a loss of glycogen from the psoas muscles which was sufficient to raise the ultimate *p*H from 5.7 to 6.1 and in some way appeared to *lower* the water content by about 0.4%. Such inanition caused an even more marked elevation of ultimate pH in the rabbit (Bate-Smith and Bendall, 1949). Steers, on the other hand, can be fasted for periods up to 28 days without affecting the ultimate pH, although the muscle glycogen reserves fall somewhat after 7 days. Even if succeeded by heavy exercise preslaughter, fasting has normally no effect on the glycogen reserves of steers (Table 9.1; and Howard and Lawrie, 1956*a*).

As the protein intake rises, the release of ACTH from the pituitary is enhanced (Munro *et al.*, 1962). It appears that a diet which is too rich in protein can exaggerate the effects on animals of stressors generally (Munro, 1964. This finding may be related to the fact that those pigs which are highly efficient food converts are especially liable to produce the so-called white muscle condition (Ludvigsen, 1954). Dietary imbalance or excesses of specific amino acids — in particular, tyrosine, methionine, tryptophan, and histidine — can exaggerate the deficiences of other amino acids which are limiting (Harper, 1964). This toxic effect is more marked in diets with high protein intake (Grau, 1948). Deficiencies and excesses of various other nutrients cause stress in muscle. An insufficiency of vitamin E, in particular, causes marked dystrophy (Blaxter, 1952). There is swelling, loss of pigmentation, and, microscopically, hyaline degeneration. Vitamin E–deficient musculature has impaired respiratory and increased autolytic activity, both factors exacerbating atrophy (Koszalka, Mason, and Krol, 1961). A deficiency of selenium causes a similar syndrome, whereas an excess causes loss of muscle tone.

Deficiencies in copper, cobalt (Marston, 1952), biotin (Sullivan, Kolb, and Nicholls, 1942), and vitamin C also produce atrophy. Excesses of nitrate (or nitrite) and fluoracetate cause tissue anoxia by their effects on oxygen carriage by the blood, and on the respiratory chain, respectively. In both cases muscle glycogen reserves are depleted and there is discoloration (Gallagher, 1964).

Dietary deficiencies of calcium and magnesium cause symptoms referred to as "milk" and "grass" tetany respectively. When reflected in the blood, a deficiency of Mg or an excess of Ca increases the excitability of muscle, leading to a fast rate of onset of rigor mortis postmortem, and to loss of water-holding capacity at a given ultimate pH. Conversely, an excess of Mg or a deficiency of Ca decreases the excitability of the muscular tissue and leads to a slow rate of onset of rigor mortis, and to enhanced water-holding capacity at a given ultimate pH (Table 9.5; and Howard and Lawrie, 1956*a*).

TABLE 9.5

The typical effects of serum levels of Mg and Ca on the onset of rigor mortis in the muscles of steers

Condition	Blood serum, mg / 100 ml		Time to onset of rigor mortis, in min at 37 C (N_2 atmosphere)	
	$Mg++$	$Ca++$	L. dorsi	Psoas
Controls	2	10	220	130
Relaxation by hypermagnesemia	21	9	310	300
Hypercalcemia	2	42	120	45
Hypocalcemia	4	1	210	180

STRESS AND INJURY

Injury results in damage to, or loss of, protein at the injured site and to loss of protein generally as part of the reaction to the stress imposed (Cuthbertson, 1964). Most of this general increase in protein catabolism, and the concomitant rise in temperature, is due to the breakdown of muscle protein which is utilized, as in nutritional stress, in an endeavor to spare more essential proteins. A definite pattern of changes occurs irrespective of the nature of the injury stressor (Cuthbertson, 1942). A few minutes after injury there is increased secretion and excretion of adrenaline, noradrenaline, and adrenal cortical hormones, as the general adaptation syndrome operates. Blood sugar and heart rate are augmented. After a few hours, and up to 24 hr or beyond, the effects of injury may develop into traumatic shock, when there is a period of circulatory failure due to loss of blood (through hemorrhage and fluid leakage into tissues). Body temperature and oxygen consumption fall at this point, reflecting lowered muscle metabolism. Some days after the injury a repair phase ensues when the oxygen consumption rises once more and fever develops as an adaptive mechanism. There is an increased excretion of N, S, P, and K, and an excessive output of antidiuretic hormone from the posterior pituitary which suppresses aldosterone secretion (Cuthbertson, 1964). Subsequently the normal water balance is restored.

Apart from catabolism of its protein as a general reaction to injury of the body, muscle also reacts to specific local injury characteristically. According to Denny-Brown (1961)

The initial reaction to injury is inevitably some degree of reversion to foetal structure. This may amount only to nuclear enlargement and central migration. The next stage in either repair or degeneration is accumulation of granular, basophilic sarcoplasm around the nuclei. Increasing amounts of sarcoplasm may then be a prelude to either pseudopodal budding or else a fragmentation and splitting into spindle cells.

This "cloudy swelling" is accompanied by inhibition of oxidative phosphorylation and an increase in anaerobic glycolysis (Fonnesu, 1960). Under extremely severe conditions the muscle nuclei multiply in an abortive attempt to restore normality.

As indicated above, the general adaptation syndrome is not precisely followed in an animal exposed to heat stress (Hellman *et al.*, 1956). Nevertheless the reaction of muscle to a degree of heat or cold severe enough to cause *local* injury is similar (Fishback and Fishback, 1932; Denny-Brown, 1961). Histologically, changes proceed from a slight granularity and swelling of the fiber to edema, vacuolization, and finally to segmented fragmentation (Adams, Denny-Brown, and Pearson, 1953) in which the myofibrillar proteins form discrete clots or bands of exremely contracted fibers. At environmental temperatures below $0\,C$, local damage to muscle may be sufficiently severe to cause coagulation of sarcoplasmic proteins (Friedman, Lange, and Wiener, 1950). Under the microscope, the necrotic muscle fibers show transverse bands of dense material separated by clear areas which, according to Adams *et al.* (1953), reflect a state of extreme contraction.

Where there is prolonged exposure of parts of the body, such as limbs, to a temperature only $20\,C$ lower than deep body temperature there can be considerable damage to muscles (e.g., trench foot), which is superficially manifested by swelling or necrosis (Pichotka, Lewis, and Freytag, 1951). Such changes probably reflect impaired circulation and are similar to those in severe oxygen lack.

Owing to the low renal threshold of myoglobin this pigment will be excreted in the urine whenever sufficiently large quantities are released from muscle. This happens when muscle is damaged directly, as in crushing. In the "crush syndrome" (Bywaters, 1944), 75% of the myoglobin, 75% of the phosphorus, 65% of the potassium, 70% of the creatine, and 95% of the glycogen are discharged from muscles. The latter are invaded by blood plasma and present an exudative, "fish-paste" appearance. The picture is similar when the muscle is extensively injured through high voltage electricity (Biörck, 1949).

With low voltage electricity the changes are much less severe. Mild periodic electrical stimulation — for example, by administering three or four electric shocks every 20 min for 24 hr before slaughter — causes little effect beyond the lowering of muscle glycogen, though the ultimate pH may thereby be raised sufficiently to give a dark color in the muscles of both pigs and cattle (Lewis, Brown, and Heck, 1961, 1963).

On the other hand even relatively low doses of ionizing radiation (ca. 3,000 rad) applied to muscles physiologically, cause a fall in creatine, aldolase, and potassium, and an increase in sodium and chloride, in the tissue (Dowben and Zuckerman, 1963). Superficially there is edema which presents an aspect similar to that in many dystrophic conditions. An even smaller (1,000 rad) dose, however, administered to the live animal, is said to inhibit subsequent autolytic changes postmortem and to enhance water-holding capacity of the meat (Silaev, 1962).

PSYCHOLOGICAL STRESS

It is rather easier to appreciate that such agents as activity, temperature, and injury can cause stress in muscle than that factors which have no obvious physical basis can do so. Nevertheless, the hypothalamus is responsive to stimuli from the higher centers as well as from the external environment; and it has been shown that the sequence of reactions of the general adaptation syndrome is followed with psychological stress, also, however mysterious the details may appear superficially.

The induction of psychological stress can, indeed, have a physical basis. Thus, it can be caused by sound of sufficient intensity or duration; and it is then reflected in an increased secretion of ACTH and of adrenal cortical hormones (Sackler and Weltman, 1963). Convulsions, with consequent lowering of muscle glycogen levels, may ensue. A diminution of muscle glycogen and a build-up of liver glycogen also occur on initial exposure to acceleration stressors (e.g., 4–5 g); but normal equilibruim is restored as exposure is continued (Oyama and Platt, 1965). There is no obvious physical basis for social stress, however, which is perhaps the most curious of all psychological effects. This may arise from the pressure of living in populations of high density or, as shown by the behavior of rats, from the presence of an interloper in an established population (Barnett, 1958). In these cases, even without physical injury and before there is any indication of depleted adrenal cortex hormones to counteract a prolonged alarm reaction, death may ensue.

Since they may attain commercial importance[3] it is appropriate to give more detailed consideration to two striking examples of metabolic stresses which affect the musculature and which can have a psychological origin, namely, dark-cutting beef and pale, soft, exudative pork.

Dark-cutting beef

The effect of psychological stress on muscle first came to my attention in 1953, during experiments in Queensland. Since it had not proved possible to deplete the muscle glycogen reserves of steers sufficiently to raise the

3. Emotional stress causes vasodilatation of the blood vessels in skeletal muscle (Greenfield, 1962), and may enhance fibrinolytic activity in entrained blood. These effects, especially if combined with electrical stunning, could perhaps explain the higher incidence of intramuscular bleeding ("blood splash") reported in excitable animals (Macgregor, 1952) — another condition which can attain commercial significance.

ultimate pH even by a combination of enforced preslaughter exercise with inanition, it was particularly surprising to find such depletion in the muscles of certain steers which had been well fed and rested. They were of excitable temperament, however (Table 9.1; and Howard and Lawrie, 1956a). Even when at rest, such animals appeared to tremble, and it was clear that a more or less continuous short-range muscular twitching, not manifested by marked movement of the body, was lowering the equilibrium level of muscle glycogen. A similar degree of lowering was caused by protein (tuberculin) shock; but rather surprisingly the intravenous injection of adrenaline 30 min preslaughter was ineffective (Howard and Lawrie, 1957), although the reaction of excitable animals indicated a chronic alarm phase of the general adaptation syndrome (Selye, 1946). On the other hand subcutaneous injection of adrenaline some hours before death (Cori and Cori, 1928) in cattle (Hedrick, Brady, and Turner, 1957) and pigs (Penny, Voyle, and Lawrie, 1964) effectively reduces reserves of muscle glycogen (Table 9.1), as also does the induction of intense trembling with tremorine (Bendall and Lawrie, 1962).

The chronic release of adrenaline into the circulation in excitable animals presumably achieves its effect on muscle glycogen stores not only by direct stimulation of phosphorylase (Sutherland and Cori, 1951) but also by the conversion of phosphorylase b to phosphorylase a (Krebs and Fischer, 1955), thus wasting glycogen by promoting lactic acid production in vivo in preference to respiration. (Both adrenaline and noradrenaline speed up glycolysis postmortem; but the latter has no effect on the stores of muscle glycogen even when administered at 20 times the level of adrenaline; see Bendall and Lawrie, 1962.) It may be of significance in understanding the chronic effect of adrenaline that the arterial blood of subcutaneously injected animals is venous in color. This strongly suggests that the animal is in a condition of partial anoxia, possibly because adrenaline keeps arterioles contracted, thus making oxygenation of the blood in the lungs more difficult and reducing the supply of oxygen to the muscles. It is also significant that the glycogen-depleting effect of chronic adrenaline can be largely prevented by the administration of cortisone about 24 hr before the adrenaline injections (Hedrick et al., 1957; Bendall and Lawrie, 1962). The secretion of glucocorticoids is characteristic of the recovery phase of the general adaptation syndrome, and it may be presumed that endogenously administered cortisone helps to counteract the excessive and prolonged alarm reaction evoked by the subcutaneous injection of adrenaline. Although these mechanisms are not precisely known, cortisone certainly promotes the deposition of glycogen in skeletal muscle (Glenn, Bowman, and Richardson, 1961). The gluconeogenic effect of glucocorticoids involves direct inhibition of the utilization of amino acids for protein synthesis and their diversion for carbohydrate production (Chester-Jones and Bellamy, 1964). It would seem that dark-cutting beef can be accounted for by the exposure of animals to stressors which are sufficiently severe (1) to prolong the release of adrenaline in the alarm reaction to stress, (2) to exhaust, thereby, the gluconeogenic, restorative hormones of the adrenal cortex, and (3) to result in the establishment of a low equilibrium level of muscle glycogen. Notwithstanding their effect in tranquilizing animals, substances such as chlorpromazine and reserpine do not prevent the action of chronic adrenaline in depleting glycogen reserves (Hedrick et al., 1959; Bendall and Lawrie, 1962).

Pale, soft, exudative pork

The efficiency of the stress defense mechanisms involved in gluconeogenesis probably varies between individual animals (Hedrick et al., 1959), and this naturally leads to a consideration of another condition in livestock which involves striking changes in the musculature — a condition against which cortisone is also prophylactic, and in which the animal's adrenal cortical hormones are unable to effect the initial changes arising in response to stress (Ludvigsen, 1957). The condition, which occurs most notably in pigs, is superficially the antithesis of dark-cutting beef, for the musculature is pale, soft, and exudative (PSE; see Briskey, 1964) instead of dark, hard, and dry. Referred to as "wässeriges Fleisch," "muskeldegeneration," or "white muscle disease" by various investigators over the last 50 years, it has received increasing attention, and aroused some controversy, since 1954. As detailed assessments of the condition have been made recently (Briskey, 1964; Bendall and Lawrie, 1964), it is not proposed to elaborate on them here; but certain comments appear relevant.

Unlike the dystrophies and other diseases of muscle, PSE character postmortem is not usually associated with any impairment of movement in the live animal. It seems generally agreed that the massive exudation and textural aspects postmortem reflect denaturation of the muscle proteins. The sarcoplasmic proteins, particularly, are involved; and creatine phosphorylkinase is especially labile (Fig. 9.2). The sarcoplasmic proteins can be seen to form aggregates around the myofibrils, when examined microscopically (Bendall and Wismer-Pedersen, 1962). The denaturation results from "thermoprotonic stress" (Scopes, 1964b), a term denoting the combined effects of high temperature and low pH. A high ultimate pH will tend to protect the proteins postmortem (Fig. 9.3). Usually the thermoprotonic stress is caused by the attainment by the muscle of a low pH while the temperature of the carcass is still high; and this circumstance arises when there is a very fast rate of postmortem glycolysis, as Ludvigsen

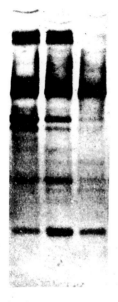

Fig. 9.2. — Electrophoretogram of extracts of sarcoplasmic proteins from pig longissimus dorsi muscle: (*a*) normal pig muscle, (*b*) pale, exudative pig muscle, (*c*) as in (*b*), but very severe. From Scopes and Lawrie, 1963.

(a) (b) (c)

Fig. 9.3. — Electrophoretogram of extracts of sarcoplasmic proteins of longissimus dorsi muscles from normal and adrenaline-treated pigs undergoing postmortem glycolysis at two temperatures: (*a*) adrenaline-treated (ult. *p*H, 6.55), 0 C, (*b*) normal (ult. *p*H, 5.45), 0 C, (*c*) adrenaline-treated (ult. *p*H, 6.55), 37 C, (*d*) normal (ult. *p*H, 5.45), 37 C. Scopes and Lawrie, unpublished.

(a)　(b)　(c)　(d)

suggested in 1954. Such conditions can be caused artificially in vitro by holding muscles at 37 C during the onset of rigor mortis or in vivo by slow cooling of the carcass and by holding pigs at temperature above 40 C for 30 min before death (Kastenschmidt, Briskey, and Hoekstra, 1964). Nevertheless, to explain the natural incidence of the condition some other factor must obviously be found, for under identical cooling conditions postmortem some carcasses are affected and some are not. Moreover, even within a given muscle where the temperature is uniform, one portion can show PSE characteristics and another, only 1 cm away, can be normal (Lawrie, Gatherum, and Hale, 1958). Among pigs which do not yield PSE musculature postmortem, there can be a threefold difference in the rate of pH fall between given pH levels at a given temperature (Lawrie, 1960). Experiments by Hallund and Bendall (1965) have shown that susceptibility to preslaughter stress has a long-term effect in accelerating postmortem pH fall and hence in eliciting the symptoms of PSE musculature. Since the latter has a high content of glycogen and marked phosphorylase activity (as shown by biopsy techniques; see Briskey and Wismer-Pederson, 1961b) and low contents of cytochrome c (Bernard, 1959) and of myoglobin (Lawrie, 1960) it seems likely that differences in susceptibility to preslaughter stress must reflect inherent factors operating over a considerable period in the animals' life. As indicated above, these are the characteristics of a muscle which is poorly developed for sustained, aerobic activity. The PSE condition is more prevalent in pigs of breeds which have involved intensive selection for a marked ability to grow muscles. Ludvigsen (1954) suggested that, in such animals, there had been automatic selection for a high content of GSH in the pituitary and *thereby* a lower content of TSH and ACTH. Both high GSH and low TSH predispose towards the elaboration of an anaerobic type of musculature (Krebs and Fischer, 1955; Russell and Wilhelmi, 1960).

Obviously an anaerobic type of musculature cannot be the sole prerequisite for producing PSE characteristics, since most rabbit muscle, like much of the musculature of normal pigs, is of this type and yet does not have PSE characteristics. The rate of postmortem pH fall in PSE musculature is so fast, however, as to indicate some internal disruption or damage to the sarcolemma. Very fast rates of postmortem glycolysis occur in thaw rigor (when muscle is frozen before the onset of rigor mortis) and may indeed attain 20 to 30 times the normal rate in that temperature range (Bendall and Marsh, 1951); the fast rates also occur when there are high concentrations of salt in the muscle, as when it is partially frozen (Smith, 1930; Howard and Lawrie, 1956b). The importance of disruption can be clearly and simply shown by comparing the time taken for beef longissimus dorsi to fall from pH 6.8 to 5.6, at a given temperature, in intact muscle, as a mince, and as a homogenate. Such times are in the ratio 30:8:1, respectively. Moreover the ultimate pH is *lower* in the latter two cases (unpublished data). According to Bendall (1960), the myofibrillar adenosine triphosphatase is greatly accelerated by damage to the sarcolemma through ionic imbalance, as in thaw rigor and PSE muscles. If, having this fact in mind, there is considered the hyperkalemia, which is evident in pigs which eventually produce PSE muscle (Ludvigsen, 1954), and the defective operation of mineralocorticoids, resulting from the above-mentioned deficiency of ACTH, it seems likely that an uncorrectable imbalance may well be precipitated by the psychological stress of preslaughter conditions.

CONCLUSION

If pale, watery pork is the manifestation of short-term adrenaline release in causing uncompensated mineral imbalance in muscles adapted for anaerobic activity, dark-cutting beef is the manifestation of long-term adrenaline release in causing uncompensated carbohydrate imbalance in muscles adapted for aerobic activity. Both appear to reflect the inability of adrenal cortex hormones to offset the disequilibrium in muscle caused by stressors.

It is scarcely surprising that muscle, which in bulk constitutes the major tissue of the body, should reflect physiological stresses of both internal and external origin. Its metabolism can be invoked, through shivering and other forms of thermogenesis, to assist the body as a whole to withstand a cold environment. In injury and inanition its proteins can be called upon as a reserve supply of essential amino acids for the elaboration of vital proteins. Its versatility in accommodating the stress in activity is attested by a many-sided biochemical differentiation.

This metabolic responsiveness to stress alters its composition and thus cannot fail to affect its nature as meat. Thus the over-all subjection of its metabolism to the higher centers of the brain through the adrenal-pituitary-hypothalamus axis can cause it to present superficial characteristics which are most unpleasant as meat attributes. That these can have a psychological basis is a salutary reminder of the subtlety of the factors which affect eating and keeping quality. It is also desirable to appreciate that there are a large number of metabolic stresses which undoubtedly depreciate quality, even if they do not produce effects which are quite so spectacular as those in dark-cutting beef or pale, exudative pork. Their elucidation could permit a more accurate prediction and control of the commodity than has hitherto been possible.

References

Adams, R. D., D. Denny-Brown, and C. M. Pearson. 1953. *Diseases of Muscle: A Study in Pathology.* Cassell & Co., Ltd., London.

Addis, T., L. J. Poo, and W. Lew. 1936. The quantities of protein lost by the various organs and tissues of the body during a fast. *J. Biol. Chem. 115:*111.

Armstrong, M. D., and A. McMillan. 1957. Identification of a major urinary metabolite of norepinephrine. *Fed. Proc. 16:*146.

Axelrod, J. 1960. N-methyladrenaline, a new catecholamine in the adrenal gland. *Biochim. Biophys. Acta 45:*614.

Bach, L. M. N. 1948. Conversion of red muscle to pale muscle. *Proc. Soc. Exp. Biol. 67:*268.

Baldwin, E. 1963. *Dynamic Aspects of Biochemistry* (4th ed.). Cambridge Univ. Press.

Barnett, S. A. 1958. Physiological effects of "social stress" in wild rats. 1. The adrenal cortex. *J. Psychosom. Res. 3:*1.

Barnett, S. A., and E. M. Widdowson. 1965. Organ-weights and body-composition in mice bred for many generations at $-3°C$. *Proc. Roy. Soc.* (London), B, *162:*502.

Bate-Smith, E. C. 1948. Observations on the pH and related properties of meat. *J. Soc. Chem. Ind. 67:*83.

Bate-Smith, E. C., and J. R. Bendall. 1949. Factors determining the time course of rigor mortis. *J. Physiol. 110:*47.

Bendall, J. R. 1960. Post mortem changes in muscle, p. 227. In G. H. Bourne (ed.), *The Structure and Function of Muscle*, Vol. 3. Academic Press, New York.

Bendall, J. R., and R. A. Lawrie. 1962. The effect of pretreatment with various drugs on post mortem glycolysis and the onset of rigor mortis in rabbit skeletal muscle. *J. Comp. Pathol. 72:*118.

———. 1964. Watery pork: a discussion of symptoms and causes. *Fleischwirts. 16:*411.

Bendall, J. R., and B. B. Marsh. 1951. The biochemistry of muscular tissue in relation to loss of drip during freezing. *Proc. 8th Int. Congr. Refrig.* (London, 1951), p. 351.

Bendall, J. R., and J. Wismer-Pedersen. 1962. Some properties of the fibrillar proteins of normal and watery pork muscle. *J. Food Sci. 27:*144.

Bernard, C. 1876. *Leçons sur la chaleur animale.* Baillière, Paris.

———. 1877. *Leçons sur la Diabète et la Glycogenèse animale.* Baillière, Paris.

Bernard, C. 1959. Recherches sur la teneur en cytochrome *c* des muscles de porc destinés à la préparation du jambon. Dissert. Ingén. Diplome, Conserv. Nat. des Artes et Métiers, Paris.

Beyer, R. E. 1963. Regulation of energy metabolism during acclimation of laboratory rats to a cold environment. *Fed. Proc. 22:*874.

Biörck, G. 1949. On myoglobin and its occurrence in man. *Acta Med. Scand. 133 (suppl.):*226.

Blaxter, K. L. 1952. Muscular dystrophy in farm animals: its cause and prevention. *Proc. Nutr. Soc. 21:*211.

Bogdanski, D. F., and S. Udenfriend. 1956. Serotonin and monoamine oxidase in brain. *J. Pharmacol. Exp. Therap. 116*:7.

Bouton, P. E., A. Howard, and R. A. Lawrie. 1957. Studies on beef quality. VI. Effects on weight losses and eating quality of further preslaughter treatments. *Spec. Rep. Food Invest. Board* (London), No. 66.

Briskey, E. J. 1964. Etiological status and associated studies of pale, soft, exudative porcine musculature. *Advance. Food Res. 13*:89.

Briskey, E. J., and R. A. Lawrie. 1961. Comparative *in vitro* activities of phosphorylase *b* and cytochrome oxidase in preparations from two ox muscles. *Nature 192*:263.

Briskey, E. J., and J. Wismer-Pedersen. 1961a. Biochemistry of pork muscle structure. 1. Rate of anaerobic glycolysis and temperature change versus the apparent structure of muscle tissue. *J. Food Sci. 26*:297.

———. 1961b. Biochemistry of pork muscle structure. 2. Preliminary observations of biopsy samples versus ultimate muscle structure. *J. Food Sci. 26*:306.

Brodie, B. B., A. Pletscher, and P. A. Shore. 1956. Possible role of serotonin in brain function and in reserpin action. *J. Pharmacol. Exp. Therap. 116*:9.

Burton, A., and D. Bronk. 1937. The motor mechanism of shivering and of thermal muscular control. *Amer. J. Physiol. 119*:284.

Bywaters, E. G. L. 1944. Ischaemic muscle necrosis. *J. Amer. Med. Ass. 124*:1103.

Callow, E. H. 1935. The electrical resistance of muscular tissue in relation to curing. *Annu. Rep. Food Invest. Board* (London), p. 57.

———. 1938. Muscular fatigue and pH. *Annu. Rep. Food Invest. Board* (London), p. 53.

Chester-Jones, L., and D. Bellamy. 1964. Hormonal mechanisms in the homeostatic regulation of the vertebrate body with special reference to the adrenal cortex. *Symp. Soc. Exp. Biol. 18*:195.

Conn, J. N., L. H. Louis, S. S. Fajans, D. H. P. Streeten, and R. D. Johnson. 1957. Intermittent aldosteronism in periodic paralysis. *Lancet 1*:802.

Cori, C. F., and G. T. Cori. 1928. The mechanism of epinephrine action. 1. The influence of epinephrine on the carbohydrate metabolism of fasting rats, with a note on new formation of carbohydrates. *J. Biol. Chem. 79*:309.

Cross, B. A. 1964. The hypothalamus in mammalian homeostasis. *Symp. Soc. Exp. Biol. 18*:157.

Cuthbertson, D. P. 1942. Post-shock metabolic response. *Lancet 1*:433.

———. 1964. Physical injury and its effect on protein metabolism, p. 373. *In* H. N. Munro and J. B. Allison (eds.), *Mammalian Protein Metabolism*, Vol. 2. Academic Press, New York.

Davey, C. L. 1960. The significance of carnosine and anserine in striated skeletal muscle. *Arch. Biochem. Biophys. 89*:303.

Davis, T. R. A., D. R. Johnstone, F. C. Bell, and B. J. Cremer. 1960. Regulation of shivering and non-shivering heat production during acclimation of rats. *Amer. J. Physiol. 198*:471.

Dawes, G. S., J. C. Mott, and H. J. Shelley. 1959. The importance of cardiac glycogen for the maintenance of life in foetal lambs and new-born animals during anoxia. *J. Physiol. 146*:516.

Denny-Brown, D. 1961. Experimental studies pertaining to hypertrophy, regeneration and degeneration. *Neuromuscular Disorders* 38:147.

Dowben, R. M., and L. Zuckerman. 1963. Alterations in skeletal muscle after X-irradiation and their similarity to changes in muscular dystrophy. *Nature* 197:400.

Drabkin, D. L. 1950. The distribution of the chromoproteins haemoglobin, myoglobin and cytochrome *c*, in the tissues of different species and the relationship of the total content of each chromoprotein to body mass. *J. Biol. Chem.* 182:317.

Dubowitz, V., and A. G. E. Pearse. 1960. Reciprocal relationship of phosphorylase and oxidative enzymes in skeletal muscle. *Nature* 185:701.

Fawcett, D. W., and C. P. Lyman. 1954. The effect of low environmental temperature on the composition of depot fat in relation to hibernation. *J. Physiol.* 126:235.

Fawcett, D. W., and J. P. Revel. 1961. The sarcoplasmic reticulum of a fast-acting fish muscle. *J. Biophys. Biochem. Cytol.* 10(suppl.):89.

Fischer, E., and V. W. Ramsay, 1946. Changes of protein during muscular atrophies. *Amer. J. Physiol.* 145:571.

Fishback, D. K., and H. R. Fishback, 1932. Studies of experimental muscle degeneration. I. Factors in the production of muscle degeneration. II. Standard method of causation of degeneration and repair of the injured muscle. *Amer. J. Pathol.* 8:193, 211.

Fonnesu, A. 1960. Changes in energy transformation as an early response to cell injury, p. 85. *In* H. B. Stoner and C. J. Threlfall (eds.), *The Biochemical Response to Injury.* Blackwell, Oxford.

Friedman, N. B., H. Lange, and D. Wiener. 1950. Pathology of experimental immersion foot. *Arch. Pathol.* 49:21.

Gallagher, C. H. 1964. *Nutritional Factors and Enzymological Disturbances in Animals.* Crosby Lockwood & Sons Ltd., London.

Glenn, E. M., B. J. Bowman, and R. B. Bayer. 1961. Metabolic effects of hydrocortisone, p. 316. *In* L. C. Mills and J. H. Moyer (eds.), *Inflammation and Diseases of Connective Tissue.* Saunders, Philadelphia.

Grau, C. R. 1948. Effect of protein level on the lysine requirement of the chick. *J. Nutr.* 36:99.

Greenbaum, A. L., and F. G. Young. 1953. A comparison of the differences in the total nitrogen content of the muscles of the rat, resulting from treatment with growth hormone and from inanition. *J. Endocrinol.* 9:127.

Greenfield, A. D. M. 1962. The effects of emotional stress on the circulation through a voluntary muscle, p. 177. *In* K. D. Bock (ed.), *Shock: Pathogenesis and Therapy.* Springer-Verlag, Berlin.

Grundfest, H. 1959. Synaptic and ephaptic transmission, p. 147. *In* J. Field, H. W. Magown, and V. E. Hall (eds.), *Handbook of Physiology* (Amer. Physiol. Soc.), Vol. 1, sect. 1.

Hall, J. L., S. E. Latscher, and D. L. Mackintosh. 1944. Characteristics of dark-cutting beef. *Kan. Agr. Exp. Sta. Bull.*, No. 58, Pt. 4.

Hallund, O., and J. R. Bendall. 1965. The long-term effect of electrical stimulation on the post-mortem fall of pH in the muscles of Landrace pigs. *J. Food Sci.* *39*:296.

Hannon, J. P. 1963. Current status of carbohydrate metabolism in the cold-acclimated mammal. *Fed. Proc.* *22*:856.

Hannon, J. P., E. Evonuk, and A. M. Larson. 1963. Some physiological and biochemical effects of norepinephrine in the cold-acclimated rat. *Fed. Proc.* *22*:783.

Harper, A. E. 1964. Amino acid toxicities and imbalances, p. 87. *In* H. N. Munro and J. B. Allison (eds.), *Mammalian Protein Metabolism*, Vol. 2. Academic Press, New York.

Harris, G. W. 1951. Neural control of the pituitary gland. I. The neurohypophysis. *Brit. Med. J.* *2*:559.

Hedrick, H. B., J. B. Boillet, H. E. Brady, and H. D. Naumann. 1959. Etiology of dark-cutting beef. *Univ. Missouri Coll. Agr. Res. Bull.*, No. 717.

Hedrick, H. B., D. E. Brady, and C. W. Turner. 1957. The effect of antemortem stress on post mortem beef carcass characteristics. *Proc. 9th Res. Conf. Amer. Meat Inst.* (Chicago), p. 9.

Hellman, K., K. J. Collins, C. H. Gray, R. M. Jones, J. B. Lunnon, and J. S. Wiener. 1956. The excretion of urinary adrenocortical steroids during heat stress. *J. Endocrinol.* *14*:209.

Henson, R. A. 1960. Clinical aspects of some diseases, p. 359. *In* G. H. Bourne (ed.), *The Structure and Function of Muscle*, Vol. 3. Academic Press, New York.

Howard, A., and R. A. Lawrie. 1956a. Studies on beef quality. II. Physiological and biochemical effects of various preslaughter treatments. *Spec. Rep. Food Invest. Board* (London), No. 63, p. 18.

———. 1956b. Studies on beef quality. I. The effect of blast-freezing hot beef quarters. *Spec. Rep. Food Invest. Board.* (London), No. 63, p. 1.

———. 1957. Studies on beef quality. V. Further observations on biochemical and physiological responses to preslaughter treatments. *Spec. Rep. Food Invest. Board* (London), No. 65.

Iampietro, P. F. 1963. Heat-induced tetany. *Fed. Proc.* *22*:884.

Irving, L. 1939. Respiration in diving mammals. *Physiol. Rev.* *19*:112.

Ishikawa, Y. 1961. Some considerations on diving in whales. *J. Fac. Fish. Anim. Husb.* (Hiroshima Univ.) *3*:351.

Jansky, L. 1963. Body organ cytochrome oxidase activity in cold-water and warm-acclimated rats. *Can. J. Biochem. Physiol.* *41*:1847.

Jewell, P. A., and E. J. Zaimis, 1959. Changes at the neuromuscular junction of red and white muscle fibres in the cat induced by disuse atrophy and by hypertrophy. *J. Physiol.* *124*:429.

Johnson, A. R., and J. R. Vickery. 1964. Factors influencing the production of hydrogen sulphide from meat during heating. *J. Sci. Food Agr.* *15*:695.

Kastenschmidt, L. L., E. J. Briskey, and W. G. Hoekstra. 1964. Prevention of pale, soft, exudative porcine muscle through regulation of antemortem environmental temperature. *J. Food Sci.* *29*:210.

Koszalka, T. R., K. E. Mason, and G. T. Krol. 1961. Relation of Vitamin E to proteolytic and autolytic activity of skeletal muscle. *Nutrition* *73*:78.

Kreb, E. G., and E. H. Fischer. 1955. Phosphorylase activity of skeletal muscle extracts. *J. Biol. Chem. 216*:113.

Lawrie, R. A. 1950. Some observations on factors affecting myoglobin concentrations in muscle. *J. Agr. Sci. 40*:356.

———. 1952. Studies on myoglobin and cytochrome in muscle. Ph.D. diss., Cambridge Univ.

———. 1953*a*. The activity of the cytochrome system in muscle and its relation to myoglobin. *Biochem. J. 55*:298.

———. 1953*b*. The relation of energy-rich phosphate in muscle to myoglobin and to cytochrome oxidase activity. *Biochem. J. 55*:305.

———. 1953*c*. Effect of enforced exercise on myoglobin concentration in muscle. *Nature 171*:1069.

———. 1955. Residual glycogen at high ultimate pH in horse muscle. *Biochim. Biophys. Acta 17*:282.

———. 1958. Physiological stress in relation to dark-cutting beef. *J. Sci. Food Agr. 9*:721.

———. 1960. Post mortem glycolysis in normal and exudative longissimus dorsi muscles of the pig in relation to so-called white muscle disease. *J. Comp. Pathol. 70*:273.

Lawrie, R. A., D. P. Gatherum, and H. P. Hale. 1958. Abnormally low ultimate pH in pig muscle. *Nature 182*:807.

Lawrie, R. A., D. J. Manners, and A. Wright. 1959. α-1:4-glucosans. X. Glycogen structure and *rigor mortis* in mammalian muscles. *Biochem. J. 73*:485.

Lawrie, R. A., R. W. Pomeroy, and A. Cuthbertson. 1963. Studies on the muscles of meat animals. III. Comparative composition of various muscles in pigs of three weight groups. *J. Agr. Sci. 60*:195.

Leduc, J. 1961. Catecholamine production and release in exposure and acclimation to cold. *Acta Physiol. Scand. 53(suppl.)*:183.

Lewis, P. K., Jr., C. J. Brown, and M. C. Heck. 1961. Effect of stress from electrical stimulation and sugar on the chemical composition of bovine carcasses. *J. Anim. Sci. 20*:727.

———. 1963. Effect of preslaughter treatments on the chemical composition of various beef tissues. *J. Food Sci. 28*:669.

Ludvigsen, J. 1954. Investigations into so-called "muscular degeneration" in pigs [in Danish, English summary]. *Beretning fra Forsøgslaboratoriet* (Copenhagen), No. 272, Paper No. 1.

———. 1957. On the hormonal regulation of vasomotor reactions during exercise with special reference to the action of adrenal cortical steroids. *Acta Endocrinol.* (Copenhagen), *26*:406.

Macgregor, R. 1952. *The Structure of Meat Animals*, p. 86. Tech. Press Ltd., London.

McMinn, R. M. H., and C. Vrbová. 1962. Morphological changes in red and pale muscles following tenotomy. *Nature 195*:509.

Marston, H. R. 1952. Cobalt, copper and molybdenum in the nutrition of animals and plants. *Physiol. Rev. 32*:66.

Mitchell, H. H., and J. S. Hamilton. 1933. Effect of long-continued muscular exercise upon the chemical composition of the muscles and other tissues of beef cattle. *J. Agr. Res. 46:*917.

Munro, H. N. 1964. A general survey of pathological changes in protein metabolism, p. 267. *In* H. N. Munro and J. B. Allison (eds.), *Mammalian Protein Metabolism*, Vol. 2. Academic Press, New York.

Munro, H. N., W. C. Hutchison, T. R. Ramaiah, and F. J. Nielson. 1962. The influence of diet on the weight and chemical constituents of the rat adrenal gland. *Brit. J. Nutr. 16:*387.

Oyama, J., and W. T. Platt. 1965. Metabolic alterations in rats exposed to acute acceleration stress. *Endocrinology. 76:*203.

Page, I. H. 1958. Serotonin: the last four years. *Physiol. Rev. 38:*277.

Penny, I. F., C. A. Voyle, and R. A. Lawrie. 1964. Some properties of freeze-dried pork muscles of high or low ultimate pH. *J. Sci. Food Agr. 15:*559.

Pitchotka, J., R. B. Lewis, and E. Freytag. 1951. Sequence of increasing local cold injury. *Tex. Rep. Biol. Med. 9:*613.

Platt, B. S., C. R. C. Heard, and R. J. C. Stewart. 1964. Experimental protein-calorie deficiency, p. 445. *In* H. N. Munro and J. B. Allison (eds.), *Mammalian Protein Metabolism*, Vol. 2. Academic Press, New York.

Poel, W. E. 1949. Myoglobin and anoxemia. *Amer. J. Physiol. 156:*44.

Robinson, D. 1939. The muscle haemoglobin of scale as an oxygen store in diving. *Science 90:*276.

Romanul, F. C. A. 1964. Distribution of capillaries in relation to oxidative metabolism of skeletal muscle fibres. *Nature 201:*307.

Russell, J. A., and A. E. Wilhelmi. 1960. Endocrines and muscle, p. 141. *In* G. H. Bourne (ed.), *The Structure and Function of Muscle*, Vol. 2. Academic Press, New York.

Sackler, A. M., and A. S. Weltman. 1963. Endocrine and behavioral aspects of intense audiogenic stress. *Colloques Internationaux du Centre National de la Recherche Scientifique*, No. 112, p. 255.

Saffran, M. 1962. Mechanisms of adrenocortical control. *Brit. Med. Bull. 18.*122.

Sayre, R. N., E. J. Briskey, W. G. Hoekstra, and R. W. Bray. 1961. Effect of preslaughter change to a cold environment on characteristics of pork muscle. *J. Anim. Sci. 20:*487.

Schoenheimer, R. 1942. *The Dynamic State of Body Constituents*. Harvard Univ. Press, Cambridge, Mass.

Scholander, P. F. 1940. Experimental investigations on the respiratory function in diving mammals and birds. *Hvalrodets Skrifter*, No. 22, p. 1.

Scopes, R. K. 1964a. The influence of post mortem conditions on the solubilities of muscle proteins. *Biochem. J. 91:*201.

―――. 1964b. Protein denaturation in muscle post mortem. Ph.D. diss., Cambridge Univ.

Scopes, R. K., and R. A. Lawrie. 1963. Post mortem lability of skeletal muscle proteins. *Nature 197:*1202.

Selye, H. 1936. A syndrome produced by diverse nocuous agents. *Nature* 138:32.
———. 1946. The general adaptation syndrome and diseases of adaptation. *J. Clin. Endocrinol.* 6:117.
———. 1950. *The Physiology and Pathology of Exposure to Stress.* Acta Inc., Montreal.
Sharp, J. G., and B. B. Marsh. 1953. Whalemeat: production and preservation. *Spec. Rep. Food Invest. Board.* (London), No. 58.
Silaev, M. P. 1962. Studies of cattle irradiation prior to slaughter to prevent proteolytic spoilage of meat preserved by gamma irradiation. *Proc. 8th Conf. Europe. Meat Res. Workers* (Moscow), Paper No. 21.
Smith, A. U. 1958. The resistance of animals to cooling and freezing. *Biol. Rev.* 33:197.
Smith, E. C. 1930. The formation of lactic acid in muscles in the frozen state. *Proc. Roy. Soc.* (London), B, 105:198.
Smith, P., and A. M. H. Bennett. 1958. Vanillic acid excretion during stress. *Nature* 181:709.
Sullivan, M., L. Kolb, and J. Nicholls. 1942. Nutritional dermatoses in the rat. VII. Notes on the posture, gait and hypertonicity resulting from a diet containing unheated dried egg white as the source of protein. *Johns Hopkins Hosp. Bull.* 70:177.
Sutherland, E. W., and C. F. Cori. 1951. Effect of hyperglycemic-glycogenolytic factor and epinephrine on liver phosphorylase. *J. Biol. Chem.* 188:531.
Tasker, K., and P. G. Tulpule. 1964. Influence of protein and calorie deficiencies in the rat on the energy-transfer reactions of striated muscle. *Biochem. J.* 92:391.
Vogt, M. 1960. The control of the secretion of corticosteroid, p. 85. *In* F. Clark and J. K. Grant (eds.). *The Biosynthesis and Secretion of Adrenocortical Steroids* (Biochem. Soc. Symp.), No. 18.
Widdowson, E. M., J. W. T. Dickerson, and R. A. McCance. 1960. Severe undernutrition in growing and adult animals. IV. The impact of severe undernutrition on the chemical composition of the soft tissues of the pig. *Brit. J. Nutr.* 14:457.

Chapter 10

Summary and Discussion of Part II

PANEL MEMBERS: B. S. SCHWEIGERT, *Chairman*
R. J. BOUTHILET
M. D. JUDGE
R. K. MEYER
J. WILL

Schweigert: The three chapters of Part II reviewed factors influencing composition and properties of muscle tissue. The significance of species differences in response of muscles to hormone and other treatments was emphasized throughout. Comparative studies of the guinea pig and the rat demonstrated an interesting lack of uniformity in the response of various muscles, where increase in mass was concerned. From the standpoint of food production and food quality, it is unfortunate that the greatest increase in muscle mass was not observed for leg and loin muscles. The differences in the amounts of specific proteins synthesized attributable to hormone treatment are also of great interest, particularly since the relative concentration of the muscle pigment, myoglobin, was higher than for other proteins with certain of the treatments. In view of the work of Professor A. M. Pearson and associates, of Michigan State University (Quinn and Pearson, 1964), on the different forms of myoglobin in bovine muscle, it would be most interesting to know if a difference exists in the amounts of different myoglobins that may be present in the muscles of the experimental animals subjected to hormone treatments.

The biochemical and histochemical findings relating enzymatic activity in muscle to hormone treatment and various disease states show considerable promise and, in light of the studies reported by Dr. Lawrie, are interesting to examine in relation to quality aspects of muscle as a food. Specifically, the relation of such biochemical and histochemical changes to the flavor, color, texture, and functional properties (such as water-binding capacity of the muscle, or susceptibility to microbial spoilage) merits extensive study and is also of great interest in terms of the relative compatibility of such changes with life functions in the living animal. Thus, in studying muscle as food, we must consider many biological factors as well as environmental factors like fasting, external temperature conditions, and other stress reactions that influence the physiological state. The results reported indicate some important insights into hormonal action and biochemical events occurring in muscle, particularly in terms of certain overall enzymatic reactions. However, why certain animals show striking variations when subjected to presumably identical treatments is not at all clear.

In an even broader view of these significant research reports, several key points seem appropriate:

1. While a number of major changes have been correlated with hormonal, environmental, and disease factors, we have no idea of the significance of less dramatic and even more elusive changes, in part because we do not have precise and sensitive objective methods for measuring many of the quality attributes of foods, such as those involved in flavor, texture, and susceptibility to microbial spoilage.

2. Significant contributions have been made and will continue to be made by the use of a variety of scientific methods, several species of animals, and interdisciplinary approaches in this field.

3. When the many factors are considered interrelating the gross biological changes of an animal to the as yet poorly defined quality attributes of the resulting food (muscle), one's first impression could be that the complexities are of such magnitude that the problems defy reliable scientific attack. Many scientists with experience in emphasizing a single scientific discipline applied to studies of model reactions would eschew these problems altogether. However, it should be emphasized that workers in the interdisciplinary scientific areas do establish a reliable scientific attack, primarily because by necessity they ask scientific questions different from those asked by investigators working with model systems.

DISCUSSION

Meyer: Would Dr. Kochakian elaborate on the "wearing-off effect" in terms of nitrogen retention and growth?

Kochakian: When hormone is administered it has a potent effect on certain tissues, but the tissue itself determines the specific response to the hormone. The regulating mechanism is unknown; however, it may be part of the Jacob-Monod suggested system of repressors and inducers.

Meyer: Is fat, as well as protein, deposited in muscle during the initial anabolic phase (causing increase in weight)?

Kochakian: Nitrogen is deposited as protein. We have analyzed the animals at different times during the anabolic phase and there is definitely an increase in tissue nitrogen as well as a concomitant increase in fat. There is, however, a decrease in abdominal and subcutaneous fat.

Meyer: Could the increase in muscle size, caused by androgen, be indirectly due to increased physical activity induced by androgen?

Kochakian: Based on chemical analysis there is utilization of fat under androgen stimulation. In our initial experiments, the dogs were in cages, which allowed little activity; so therefore if the fat utilization was due to activity it must have been isometric rather than dynamic in kind.

Kauffman: How do you account for the possibility that the rate of deposition of proteins in the eye lens may not be inhibited by nutritional stress such as starvation and that the presence or absence of testosterone does not affect the rate of deposition or the total amount deposited?

Kochakian: I believe this is another instance of a difference in receptor quality of a specific tissue. This could be at the genetic level or the intermediary steps (which are unknown) between the stimulus (starvation and the presence or absence of testosterone) and the tissue receptor.

Sink: Do estrogens produce the same growth responses as androgens on muscle development?

Kochakian: Estrogens are ineffective in the stimulation of the growth responses seen after androgen administration. Also, you will recall from my report that the temporal muscle of the female guinea pig was much smaller than that of the male.

Meyer: Can androgen reduce the loss of nitrogen after growth hormone withdrawal?

Kochakian: We have not done this specific experiment but I would expect such to occur. I might cite another experiment. The daily administration of 10 μg of thyroxin to adult rats in nitrogen equilibrium will produce a negative nitrogen balance for the first six days. If testosterone propionate is given simultaneously, the negative nitrogen balance is not apparent. Thus, the decrease in urinary nitrogen produced by testosterone propionate is the same as that in the rats which received testosterone propionate and no thyroxin.

Judge: What are the principal actions of androgens on carbohydrate storage and metabolism in muscle?

Kochakian: The effect of androgens on carbohydrate storage in muscle has been extensively studied by Dr. S. Leonard at Cornell University, employing the perineal muscles which are known to be very responsive to androgens. These muscles respond to androgens by an increase in their glycogen stores. The skeletal muscles, however, are not influenced.

Judge: Have intact and castrate animals been compared with respect to their ability to withstand any type of stress?

Kochakian: I do not know of any studies in which intact and castrated animals have been compared with respect to their ability to withstand stress.

Judge: Does castration result strictly in a reduction of the total quantity of circulating androgens or are there differences in potency of testicular and adrenal androgens with regard to protein synthetic action?

Kochakian: The amount of the circulating androgens is decreased after castration, and also the adrenal androgens are much less effective in stimulating protein synthesis except in pathological conditions in which not only an excessive production of androgens but also excessive potency results in a marked stimulation of muscular growth as is seen in patients with adrenal tumors.

Will: What difference does age at castration make in the response to androgen injections?

Kochakian: The androgens are effective at all ages. The effect on body weight, however, is more apparent in the older animals, as indicated in my report.

Sair: Is it known whether the androgens selectively affect the S-RNA, M-RNA, or template RNA, or affect a combination of these types of RNA?

Kochakian: The androgens influence all of the RNA's but have a greater effect upon the microsomal RNA's. The latter, however, might be a reflection of the combination of the various RNA's to bring about protein biosynthesis.

Meyer: Why is glycine incorporated only in the diaphragm, retractor penis, and temporal muscle, and not in 45 other muscles of the body of the guinea pig?

Kochakian: Glycine, of course, is incorporated in all of the muscles. The difference between the three muscles and the others is the rate of incorporation. We were surprised at the great differences and have no explanation. This is specially interesting in the case of the masseter muscle, which shows a responsiveness to castration and androgen administration of almost the same degree as temporal muscle but did not show a significantly marked change in the rate of incorporation of glycine. I believe all this indicates that we are dealing with a very complicated system in each of these muscles.

Meyer: Do glucocorticoids prevent the anabolic effect of androgens?

Kochakian: Glucocorticoids, if given in high enough dosage, will mask the anabolic effect of the androgens. I do not believe this can be interpreted as a prevention until more specific information is obtained. I would like to consider it as the sum of two separate effects.

Lardy: Does the rat that has become refractory to testosterone after prolonged administration still respond to growth hormone administration?

Kochakian: We have not done this experiment, but I would expect the growth hormone to be effective. The two hormones work independently. I might indicate that if the dose of androgen is increased during the "wearing-off" phase, the anabolic phase will promptly appear again.

Lardy: Could this observation have some bearing on Dr. Meyer's interpretation of the influence of the degree of activity?

Kochakian: It may have some bearing on the influence of activity, but I seriously doubt if it has any influence on the "wearing-off" effect.

Bouthilet: If androgens were given to milk cows or laying hens after cessation of production, would we be able to salvage more protein for meat?

Kochakian: I think it would be a very worthwhile experiment. I would expect to increase the protein in these animals because they would be in a low anabolic phase and this is where something like testosterone would be more effective than it would be if the animals were in a high anabolic phase.

Bouthilet: Is the anabolic effect of androgens on the protein always associated with a catabolic effect on the fat?

Kochakian: Yes, our observations would give affirmative support to that statement. The catabolic effect is on the abdominal and subcutaneous fat.

Meyer: Does microscopic structure of hypertrophied muscle induced by exercise differ from the structure of the muscle which has been hypertrophied by androgen or growth hormone?

Brooke: There appears to be no difference histologically between the hypertrophy induced by exercise and that produced by the administration of androgens. I do not have any information on the histological picture following the administration of growth hormones.

Hoekstra: Does the presence of consistently smaller Type I or Type II muscle cells necessarily indicate atrophy?

Brooke: There is a difference in the average diameter of the Type I fibers and the Type II fibers normally. In humans the Type I fibers are slightly smaller than Type II. The muscle from guinea pigs and rats shows more difference between these average diameters. In this sense the smaller fibers are not abnormal. However, as has been pointed out, the process of atrophy may involve only one of the two fiber types, producing fibers of a size which is clearly less than normal for that muscle. It is this situation which is referred to as Type II atrophy, and this, I feel, is always abnormal. This problem is further discussed elsewhere (Brooke and Engel, 1966).

Meyer: Do hormones affect both Type I and Type II fibers?

Brooke: Our knowledge on the subject is incomplete. There is some evidence that the administration of steroids in humans may result in Type

II atrophy. On the other hand, such steroids are usually administered because of pre-existing disease which may itself cause changes in the muscle.

Schweigert: Can steroids have an effect on heart muscle?

Brooke: There are only minor changes, if any, in heart muscle, although
this problem requires further investigation.

Will: I believe that changes from steroid administration do occur in individuals under intensive therapy for asthma. There is apparently some
resultant myocardial change.

Brooke: In animal experimentation one can administer steroids to normal animals and subsequently examine their tissue; however, most patients
that we examine are not normal before we administer steroids. Without
question there are changes in patients with asthma, who have been on
steroids, but one cannot determine whether these changes are due to the
asthma or due to the steroids, because patients with asthma and without
steroids can also have myocardial changes.

Meyer: Has antibody against striated muscle been produced and, if so,
what is its effect on the gross and histological characteristics of muscle?

Brooke: Anti-myosin antibody has been prepared and is, of course, widely used in immunofluorescent techniques in the investigation of muscle
disease. Attempts have been made by various investigators to produce
experimental allergic myositis by techniques comparable to those used in
the production of experimental allergic encephalomyelitis, but they have
not met with any success.

Will: Are the changes in nuclear location in denervation atrophy the
result of actual migration of the nucleus or does the cytoplasm increase,
and mechanically surround the nucleus? Might centralization of the nuclei
be a protective mechanism?

Brooke: It has been suggested that the migration of nuclei toward the
center of the fiber is the result of a passive process due to a drop in the intracellular pressure. Until a better theory is developed this is as good as
any. I do not think one can say that this is a protective mechanism.
Splitting of fibers often occurs at points to which the nuclei have migrated.

Judge: What is the effect of postmortem sampling time on the pathologies you observe; i.e., if muscle is secured postrigor do the histological abnormalities appear similar to those of biopsy samples?

Brooke: Histochemical studies are usually not done on material which
has been obtained in the postrigor period, since the enzymes are often lost.
The histological picture of fixed, paraffin-embedded material does not
appear to be too different from that of biopsy material although a certain
amount of autolysis may be seen.

Judge: What degree of invasion of a muscle with fat would you consider pathologic?

Brooke: A certain amount of fat may normally be present in the inter-fascicular regions, but when free fat appears within the fascicles, lying between individual fibers, we usually consider this pathological.

Allen: During the fatty infiltration of muscle, is any of the fat synthe-sized *in situ* relative to the muscle fiber, or is it deposited in the fiber?

Brooke: This is a difficult question to answer, but my guess is that the fat is not synthesized in the muscle tissue. It is probably deposited there. Actually, free fat in the sense of fatty infiltration, does not occur within the muscle fibers but is outside. Lipid droplets, which are normally present in muscle fibers, may increase in pathological processes.

Kauffman: You did not mention the interfascicular accumulation of fat in diseased muscle — normally referred to as steatosis or myodemia — which perhaps is associated with the sebaceous glands. Would you care to com-ment on how one might experimentally produce steatosis?

Brooke: I think the accumulation of fat within the muscle tissue is a nonspecific reaction. It seems that in muscle, as in any other tissue, nature abhors a vacuum and the tissue which is lost is replaced by fibrous or fatty tissue. I think that gracing it with a name such as steatosis lends it a dignity which it does not deserve. It does, however, seem to be rather less promi-nent in the denervating diseases than in the dystrophies.

Will: What do you believe is the metabolic mechanism in the bovine species which makes it unique from other species in its response to fasting or exercise before slaughter?

Lawrie: I believe that one such mechanism is the greater capacity of ruminant muscle to gain energy by direct catabolism of fatty acids, thus sparing carbohydrate. If stresses are sufficiently severe, however, carbo-hydrate stores will be depleted, as in nonruminants.

Will: You have made the statement that arterial blood appears the same as venous blood after subcutaneous injection of epinephrine. Did you perform oximetry to substantiate this?

Lawrie: We did not determine the oxygen content of the blood. The typical, purplish-red color of deoxygenated hemoglobin was very marked and the absorption lines of oxymyoglobin abnormally weak.

Judge: What is the effect of administering adrenalin to porcine animals immediately prior to dispatch? Does administration of adrenalin, at this time, simulate the pale, soft, exudative (PSE) condition or does it elevate ultimate pH?

Lawrie: The administration of adrenalin intravenously, immediately prior to dispatch, has no effect on the ultimate pH of bovine animals. Dr.

Bendall may be able to give more information regarding the reaction of porcine animal to adrenalin injection.

Bendall: There is not sufficient evidence to establish this point; however, I do not believe that there would be a short-term effect of adrenalin. A minimum of two hours appears to be the required time, and even then the effect seems to be mostly on the ultimate pH. I believe that predispatch conditions may be of equal or greater importance to the PSE porcine muscle problem, than the heredity of the animal. We conducted a survey of progeny-tested porcine animals, of essentially similar breeding, which were slaughtered in two different meat processing plants. One plant used carbon dioxide immobilization while the other plant stunned their animals with electric equipment. The plant that used carbon dioxide had a much greater incidence of PSE muscle than the plant with electric stunning.

Lawrie: Preslaughter conditions may increase the incidence of PSE muscle in many breeds of porcine animals. However, when preslaughter conditions are essentially identical there still seem to be stress-susceptibility differences between individual animals.

Sybesma: There is perhaps too much emphasis placed on the stress theory in the development of the PSE condition. Work at our institute (Sybesma, 1965) has shown: (1) When blood circulation is poor, electrical stimulation of the longissimus dorsi, immediately after stunning, can create the PSE condition. (2) A smaller blood volume has been found in pigs which are susceptible to the development of the PSE condition. (3) Improvement of muscle quality has been attained by injecting isoxsuprine, which causes a peripheral dilation.

Could oxygen retention in the tissue be an important factor in postmortem change?

Lawrie: The capability of mobilizing the blood is less in PSE-susceptible than in normal animals and this may have something to do with the development of PSE muscle. Enhancement of the blood supply, and therefore the oxygen supply, to tissue might prove beneficial.

Meyer: Dr. Lawrie, if I understand your postulate, you ascribe both types of meat (DFD, or dark, firm, and dry, as well as the PSE muscle) to a deficiency of adrenocortical hormones, presumably glucocorticoids. Is this correct? If so, what is the evidence that the adrenal cortex is exhausted and not capable of producing glucocorticoids to counteract the stimulus?

Lawrie: Dark-cutting bovine muscle may be explained on the basis of an absence of the glucocorticoids, where the PSE condition may be explained by absence of mineralocorticoids. Ludvigsen (1954) found hypertrophy of the hypothalamus in PSE pigs, which he inferred represented an excessive attempt by the hypothalamus to stimulate the pituitary which was deficient in ACTH and which could not induce enough mineralocorticoid from the adrenal cortex to restore the potassium balance in the muscle. According to his interpretations the PSE condition was due to the excessive attempt of the hypothalamus and thereby pituitary and adrenal to correct the mineral imbalance resulting from the initial reaction to stress.

Meyer: What is the evidence that stress causes the exhaustion of the adrenal cortex to the point where glucocorticoids are no longer being secreted or are being secreted in insufficient quantities?

Lawrie: There is no direct evidence confirming glucocorticoid deficiency in the problem of dark-cutting bovine muscle. There is some evidence in Ludvigsen's (1954) work on PSE muscle that the adrenal cortex is impaired. I also gather from this symposium that Dr. Judge has such evidence for PSE pigs. One could test this by giving dichlorodiethyl dichloroethane, because that would presumably inactivate the adrenal cortex, but as far as I know this has not been done to see if one could thereby produce the PSE or DFD muscle condition.

Meyer: Have the levels of aldosterone been determined in animals which have been stressed and have subsequently shown either the dark-cutting or the pale characteristic?

Lawrie: A relation between excessive production of aldosterone and PSE musculature in porcine animals has been reported by Henry, Billon, and Haouza (1955). I do not know of such a study in animals yielding dark-cutting bovine muscle, but of course there are many studies relating stress with aldosterone in laboratory animals and humans.

Meyer: Is it at all reasonable to believe that the dark and pale muscle may be due to exhaustion of the epinephrine and/or norepinephrine producing tissues?

Lawrie: Since dark-cutting bovine muscle can be caused by chronic adrenaline release in the animal, and this effect can be counteracted by prior administration of cortisone, it seems that exhaustion of adrenaline stores is not involved. Noradrenaline, administered at 20 times the effective adrenaline level, does not produce dark-cutting characteristics. In the literature there is some suggestion that the thyroid-to-adrenal ratio is high in pigs which give PSE musculature; but this is due rather to the swelling of the thyroid than to atrophy of the adrenals. There is no evidence that exhaustion of adrenaline is involved.

Judge: In recent research, at the University of Wisconsin, on adrenal gland function and histology, we observed that pigs having pale, soft, exudative, and highly contracted muscles tend to excrete lowered quantities of 17-ketosteroids and 17-*OH*-corticosteroids during the stress of close confinement. These animals also had adrenal glands which showed lipid invasion and possible degeneration in the cells of the *zona reticularis*. Since the results implicated the glucocorticoids and since the abnormal cells were seen only in the inner zone of the cortex, are these findings in harmony with your theory that defective operation of mineralocorticoids and an uncompensated mineral imbalance occur in animals with the PSE muscle condition?

Lawrie: Although the superficial symptoms of dark-cutting bovine muscle and of PSE musculature in porcine animals can be rationalized by defective operation, during stress, of glucocorticoids and of mineralocorticoids, respectively, this may well be an oversimplification of the issues involved, as your histological data suggest.

Topel: We found that there were somewhat lower levels of the 17-hydroxyglucocorticoids in the plasma of pigs which ultimately had PSE muscle, than in those which had normal muscle. Nevertheless, through a blocking of the adrenal gland with excessive dosages of prednisolone, we were unable to produce the PSE condition with any consistency.

Judge: It has been suggested that the inherent rate of pH fall is important in the development of pale, soft, exudative porcine muscle. How likely are the following possibilities? (1) Accumulation of lactic acid in muscle prior to death as a result of impaired circulatory function. (2) Elevation of body temperature caused by psychological stress in the preslaughter period.

Lawrie: I think both an accumulation of lactic acid in muscle preslaughter, and an elevation of body temperature, may sometimes be manifestations of an inherent stress susceptibility, and concomitant with an enhanced rate of pH fall postmortem. The relative absence of cytochromes and of myoglobin in PSE musculature is also symptomatic of a long-term condition rather than of one which is entirely explainable by immediate preslaughter circumstances.

Bouthilet: It has been suggested that we use some sort of medication to relieve stress in animals before slaughter. Do you know of any which would have a direct effect on the hypothalamus?

Lawrie: The tranquilizer, reserpine, is said to be effective through its discharge of serotonin from sites where it is stored, especially the hypothalamus. Since such tranquilizers do not prevent the glycogen-depleting action of adrenaline, it is clear that they do not suppress all aspects of hypothalamic activity.

Sair: Have any studies on Ca^{++} and Mg^{++} concentrations as well as histological studies on the sarcoplasmic reticulum been done ante- and postmortem on the same animals which ultimately develop PSE? A disruption of the sarcoplasmic reticulum at death would release Ca^{++} previously bound to the reticulum and hence increase the myofibrillar adenosine triphosphatase activity with a resulting rapid glycolysis.

Lawrie: No such studies have been carried out as far as I know; but I feel they would be most pertinent in demonstrating whether or not there is some common feature between PSE musculature and the phenomena of "thaw rigor" and "cold shortening."

Kim: Have you found a difference in the isoelectric point between normal and PSE muscle?

Lawrie: Bendall and Wismer-Pedersen (1962) showed that the IEP of PSE musculature is little different from normal.

Wierbicki: Would Dr. Lawrie comment on the antemortem use of sublethal doses of irradiation to raise the postmortem carcass pH?

Lawrie: I mentioned the Russian work (Belenky, 1962) wherein a thousand rad had been given to animals to increase the autolytic enzyme activity. I think that this increase in autolytic enzyme activity might be associated with an increase in water-holding capacity.

Bouthilet: I was particularly interested in your comment on the effect of hibernation on the saturation of body fats. Do you think we can expect to achieve unsaturation by such means in meat animals in the future?

Lawrie: Even if means to achieve unsaturation by hypothermia were available I think it would be impractical commercially.

Charpentier: What is the most active adenosine triphosphatase postmortem? sarcoplasmic or actomyosin?

Bendall: I do not know the answer.

Bouthilet: Could we produce an all white meat turkey through proper long-term restraint?

Lawrie: I do not think so. To some extent one could achieve a whiter flesh by some form of inactivity, but genetic aspects would undoubtedly persist.

Sink: Is the distribution pattern of dark and light fibers the same for different muscles?

Brooke: No. The soleus muscle, for example, in many animals is a "slow" muscle which contains predominantly Type I fibers. Thus the proportion of Type I to Type II fibers may vary depending upon the muscle examined and the species. In the human we usually biopsy the deltoid, biceps brachii, quadriceps femoris, gastrocnemius, or anterior tibial, and these are "mixed" muscles, although, as far as I am aware, no specific data are available on the exact proportion of the histochemical types.

Thomas: What effect does muscular dystrophy, or muscular degeneration in general, have on the pigment (myoglobin) concentration of muscle?

Brooke: A number of workers have reported a fall in the myoglobin content in the muscular dystrophies (Hughes, 1961). Others have maintained that the myoglobin is qualitatively altered (Whorton *et al.*, 1961). This work is interesting, but further studies will be needed to substantiate and elaborate these findings.

Snyder: In Dr. Lawrie's presentation, a comment was made about the O_2 storage function of myoglobin in muscle: "if that is, in fact, the function of myoglobin in muscle," were Dr. Lawrie's words. Is there some evidence for other functions of myoglobin?

Lawrie: There is some evidence that the oxidized form of myoglobin, that is, metmyoglobin, can act to reduce the cytochromes; however, it is hard to tell exactly at which point this would occur. It seems possible, quite apart from oxygen storage, that it could act as an oxidation-reduction catalyst of some kind, but there is no firm foundation for this postulate.

Snyder: Are there any conditions in muscle where one can see metmyoglobin accumulating?

Lawrie: During improper postrigor handling.

Blumer: How do you account for the difference in myoglobin content of heavily used muscles, such as cardiac and the wings of birds, compared to muscles developing a high concentration of pigment due to exercise, such as the biceps femoris?

Lawrie: The nature of the contraction/relaxation cycle in relation to oxygen appears to determine the concentration of myoglobin. Muscles which must act for long periods and cannot, therefore, develop an oxygen debt, invariably have a high concentration of cytochrome enzymes by which, in the mitochondria, "energy-rich" phosphate is synthesized by coupling with oxygen uptake. Muscles which are used in relatively infrequent bursts and can develop an oxygen debt, have little cytochrome enzyme activity. Except in diving animals, such muscles store little oxygen as oxymyoglobin. In muscles with appreciable cytochrome activity, an auxiliary oxygen store in the form of oxymyoglobin is found if the contraction phase of the muscle's action restricts the oxygen supply for a second or two. Where the contraction phase is less prolonged, and especially where blood-borne oxygen is supplied lavishly (as in the heart) or from an elaborated air sac network from the lungs (as in the pectoral muscles of flying birds) there is little need for myoglobin. The concentrations of myoglobin in the pectoral muscles of Manx Shearwater, pigeon, and Willow Warbler are, respectively, 0.7%, 0.3%, and 0.02% — and these are approximately proportional to the duration of the contraction phase of their characteristic wing movements. In each, the activity of the cytochrome enzymes is of the same high order. On the other hand the concentration of myoglobin in the pectoral muscles of the nonflying domestic fowl is very low; but so also is cytochrome activity, as would be expected. Limb muscles like biceps femoris in the ox resemble the pectoral muscle of the Manx Shearwater in myoglobin content and in the duration of the contraction phase, although the cytochrome concentration is somewhat lower.

References

Belenky, W. G. 1962. Demotin. *Proc. 8th Conf. Europe. Meat Res. Workers* (Moscow).

Bendall, J. R., and J. Wismer-Pedersen. 1962. Some properties of the fibrillar proteins of normal and watery pork muscle. *J. Food Sci.* 27:144.

Brooke, M. H., and W. K. Engel. 1966. *Arch. Phys. Med. Rehabilitation.* (In press.)

Henry, J., J. Billon, and G. Haouza. 1955. Contribution à l'étude de l'acidose des viandes du porc, dites exsudatives. *Rev. Pathol. Gén. Comp.*, No. 669, p. 857.

Hughes, B. P. 1961. Studies on starch gel electrophoresis of some human muscle proteins. *Clin. Chim. Acta.* 6:794.

Ludvigsen, J. 1954. On the hormonal regulation of vasomotor reactions during exercise with special reference to the action of adrenal cortical steroids. *Acta Endocrinol.* 26:406.

Quinn, J. R., and A. M. Pearson. 1964. Characterization studies of three myoglobin fractions from bovine muscle. *J. Food Sci.* 29:429.

Sybesma, W. 1965. Exudative meat in the Netherlands. *Meeting Europe. Soc. Anim. Production.*

Whorton, E. M., P. C. Hudgins, and J. J. Conners. 1961. Abnormal spectrophotometric absorption spectrums of myoglobin in two forms of progressive muscular dystrophy. *New England J. Med.* 265:1242.

PART III

Behavior of Muscle Postmortem

Chapter 11

General Aspects of Postmortem Changes

R. G. CASSENS

A consideration of postmortem change in muscle may be subdivided into three general areas: (1) the influence of antemortem conditions on postmortem change, (2) the actual postmortem change, and (3) the impact of postmortem change on the use of muscle as a food.

I will direct the emphasis of this chapter toward the actual postmortem changes, since antemortem factors such as muscle development, metabolic processes, and muscle regulation have been discussed in preceding chapters, while the subject of muscle as food will be treated in later chapters. In view of the wealth of scientific knowledge concerning postmortem change in muscle, this brief introduction to the subject must be superficial in most respects; furthermore I have not commented on work concerned with poultry and fish muscle, since Chapter 12 and Chapter 13 treat these two aspects of the subject. To illustrate this chapter I have called freely upon a good deal of information involving postmortem changes in porcine muscle deriving from a project which has been supervised by Dr. E. J. Briskey at the University of Wisconsin for a number of years.

VISUAL POSTMORTEM CHANGES

Color change is perhaps the most obvious visual alteration postmortem, and in normal porcine muscle the color is converted from a relatively dark red to a lighter grayish pink. Figure 11.1 illustrates the appearance of muscles in a porcine ham which are normal to slightly dark in color. Figure 11.2 shows ham muscles which have been affected with the condition known as pale, soft, and exudative. As can be easily seen, the muscles of the first ham appear darker and firmer, while those of the other ham are very pale and soft. The pale, soft, exudative condition was first described in 1954 by Ludvigsen and has since received attention from laboratories in many parts of the world (Briskey, 1964; Lawrie, 1960; Hart *et al.*, 1963; Henry, Billon, and Haouza, 1955; and Bendall and Wismer-Pedersen,

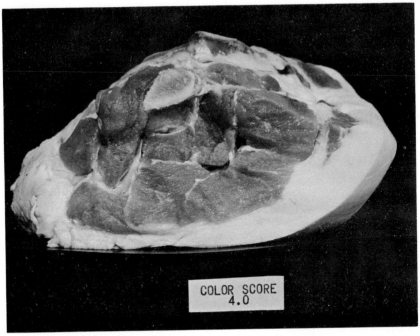

Fig. 11.1. — Porcine ham muscles classified as normal to slightly dark in color. From Briskey, 1964.

1962). In contrast to normal muscle, PSE muscle changes from dark red to an abnormal very pale color.

Another visual postmortem development is exudation, or the loss of moisture. During normal postmortem change there may be a shift in the bound water of muscle resulting in some small amount of loss in water-binding capacity. Again, a large exudation of moisture is quite obvious in the abnormal change associated with the development of PSE muscle.

Surface texture of muscle also changes postmortem from a rather close-ly packed, sticky character to a smooth, moist, and relatively loose struc-ture.

RIGOR MORTIS

The grossly evident results of postmortem change, of course, have their basis in more complex biochemical conversions during postmortem an-aerobic glycolysis. Perhaps the most important consequence is the often discussed, but sometimes obscure, process of rigor mortis. Classically, muscle stiffening has been associated with rigor mortis and has been con-sidered a result of changes in muscle proteins and not of a setting or hardening of the fat. However, the very rigid stiffening generally asso-

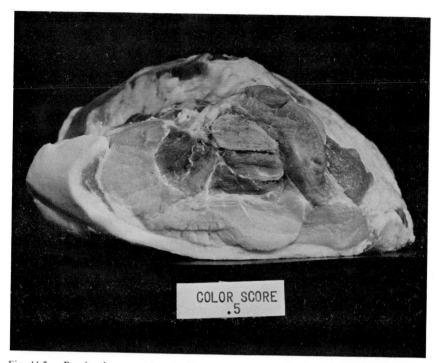

Fig. 11.2. — Porcine ham muscles classified as extremely pale, soft, and exudative. From Briskey, 1964.

ciated with rigor mortis may not always occur; in fact, the muscle may pass into rigor mortis with little detectable change in stiffening or hardness. A number of devices are available for measuring the time course of rigor mortis by following the changes in extensibility of muscle strips under controlled conditions (Bate-Smith and Bendall, 1949; Briskey, Sayre, and Cassens, 1962; Partmann, 1963). Figure 11.3 shows the apparatus being used in the muscle biology laboratory at the University of Wisconsin for measurement of time course of rigor mortis. A muscle strip is held between jaws inside the Plexiglas chamber, and weight is automatically loaded and unloaded from the strip. The change in extensibility of the strip is recorded on the chart. I will not pursue the physiochemical basis of rigor mortis further, since Chapter 14 deals with this subject, but will comment on some observations relating to rigor mortis which have been made in our laboratory.

Let us first consider the relation of time course of rigor mortis to extent of shortening. Previous reports have indicated that greater contraction is associated with a short-time course as compared to a long-time course of rigor mortis (Bendall, 1960; Marsh, 1954). Recently, Dr. J. D. Sink has

Fig. 11.3. — Rigorometer. From Briskey, 1964.

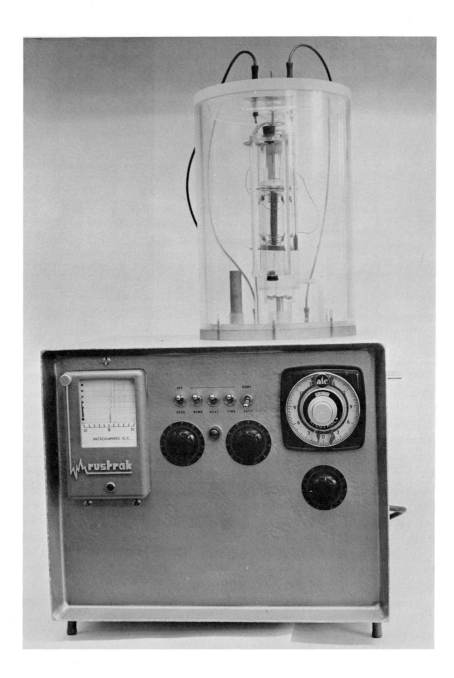

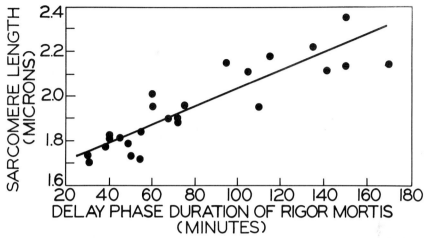

Fig. 11.4. — Association of rigor mortis delay phase duration with sarcomere length. From Sink *et al.*, 1965.

confirmed these observations with porcine muscle, using sarcomere length as an estimate of extent of muscle contraction (Sink *et al.*, 1965). Figure 11.4 shows the very high positive association which was found between duration of rigor mortis delay phase and sarcomere length in the same muscle measured 24 hr postmortem. The results were interpreted as indicating that very different amounts of contraction occurred postmortem in muscle which had remained attached to the carcass, and the amount of contraction was dependent, to a large extent, on the time course of rigor mortis. This information appeared to have exciting practical significance in view of Locker's (1960) earlier report which implicated state of muscle contraction in the problem of meat tenderness. Additional direct evidence has been offered (Marsh, 1964; Herring, Cassens, and Briskey, 1965*a*) to support the postulation that state of muscle contraction does indeed contribute to tenderness. Herring *et al.* (1965*b*) further examined the changes in postmortem sarcomere length concomitant with changes in fiber diameter. They found that the sarcomere length of bovine psoas major could be drastically altered (Fig. 11.5) by immediate postmortem carcass positioning.

Figure 11.5 illustrates cross sections of the psoas major muscle from opposite sides of the same carcass. The section with small fiber diameter and long sarcomere length (3.6 microns) was taken from the side which was vertically suspended in the normal manner. If the carcass was horizontally placed, which released tension on the psoas and allowed it to shorten, the sarcomeres shortened to 2.7 microns, and the fiber diameter increased about 30%, as shown in the other section. The muscle with long sarcomere

Fig. 11.5. — Cross sections and corresponding sarcomere lengths of bovine psoas major muscle. Neg. mag. × 80. From Herring *et al.*, 1965*b*.

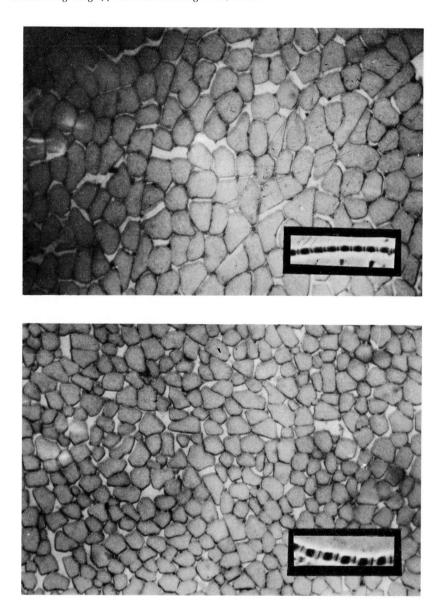

length and small fiber diameter was more tender than its counterpart. This poses an interesting question. What role do fiber cell walls play in tenderness? In a given unit area of muscle, with small fiber diameter, more cell walls are present to impede the chewing or shearing process, but in the example just cited the muscle with small fiber diameter was more tender than the paired muscle with a large fiber diameter. This means either that cell walls do not contribute substantially to meat tenderness or that the possible effect of protein alterations induced by muscle stretching (long sarcomeres) is of overriding importance.

ELECTRICAL STIMULATION PROPERTIES OF POSTMORTEM MUSCLE

Electrical stimulation was used by Hallund and Bendall (1965) to accelerate pH fall over the entire pH-time curve in porcine muscle which was at the time of stimulation undergoing a relatively slow pH fall. Muscles which were at the time of stimulation undergoing a fast pH fall gave no apparent response to the same stimulation. The long-term stimulation effect in porcine muscle as described by these authors is quite different from the well-known short-term effect in other mammalian muscle which gives rise to a rapid pH fall for a short time only. These researchers felt that the new phenomenon was due to an induced higher adenosine triphosphatase activity. Nonetheless it appears that the role of the nervous system may be important in influencing some postmortem muscle changes, particularly in certain animals.

Work by Forrest, Ludvigsen, and Briskey (unpublished) has been directed at stimulating the exposed spinal cord in split carcasses as soon after exsanguination as normal handling procedures would permit. The effects of this treatment have been variable, as indicated by subsequent pH fall and color-gross morphology score, with some longissimus dorsi muscles reacting as reported by Hallund and Bendall, while others gave no apparent response. This variation could possibly be explained by damage inflicted on the spinal cord during splitting of the carcass or perhaps by inherent differences in the nervous system.

The electrical stimulation studies of Forrest *et al.* (1966) on excised porcine muscle have been conducted in a slightly different manner. They found that electrical stimulation could be used quite successfully on postmortem muscle strips to predict time course of rigor mortis, rate of postmortem glycolysis, and ultimate color morphology rating. Figure 11.6 illustrates typical results from electrical stimulation of muscle strips and compares the results with rigor mortis patterns from the same muscle. To begin with, a series of single electrical stimulations was administered at 1, 3, 5, 10, 25, and 50 volts at approximately 3 sec intervals. The voltage at which the first contractile response was elicited was termed the "ex-

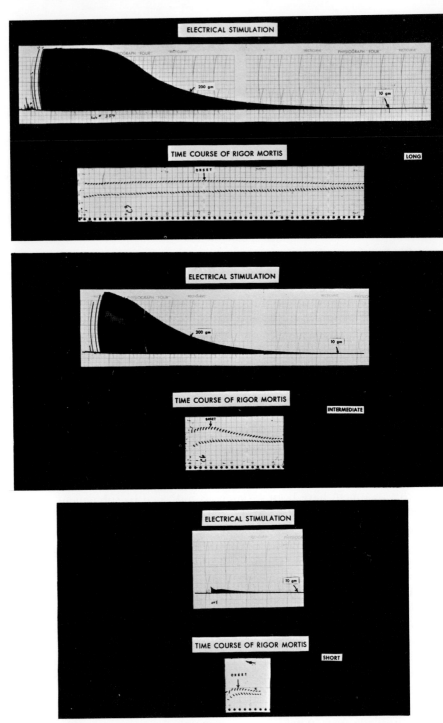

Fig. 11.6. — Typical results from electrical stimulation and rigor mortis determination of the same muscle. From Forrest *et al.*, 1966.

citability threshold." "Strength of contraction" was measured in grams for the contractions at stimulus voltages of 5, 10, 25, and 50. At the 50 volt level, a series of continuous stimulations was administered at a frequency of 2 per sec until the muscle contracted with a strength of less than 10 g. "Duration of contractility" was measured to both 200 g and 10 g. Those muscles which had a short-time course of rigor mortis, fast rate of post-mortem glycolysis, and which ultimately appeared PSE had a high excitability threshold, low strengths of contraction, and short duration of contractility. Multiple regression analysis indicated that up to 87% of the variability in ultimate color-morphology rating could be predicted by combining the various parameters of muscle response to electrical stimulation. Time course of rigor mortis was also highly associated with the electrical stimulation properties.

CHEMICAL CHANGES

The preceding visual and rigor mortis associated postmortem properties are primarily due to a series of postmortem chemical changes termed glycolysis. Very simply, this is the conversion of glycogen to lactic acid and can be easily estimated by following pH decline.

Different rates of pH decline are easily illustrated in porcine muscle. The rates are extremely variable, ranging from a slow gradual decline to an extremely rapid decline with a subsequent slight elevation of pH to the ultimate value. The rate of postmortem pH decline has been divided into four categories by Briskey and Wismer-Pedersen (1961). More recently, Briskey (1963) described six distinct types of pH pattern, which are shown in Figure 11.7. The classifications are as follows: (1) a slow, gradual decrease to an ultimate (24 hr) pH of 6.0–6.5 or above (dark muscle); (2) a slow, gradual decrease to an ultimate pH of 5.7–6.0 (slightly dark); (3) a gradual decrease to approximately 5.7 at 8 hr, with an ultimate pH of 5.3–5.7 (normal muscle); (4) a relatively rapid decrease to approximately 5.5 at 3 hr, with an ultimate pH of 5.3–5.6 (slightly PSE); (5) a rapid to a slightly gradual but extremely extensive decrease to an ultimate pH of approximately 5.0 (slightly dark to extremely pale, but in all cases extremely exudative); (6) a rapid decrease to a pH of 5.1–5.4 at 30 to 90 min, and retention of this low pH, or a slight subsequent elevation to 5.3–5.6 (extremely PSE).

Forrest (1966) has recently reported on the influence of blood oxygen and carbon dioxide levels on postmortem porcine muscle pH. He found that Poland China pigs reacted to a warm antemortem environment by significantly increasing blood PCO_2 and drastically lowering blood PO_2. The longissimus dorsi muscle from these same animals reached a low pH of about 5.8 within 30 min following death, while the muscles from the

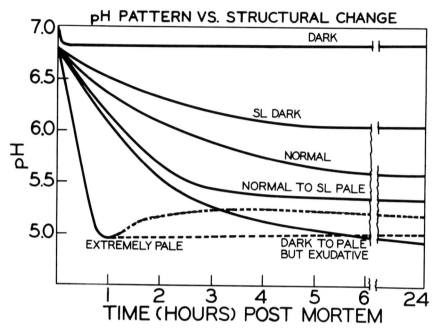

Fig. 11.7. — pH pattern types. From Briskey, 1964.

control animals which were not subjected to a warm antemortem environment exhibited a more normal pH decline.

As indicated in the previous discussion, pH may reach a very low value soon after death of the animal, and the exothermic reactions may actually raise the muscle temperature over that found in normal living muscle. This combination of low pH and high temperature soon after death may be detrimental to the muscle protein and in fact be responsible for the visual loss of color and drastic lowering of water-binding capacity.

Bendall and Wismer-Pedersen (1962) were the first to examine the effect of low postmortem pH in combination with relatively high muscle temperatures on the properties of the porcine muscle proteins. They reported that the fibrillar proteins were not changed or denatured by the aforementioned conditions but that the sarcoplasmic proteins were quite susceptible to change under the same conditions.

Sayre and Briskey (1963) and McLoughlin (1963) both reported a marked decrease in solubility of the sarcoplasmic protein fraction under conditions of low pH (5.7) and high temperature (35 C) when these conditions were reached soon after death of the animal. Scopes and Lawrie (1963) singled out creatine phosphoryltransferase as being particularly susceptible to the low pH–high temperature combination.

Postmortem alteration of muscle proteins could, of course, play a major role in the characteristic visual and physical changes which we know muscle undergoes in its postmortem conversion. In this regard it should be mentioned that surface freezing with liquid nitrogen (Borchert and Briskey, 1964, 1965) has been used successfully to accelerate cooling rate and thereby slow postmortem change; specifically, pH fall was retarded and concurrently loss of protein solubility was diminished.

HISTOLOGICAL ASPECTS OF POSTMORTEM CHANGE

A detailed histological study of postmortem change in bovine muscle was reported by Paul, Love, and McClurg (1944). The microscopic alterations which these workers found in beef muscle during postmortem change were quite distinct. Muscle from freshly killed beef had poorly differentiated fibers which were straight to slightly wavy, and longitudinal striations were more prominent than cross striations. After one-day storage the fibers were much more distinct. Some showed contraction nodes and others the kinks or crinkles of passive retraction. Breaks appeared during the second day of storage and became more numerous as storage time increased; kinks and crinkles disappeared after four to ten days storage.

Beecher *et al.* (1965) have tried to relate red fiber content to postmortem muscle properties. Their conclusions were that muscle containing a high percentage of red fibers ($> 30\%$) also had higher succinic dehydrogenase activities, and generally these muscles underwent a slower postmortem glycolysis as estimated by pH decline. It is interesting to note that the muscles with a high percentage of red fibers are least susceptible to the PSE condition and also have longer postmortem sarcomere lengths. This relationship is illustrated in Figure 11.8. The interrelationship of time course of rigor mortis, sarcomere length (i.e., extent of filament overlap), and ultimate postmortem appearance seems to merit further consideration. Could number of cross bridges or density of thick and thin filaments per unit volume affect the characteristics we have been discussing, such as color, water-binding capacity, and tenderness?

The PSE condition has been histologically examined by Ludvigsen (1954), who reported some nuclear changes and the formation of vacuoles. Lawrie (1960) reported that certain gross changes of the fibers, such as twisting or kinking, were possibly due to postmortem changes in the muscle. Bendall (1960) has suggested that only a minority of the fibers contract actively during onset of rigor, and that these actively contracting fibers force or pull many of the adjacent fibers into the typical kinked or S-shaped configuration.

Paul *et al.* (1944) have described the appearance of rigor nodes in postmortem bovine muscle as swollen, dense areas in the fiber. The rigor nodes

Fig. 11.8. – Association of red fiber content with postrigor contraction state. Neg. mag. × 71 and × 320. From Briskey *et al.*, 1966.
Copyright © 1966 by American Chemical Society.

Sarcomere Length

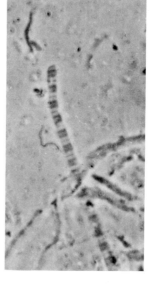

SHORT

1-6

LONG

2-8

Dark Fiber Content

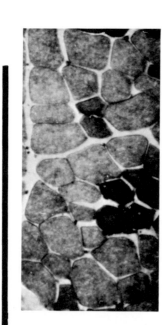

LOW
(G. medius)

HIGH

were often too dense to show cross striations, and on either side of the rigor node the fiber appeared narrower and less deeply stained.

Very severe contraction may cause a disarrangement of the fibrillar structure in localized areas of muscle fibers. The ultrastructure of these so-called contraction clots has been described by Cassens, Briskey, and Hoekstra (1963a).

Norman (1966), who examined a number of postmortem porcine muscles for specific symptoms of muscular dystrophy, found pathological lesions such as hyaline degeneration, ringbinden, and granular degeneration to be rather common in postmortem porcine muscle; but no relationship was found between the pathological conditions and PSE or in a general sense between pathological lesions and postmortem change. It would be interesting to establish if such lesions exist to the same extent in other large laboratory animals as they apparently do in porcine animals.

An investigation of ultrastructural changes in porcine muscle postmortem (Cassens et al., 1963b) revealed that the disruption of sarcoplasmic components appeared to be a function of rate of postmortem glycolysis. Abnormally fast glycolytic rates led to such disruption within 30 min postmortem while in normal muscle, components such as mitochondria of apparently good preservation were still evident 24 hr postmortem. The interrelationships among the rate of disruption of sarcoplasmic components, release of Ca^{++}, change in adenosine triphosphatase activity, electrical stimulation properties, and PSE muscle appear to be intricate, but an elucidation of the entire complex must be made for a thorough understanding of the significance of postmortem change.

Figure 11.9 illustrates the 24 hr postmortem appearance of normal porcine muscle and PSE muscle. The PSE condition was artificially produced by exposing the animal to an elevated environmental temperature immediately prior to exsanguination. The normal muscle shows a preservation of the fibrillar structure, while the PSE muscle appears to be granular instead of filamentous in the A band. This may indicate a disruption of the protein filaments which could possibly be responsible for the abnormal color and water-binding properties of the PSE muscle.

SUMMARY

A cursory review of postmortem change in muscle has been presented. Many excellent publications were omitted, while emphasis focused on postmortem changes occurring in porcine muscle. Grossly evident events such as change in color and exudation of moisture must have their origin at the molecular level, and the process of rigor mortis certainly plays a dominant role in the complete concept. The use of muscle as a food necessitates a more complete understanding of postmortem behavior of muscle.

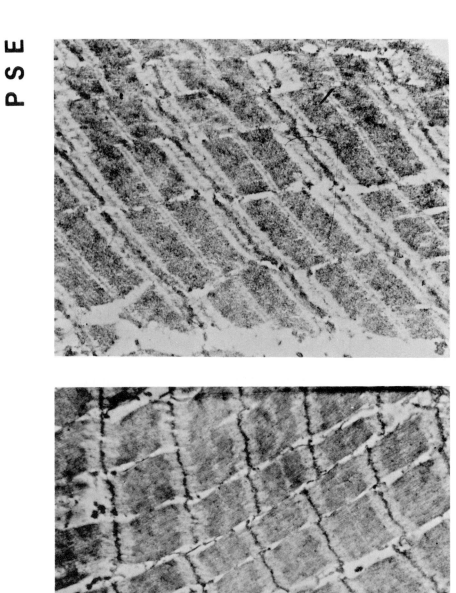

P S E

Normal

Fig. 11.9. — Electron micrographs of normal and PSE porcine muscle. × 16,000. From Cassens *et al.*, 1963*b*.

References

Bate-Smith, E. C., and J. R. Bendall. 1949. Factors determining the time course of rigor mortis. *J. Physiol. 110:*47.

Beecher, G. R., R. G. Cassens, W. G. Hoekstra, and E. J. Briskey. 1965. Red and white fiber content and associated post-mortem properties of seven porcine muscles. *J. Food Sci. 30:*969.

Bendall, J. R. 1960. Post-mortem changes in muscle, p. 227. *In* G. H. Bourne (ed.), *The Structure and Function of Muscle*, Vol. 3. Academic Press, New York.

Bendall, J. R., and J. Wismer-Pedersen. 1962. Some properties of the fibrillar proteins of normal and watery pork muscle. *J. Food Sci. 27:*144.

Borchert, L. L., and E. J. Briskey. 1964. Prevention of pale, soft, exudative porcine muscle through partial freezing with liquid nitrogen post-mortem. *J. Food Sci. 29:*203.

————. 1965. Protein solubility and associated properties of porcine muscle as influenced by partial freezing with liquid nitrogen. *J. Food Sci. 30:*138.

Briskey, E. J. 1963. Influence of ante and post-mortem handling practices on properties of muscle which are related to tenderness. *Proc. Campbell Soup Co. Meat Tenderness Symposium* (Camden, N.J.), p. 195.

————. 1964. Etiological status and associated studies of pale, soft, exudative porcine musculature. *Advance. Food Res. 13:*89.

Briskey, E. J., L. L. Kastenschmidt, J. C. Forrest, G. R. Beecher, M. D. Judge, R. G. Cassens, and W. G. Hoekstra. 1966. Biochemical aspects of post-mortem change in porcine muscle. *J. Agr. Food Chem. 14:*201.

Briskey, E. J., R. N. Sayre, and R. G. Cassens. 1962. Development and application of an apparatus for continuous measurement of muscle extensibility and elasticity before and during rigor mortis. *J. Food Sci. 27:*6.

Briskey, E. J., and J. Wismer-Pedersen, 1961. Biochemistry of pork muscle structure. I. Rate of anaerobic glycolysis and temperature change versus the apparent structure of muscle tissue. *J. Food Sci. 26:*297.

Cassens, R. G., E. J. Briskey, and W. G. Hoekstra. 1963a. Similarity in the contracture bands occurring in thaw rigor of muscle and other violent treatments. *Biodynamica 9:*163.

————. 1963b. Electron microscopy of post-mortem changes in porcine muscle. *J. Food Sci. 28:*680.

Forrest, J. C. 1966. Porcine physiology as related to post-mortem muscle properties. *Proc. 18th Reciprocal Meat Conf.* (Manhattan, Kansas.) (In press.)

Forrest, J. C., M. D. Judge, J. C. Sink, W. G. Hoekstra, and E. J. Briskey. 1966. Prediction of the time course of rigor mortis through response of muscle tissue to electrical stimulation. *J. Food Sci.* (In press.)

Hallund, O., and J. R. Bendall, 1965. The long-term effect of electrical stimulation on the post-mortem fall of pH in the muscles of Landrace pigs. *J. Food Sci. 30:*296.

Hart, P. C., D. Kroeske, W. Sybesma, and H. E. van den Veen. 1963. Influence of anabolic steroids versus effect of glucose on muscular degeneration in pigs. *Nature* 198:716.

Henry, M., J. Billon, and G. Haouza. 1955. Contribution à l'étude de l'acidose des viandes du porc, dites exsudatives. *Rev. Pathol. Gén. Comp.*, No. 669, p. 857.

Herring, H. K., R. G. Cassens, and E. J. Briskey. 1965a. Sarcomere length of free and restrained bovine muscles at low temperatures as related to tenderness. *J. Sci. Food Agr.* 16:379.

――――. 1965b. Further studies on bovine muscle tenderness as influenced by carcass position, sarcomere length and fiber diameter. *J. Food Sci.* 30:1049.

Lawrie, R. A. 1960. Post-mortem glycolysis in normal and exudative longissimus dorsi muscles of the pig in relation to so-called white muscle disease. *J. Comp. Pathol. Therap. 70:273.*

Locker, R. L. 1960. Degree of muscular contraction as a factor in tenderness of beef. *Food Res.* 25:304.

Ludvigsen, J. 1954. Investigations into so-called "muscular degeneration" in pigs [in Danish, English summary]. *Beretning fra Forsøgslaboratoriet* (Copenhagen), No. 272, Paper No. 1.

Marsh, B. B. 1954. Rigor mortis in beef. *J. Sci. Food Agr.* 5:70.

――――. 1964. Meat quality and rigor mortis. *In* D. E. Tribe (ed.), *Carcass Composition and Appraisal of Meat Animals.* CSIRO, Australia.

McLoughlin, J. V. 1963. The effect of rapid post-mortem pH fall on the extraction of the sarcoplasmic and myofibrillar proteins of pig muscle. *Proc. 9th Conf. Europe. Meat Res. Workers* (Budapest), Paper 33.

Norman, W. P. 1966. Pathological conditions in muscle. *Proc. 18th Reciprocal Meat Conf.* (Manhattan, Kansas). (In press.)

Partmann, W. 1963. Post-mortem changes in chilled and frozen muscle. *J. Food Sci.* 28:15.

Paul, P., B. Love, and B. R. McClurg. 1944. Changes in histological structure and palatability of beef during storage. *Food Res.* 9:221.

Sayre, R. N., and E. J. Briskey. 1963. Protein solubility as influenced by physiological conditions in the muscle. *J. Food Sci.* 28:675.

Scopes, R. K., and R. A. Lawrie. 1963. Post-mortem lability of skeletal muscle proteins. *Nature* 197:1202.

Sink, J. D., R. G. Cassens, W. G. Hoekstra, and E. J. Briskey. 1965. Rigor mortis pattern of skeletal muscle and sarcomere length of the myofibril. *Biochim. Biophys. Acta* 102:309.

Chapter 12

Some Aspects of Postmortem Changes in Fish Muscle

H. BUTTKUS *and* N. TOMLINSON

The macroscopic arrangement of skeletal fish muscle differs from that of mammals and birds. While long fibers can be separated from the latter two, in fish short fibers are arranged between sheets of connective tissue, the myocommata (Fig. 12.1). In over-all composition, fish muscle contains less connective tissue (cod, 3%; sole, 4%; dog fish, 10%) compared with rabbit (15% to 21%). Under the microscope, the myofibrils have a striated appearance like those from mammalian muscle, and the same major myofibrillar proteins — myosin, actin, actomyosin, and tropomyosin — have been isolated (Hamoir, 1955; Mackie and Connell, 1964; Richards *et al.*, 1965). However, the rate of aggregation and the loss of enzymatic activity (adenosine triphosphatase) are faster in the proteins prepared from fish muscle (Connell, 1961; Buttkus, 1966). Myofibrils from cod are also more readily degraded than beef myofibrils when subjected to tryptic digestion (Connell, 1964).

Muscle of fish can be divided into red and white muscle, the former generally amounting to less than 10% (Fig. 12.1). Red muscle is distinguished not only by its higher myoglobin content (1% to 3%) but also by its characteristic sarcoplasmic proteins (Hamoir and Konosu, 1965). A higher content of succinic dehydrogenase and respiratory enzymes was also found in red muscle from fish (Lawrie, 1953; Fukuda, 1958). Fatty acid oxidation and lecithinase activity are greater in the red muscle of trout (Bilinski, 1963; Bilinski and Jonas, 1966), and a distinct difference has been shown to exist in the fine structure of white and red myofibrils of lingcod (Figs. 12.2 and 12.3). During the development of rigor mortis in lingcod, the increase in rigidity and contraction in the red muscle is similar to that found in warm-blooded animals. In white muscle of lingcod and halibut, these changes are less pronounced (Buttkus, 1963). Red muscle of fish also contributes to postmortem oxidative spoilage problems.

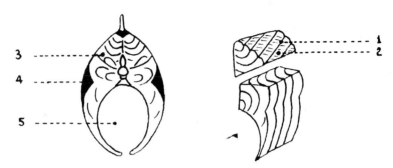

Fig. 12.1. — Transverse section through a lingcod: (1) myocommata, (2) muscle fibers of white muscle, (3) white muscle, (4) red, or lateral muscle, (5) peritoneal cavity.

Although red muscle is undoubtedly very important in the physiology and biochemistry of fish, it is usually the white muscle that is considered as food. Postmortem biochemical changes of white muscle have therefore been investigated most extensively and some of these changes are outlined below.

Rigor mortis

After death, lactic acid is produced by anaerobic glycolysis and creatine phosphate concentrations decrease, while ATP may be resynthesized at the same or even at a slightly greater rate than that at which it is broken down. After such a delay period, a steady decrease in ATP concentration is observed with increasing postmortem time. In fish muscle, the relation between these changes and rigor mortis appears similar to that in mammals (Partmann, 1964). However, rigor mortis may at times develop more rapidly in the red than in the white muscle of fish. Rigor stiffening has been observed in rainbow trout whose ATP concentrations had been depleted in the red, but not in the white muscle (Tomlinson, Geiger, and Kay, 1964b). The development of rigor mortis, glycolysis, and the loss of ATP are also related to changes in the permeability of fish muscle. Penetration of Na^+ from sea water into the muscle of a freshly killed trout did not become appreciable until ATP concentrations in the muscle had been greatly reduced and rigor mortis had been established. Loss of K^+ from the fish muscle did not begin until lactic acid formation had ceased (Tomlinson and Geiger, 1964; Tomlinson et al., 1965a).

Postmortem fate of nucleotides

ADP produced from the hydrolysis of ATP does not accumulate but is converted to AMP, probably by the action of myokinase. AMP is then

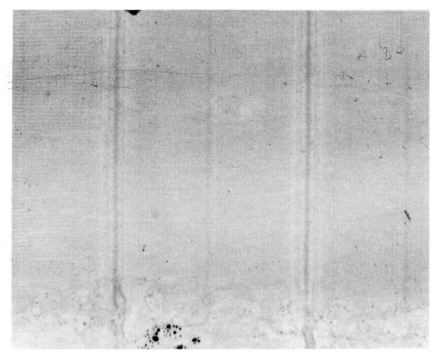

Fig. 12.2. — Electron micrograph of one sarcomere from the white muscle of lingcod. Note the short I band and the proportionately longer A band. × 15,000.

deaminated to form IMP (Saito and Arai, 1958a) which is dephosphory-lated to yield inosine. By the action of riboside hydrolase (Tarr, 1955) inosine is hydrolyzed to hypoxanthine. Hypoxanthine accumulates in fish muscle with increasing postmortem time and has been suggested as a chemical index for freshness (Saito, Arai, and Matsuyoshi, 1959; Spinelli, Eklund, and Miyauchi, 1964). Further aspects of postmortem biochemical changes in fish muscle have been reviewed (Tarr, 1958; Gubmann, Brown, and Tappel, 1958; Tomlinson and Geiger, 1962; Partmann, 1964).

Effect of postmortem pH changes on muscle proteins

The lowest postmortem pH which is reached in many species of food fish is in the range of about 6.2 to 6.6; but in some species, such as halibut, tuna, mackerel, and shark, it may fall to between 5.5 and 6.0. The effect of decreasing pH on the solubility of sarcoplasmic and myofibrillar proteins, as well as on the water-holding capacity of mammalian muscle, has been extensively investigated (Bendall and Wismer-Pedersen, 1962; Scopes and Lawrie, 1963; Sayre and Briskey, 1963). However, in fish muscle rela-

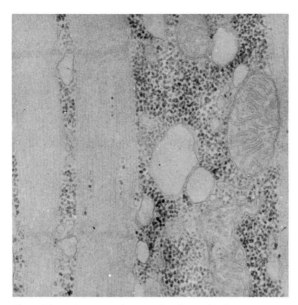

Fig. 12.3. — Electron micrograph of myofibrils, one sarcomere length from the red muscle of lingcod. The H zone, present in all types of relaxed skeletal muscle of vertebrates and invertebrates, is not visible. In the sarcoplasmic region, note the mitochondria, negative images of fat droplets, and the glycogen granules. $\times$ 12,000.

tively little work has been carried out on these aspects. Tarr (1942) demonstrated that the water-holding capacity of halibut muscle reached a minimum between pH 4.5 and 6.0 while adjustment of the pH below and above this range progressively increased the water-holding capacity. Recently it has been found that changes in the solubility of sarcoplasmic and myofibrillar proteins of halibut are influenced by the postmortem pH attained in the muscle. With increasing storage time and decreasing pH, below about 6.0, the muscle proteins became more insoluble as the region of the isoelectric zone was approached (Tomlinson, Geiger, and Dollinger, 1964a, 1965b). As the solubility of the proteins decreased, the appearance of the meat changed from translucent to opaque, free and cooked drip increased, the nitrogen content of drip decreased, and the meat became increasingly tough and dry when cooked (Patashnik, 1966, and personal communication; Tomlinson, Geiger, and Dollinger, unpublished). The condition in halibut has been termed "chalky" and in many respects resembles the pale, soft, exudative condition of pork (Briskey, 1964). However, in halibut muscle the loss in solubility of the myofibrillar proteins may occur at higher pH and lower temperature (Tomlinson *et al.*, 1965b), reflecting the greater lability of fish proteins (Connell, 1961). Preliminary results indicate that the incidence of chalkiness can be reduced if the fish are kept alive for about ten hours after being caught (Tomlinson, Dollinger, and Geiger, unpublished). This procedure brings about a small increase in the postmortem pH, presumably through the removal of lactic acid formed during catching, without a corresponding resynthesis of glycogen.

Autolysis

Another aspect leading to postmortem changes in fish muscle may be autolysis. Cathepsin activities in fish muscle are approximately ten times greater than in mammals and possibly contribute to postmortem changes leading to softening and deterioration (Siebert and Schmitt, 1964; Siebert, Schmitt, and Bottke, 1964). However, exactly what effect these proteolytic enzymes have on fish proteins, at a physiological postmortem pH (5.5 to 6.6), has not been extensively investigated.

References

Bendall, J. A., and J. Wismer-Pedersen. 1962. Some properties of the fibrillar proteins of normal and watery pork muscle. *J. Food Sci.* 27:144.

Bilinski, E. 1963. Utilization of lipids by fish. I. Fatty acid oxidation by tissue slices from dark and white muscle of rainbow trout. *Can. J. Biochem. Physiol.* 41:107.

Bilinski, E., and R. E. E. Jonas. 1966. Lecithinase activity in the muscle of rainbow trout (*Salmo gairdnerii*). *J. Fish. Res. Bd. Can.* (In press.)

Briskey, E. J. 1964. Etiological status and associated studies of pale, soft, exudative porcine musculature. *Advance. Food Res.* 13:89.

Buttkus, H. 1963. Red and white muscle of fish in relation to rigor mortis. *J. Fish. Res. Bd. Can.* 20:45.

———. 1966. Preparation and properties of trout myosin. *J. Fish. Res. Bd. Can.* 23:563.

Connell, J. J. 1961. The relative stabilities of the skeletal-muscle myosins of some animals. *Biochem. J.* 80:503.

———. 1964. Fish muscle proteins and some effects on them of processing, p. 255. *In* H. W. Schultz and A. F. Anglemier (eds.), *Symposium on Foods: Proteins and Their Reactions.* Avi Publishing Co. Inc., Westport, Conn.

Fukuda, H. 1958. Studies on the succinic dehydrogenase of fish. *Bull. Jap. Soc. Sci. Fish.* 24:24.

Gubmann, M., W. D. Brown, and A. L. Tappel. 1958. Intermediary metabolism of fishes and other aquatic animals. *U.S. Fish and Wildlife Service Spec. Sci. Rep. Fisheries,* No. 288.

Hamoir, G. 1955. Fish proteins. *Advance. Protein Chem.* 10:227.

Hamoir, G., and S. Konosu. 1965. Carp myogens of white and red muscles. General composition and isolation of low-molecular weight components of abnormal amino acid composition. *Biochem. J. 96*:85.

Lawrie, R. A. 1953. The activity of the cytochrome system in muscle and its relation to myoglobin. *Biochem. J. 55*:298.

Mackie, I. M., and J. J. Connell. 1964. Preparation and properties of purified cod myosin. *Biochim. Biophys. Acta 93*:544.

Partmann, W. 1964. Changes in proteins, nucleotides and carbohydrates during rigor mortis. FAO symposium on the significance of fundamental research in the utilization of fish (Husum, Germany, 26–30 May). Paper No. WP/I/3.

Patashnik, M. 1966. New approaches to quality changes in fresh, dressed, chilled halibut. *Com. Fish. Rev.* (In press.)

Richards, E. G., D. B. Menzel, C. S. Chung, and H. S. Olcott. 1965. Chromatography of myosin. *Fed. Proc. 24*:400.

Saito, T., and K. Arai. 1958a. Further studies of inosinic acid formation in carp muscle. *Bull. Jap. Soc. Sci. Fish. 23*:579.

———. 1958b. Slow freezing of carp muscle and inosinic acid formation. *Arch. Biochem. Biophys. 73*:315.

Saito, T., K. Arai, and M. Matsuyoshi. 1959. A new method for estimating the freshness of fish. *Bull. Jap. Soc. Sci. Fish. 24*:749.

Sayre, R. N., and E. J. Briskey. 1963. Protein solubility as influenced by physiological conditions in the muscle. *J. Food Sci. 28*:675.

Scopes, R. K., and R. A. Lawrie. 1963. Post mortem lability of skeletal muscle proteins. *Nature 197*:1202.

Siebert, G., and A. Schmitt. 1964. Fish tissue enzymes and their role in the deteriorative changes in fish. FAO symposium on the significance of fundamental research in the utilization of fish (Husum, Germany, 26–30 May). Paper No. WP/II/3.

Siebert, G., A. Schmitt, and I. Bottke. 1964. Enzyme des Aminosäure — Stoffwechsels in der Kabeljau-Muskulatur. *Arch. Fischereiwiss. 15*:233.

Spinelli, J., M. Eklund, and D. Miyauchi. 1964. Measurement of hypoxanthine in fish as a method of assessing freshness. *J. Food Sci. 29*:710.

Tarr, H. L. A. 1942. Effect of pH and NaCl on swelling and drip in fish muscle. *J. Fish Res. Bd. Can. 5*:411.

———. 1955. Fish muscle riboside hydrolases. *Biochem. J. 59*:386.

———. 1958. Biochemistry of fishes. *Annu. Rev. Biochem. 27*:223.

Tomlinson, N., and S. E. Geiger. 1962. Glycogen concentration and post mortem loss of adenosine triphosphate in fish and mammalian skeletal muscle: a review. *J. Fish. Res. Bd. Can. 19*:997.

———. 1964. Changes occurring in fish passing through rigor mortis while stored in refrigerated sea water. FAO symposium on the significance of fundamental research in the utilization of fish (Husum, Germany, 26–30 May). Paper No. WP/I/4.

Tomlinson, N., S. E. Geiger, and E. Dollinger. 1964 [Tomlinson et al., 1964a]. Chalky halibut. Fish. Res. Bd. Can. Tech. Res. Lab., Circular 33.

————. 1965 [Tomlinson *et al.*, 1965*b*]. Chalkiness in halibut in relation to muscle pH and protein denaturation. *J. Fish. Res. Bd. Can.* 22:653.

Tomlinson, N., S. E. Geiger, and W. W. Kay. 1964 [Tomlinson *et al.*, 1964*b*]. Apparent onset of rigor mortis in steelhead trout *(Salmo gairdnerii)* in the absence of loss of adenosine triphosphate from the ordinary muscle. *J. Fish. Res. Bd. Can.* 21:857.

————. 1965 [Tomlinson *et al.*, 1965*a*]. Sodium potassium and magnesium concentration and weight changes in fish stored in refrigerated sea water in relation to biochemical changes associated with rigor mortis. *J. Food Sci.* 30:126.

Chapter 13

Some Aspects of Postmortem Changes in Poultry Muscle

D. DE FREMERY

The biophysical and biochemical changes that poultry muscle undergoes postmortem are, in general, the same as those reported for various mammalian species (Bate-Smith, 1939; Bate-Smith and Bendall, 1947, 1949; Bendall, 1951; Erdös, 1943; Marsh, 1952, 1954; Marsh and Thompson, 1958; Lawrie, 1953; Briskey, Sayre, and Cassens, 1962). The most apparent change, of course, is the stiffening of muscle as it passes into rigor mortis. The chemical changes that accompany this physical change are (1) the disappearance of glycogen, adenosine triphosphate (ATP), and N-phosphorylcreatine; (2) the appearance of ammonia and inosinic acid from the deamination of adenylic acid; and (3) the accumulation of lactic acid as a result of the anaerobic breakdown of glycogen. The accumulation of lactic acid lowers muscle pH from above 7.0 to ultimate values of 5.7 to 5.9. In rigor mortis, a marked increase in the modulus of elasticity is accompanied by the virtual disappearance of ATP from muscle. In the two sections that follow, these physical and chemical changes are discussed in some detail.

PHYSICAL CHANGES ACCOMPANYING RIGOR MORTIS

In prerigor poultry muscle, the modulus of elasticity is generally in the range of $0.5-2 \times 10^3$ g/cm². This value is more or less constant until the muscle begins to stiffen. The modulus of elasticity then increases rapidly to $8-10 \times 10^3$ g/cm². This rapid phase does not begin until the ATP concentration has declined to about 30% of its initial level. In the breast muscles from well-fed chickens, this decline takes 2 to 4.5 hr postmortem (de Fremery and Pool, 1960). These changes are shown in Figure 13.1.

The attainment of maximum modulus in normal chicken breast muscle usually occurs 8 to 12 hr postmortem. After reaching that maximum, the modulus of elasticity is reduced approximately 40% during the next 12

205

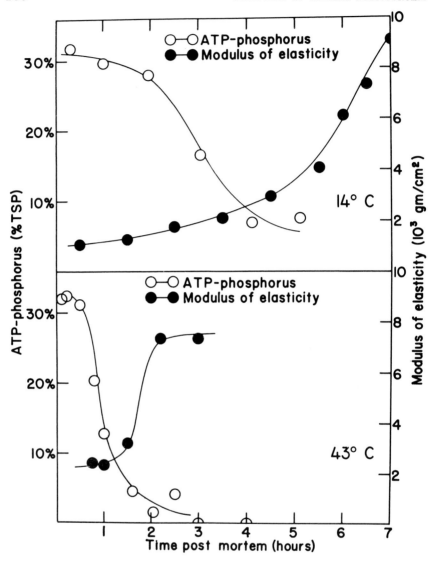

Fig. 13.1. — Postmortem changes in ATP concentration and modulus of elasticity in chicken breast muscle at two temperatures.

hr. Concurrent with stiffening, muscle strips shorten slightly under light load to about 90% of initial length, followed by a recovery almost to the original length (Pool, 1963).

Very little is known about how environmental temperature affects extensibility changes in poultry muscle. The data in Figure 13.1 suggest that lower temperatures delay the onset of rigor mortis. However, a cold-shortening effect, first described by Locker and Hagyard for beef (1963) and discussed here by Drs. Newbold and Marsh (Chaps. 14, 15), is indicated by the fact that ATP disappears more rapidly at 0 C than it does at 10 C (de Fremery and Pool, 1960). These results suggest that the loss of extensibility also proceeds more rapidly as one approaches 0 C. This suggestion, however, remains to be confirmed.

CHEMICAL CHANGES ACCOMPANYING RIGOR MORTIS

Of the postmortem chemical transformations that can be readily observed, the one that occurs most rapidly in poultry muscle is the net disappearance of N-phosphorylcreatine (PC) with the appearance of free creatine. The PC in chicken breast muscle is metabolically very labile, for the initial level declines approximately 80% when slaughter is prefaced with brief electric stunning rather than with pentobarbital anesthesia (de Fremery, 1965). These results are shown in Figure 13.2. Dodge and Peters (1960) attribute the transitory pH increase of poultry muscle immediately postmortem to the liberation of free creatine during and after slaughter.

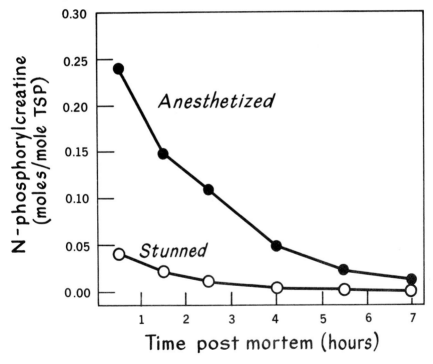

Fig. 13.2. — The postmortem disappearance of N-phosphorylcreatine from chicken breast muscle.

The disappearance of PC is followed by a breakdown of glycogen with concomitant accumulation of lactic acid. These changes have been followed in processed chickens by Shrimpton (1960) and de Fremery and Lineweaver (1962). Data on pH changes in processed turkeys have been reported by Dodge and Stadelman (1960). Shrimpton's results show that glycogen virtually disappears within 10 min of slaughter. These results do not agree with the data of de Fremery and Lineweaver. For comparison, the data are reported together in Table 13.1. Variation in struggle dur-

TABLE 13.1

Changes in the concentration of glycogen in breast muscle following commercial-type processing of fasted chickens

| Time postmortem | Glycogen concentration (mg/g fresh weight) | |
	Shrimpton (1960)	de Fremery and Lineweaver (1962)
(Live, anesthetized)	(4.1)	(8.4)*
1–3 min	2.7	3.8
10 min	0.1	3.7
30 min	0	3.3
2–2.5 hr	0	1.4
4–4.5 hr	0.3	1.0
24 hr	0.2	0.2

* Data from chickens slaughtered while anesthetized.

ing slaughter may be responsible in part for these differences. In fact, de Fremery and Lineweaver (1962) have presented data showing that slaughter conditions can markedly affect the initial glycogen concentration. In these experiments, chickens were slaughtered by bleeding (1) while under deep anesthesia (pentobarbital, 25 mg/kg live weight, iv), (2) with electric stunning sufficient to eliminate struggle, and (3) in the absence of stunning or anesthesia. The stunned birds in this experiment received a somewhat greater stunning treatment than is used commercially. The results are shown in Figure 13.3.

Under normal conditions, the concentration of ATP in chicken breast muscle (approximately 10 μmoles/g fresh weight) remains high for 1–3 hr postmortem. It then declines more or less rapidly and, as discussed previously, the muscle passes into rigor mortis when the ATP level goes below 30% of the initial value. If the muscle has received any of several stimulatory treatments prerigor (electric stimulation, higher temperature, freezing and thawing, etc.), the onset of rigor mortis is markedly accelerated (de Fremery and Pool, 1960). An extreme example is the very rapid "thaw rigor" which occurs when muscle is frozen and thawed prerigor. Data from

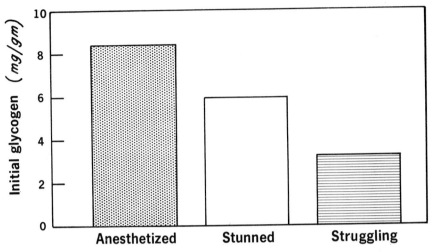

Fig. 13.3. — The effect of slaughter conditions on the glycogen concentration 3 min postmortem in chicken breast muscle.

a typical experiment are shown in Figure 13.4. In this experiment, freshly excised chicken breast muscle was frozen by immersion in a dry ice–ethanol bath, sampled for ATP and glycogen in the frozen state, and then thawed in running tap water. During thawing, the muscle underwent a massive contraction and stiffened considerably ("thaw rigor"). These observations agree with the very rapid disappearance of ATP and glycogen.

If a large dose of epinephrine (1–3 mg/kg live weight) is injected into chickens subcutaneously 16–18 hr prior to slaughter, the glycogen level in the breast muscle is reduced essentially to zero. Under these conditions the onset of rigor mortis is accelerated, but the production and accumulation of lactic acid are, of course, eliminated (de Fremery and Pool, 1963). Although the pH of the tissue never drops appreciably below 7.0, the modulus of elasticity of the muscle increases to the same extent as in normal muscle, but does so more quickly. In the experiments reported by Pool (1963), muscle strips from epinephrine-treated chickens shortened approximately 30% as they passed into rigor mortis. This shortening was somewhat greater than that which occurred in normal muscles, possibly because the temperature was usually higher when rigor mortis occurred in the treated birds.

As a concluding section of this brief review, the study of Khan and van den Berg (1964) on changes in protein extractability during the onset of rigor mortis should be mentioned. These workers showed that the nitrogen extractable from chicken breast muscle in KCl-borate or KCl-phos-

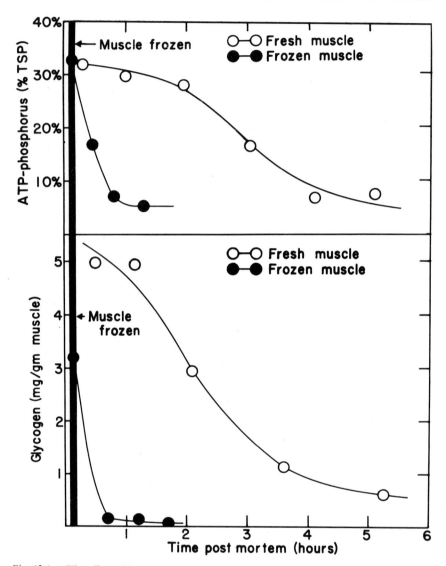

Fig. 13.4. — The effect of freezing and thawing fresh muscle on rates of ATP and glycogen breakdown.

phate buffers (ionic strength $[\gamma/2] = 1.0$ and pH 7.4) decreased from 85% of total nitrogen 30 min postmortem to approximately 71% of total nitrogen 4 hr post mortem. The extractability then increased during the next 20–44 hr to approximately the initial level. These workers attribute essentially all of this change to "myofibrillar" protein (soluble at $\gamma/2 = 0.5$, insoluble at $\gamma/2 = 0.08$), although they made no attempt to determine if the changes were due to actomyosin formation (decrease in extractability) or actin solution (increase in extractability). Since postmortem tenderization in poultry requires 12–24 hr for completion, these results have great implication for studies of the mechanism of tenderization.

References

Bate-Smith, E. C. 1939. Changes in elasticity of mammalian muscle undergoing rigor mortis. *J. Physiol. 96*:176.

Bate-Smith, E. C., and J. R. Bendall. 1947. Rigor mortis and adenosine triphosphate. *J. Physiol. 106*:177.

———. 1949. Factors determining the time course of rigor mortis. *J. Physiol. 110*:47.

Bendall, J. R. 1951. The shortening of rabbit muscle during rigor mortis: its relation to the breakdown of adenosine triphosphate and creatine phosphate and to muscular contraction. *J. Physiol. 114*:71.

Briskey, E. J., R. N. Sayre, and R. G. Cassens. 1962. Development and application of an apparatus for continuous measurement of muscle extensibility and elasticity before and during rigor mortis. *J. Food Sci. 27*:560.

De Fremery, D., 1965. The effect of anesthesia during slaughter on some biochemical properties of chicken breast muscle. *Poultry Sci. 44*:1370.

De Fremery, D., and H. Lineweaver. 1962. Early post-mortem chemical and tenderness changes in poultry. *Proc. 1st Int. Congr. Food Sci. Technol.* (In press.)

De Fremery, D., and M. F. Pool. 1960. Biochemistry of chicken muscle as related to rigor mortis and tenderization. *Food Res. 25*:73.

———. 1963. The influence of post-mortem glycolysis on poultry tenderness. *J. Food Sci. 28*:173.

Dodge, J. W., and F. E. Peters. 1960. Temperature and pH changes in poultry breast muscles at slaughter. *Poultry Sci. 39*:765.

Dodge, J. W., and W. J. Stadelman. 1960. Relationships between pH, tenderness, and moisture levels during early post-mortem aging of turkey meat. *Food Technol. 14*:43.

Erdös, T. 1943. Rigor, contracture and ATP. *Stud. Inst. Med. Chem.* (Univ. Szeged) *3*:51.

Khan, A. W., and L. van den Berg. 1964. Some protein changes during post-mortem tenderization in poultry meat. *J. Food Sci. 29*:597.

Lawrie, R. A. 1953. The onset of rigor mortis in various muscles of the draught horse. *J. Physiol. 121*:275.

Locker, R. H., and C. J. Hagyard. 1963. A cold shortening effect in beef muscles. *J. Sci. Food Agr. 14*:787.

Marsh, B. B. 1952. Observations on rigor mortis in whale muscle. *Biochim. Biophys. Acta 9*:127.

———. 1954. Rigor mortis in beef. *J. Sci. Food Agr. 5*:70.

Marsh, B. B., and J. F. Thompson. 1958. *Rigor mortis* and thaw *rigor* in lamb. *J. Sci. Food Agr.* 9:417.

Pool, M. F. 1963. Elasticity of muscle of epinephrine treated chicken. *Poultry Sci.* 42:749.

Shrimpton, D. H. 1960. Some causes of toughness in broilers (young roasting chickens). I. Packing station procedure, its influence on the chemical changes associated with *rigor mortis* and on the tenderness of the flesh. *Brit. Poultry Sci.* 1:101.

Chapter 14

Changes Associated with Rigor Mortis

R. P. NEWBOLD

Largely as a result of studies of muscle models and their constituent proteins, changes in the physical state of skeletal muscle have been related to probable interactions between actin, myosin, and ATP.

In the presence of Mg^{++} the actomyosin system is potentially a very active adenosine triphosphatase, and the splitting of ATP by this system is associated with contraction. Relaxation and the maintenance of a relaxed, resting state depend on suppression of the myofibrillar adenosine triphosphatase activity and on the plasticizing effect of ATP (see Weber and Portzehl, 1954). There is strong evidence (see Hasselbach, 1964) that contraction and relaxation, i.e., the activation and suppression of the actomyosin adenosine triphosphatase, depend respectively on the release and removal of Ca^{++} by a "relaxing factor." Relaxing factor activity has been shown to reside in tubules of the sarcoplasmic reticulum which act as a Ca pump, releasing Ca^{++} when the muscle is stimulated and recapturing them through the mediation of ATP when the stimulus ceases.

In skeletal muscle the contractile proteins actin and myosin may be considered to be arranged as two separate sets of longitudinal filaments (Hanson and Huxley, 1955). According to the sliding filament theory, shortening occurs when the actin filaments are drawn into the A band as a consequence of the development of directional forces between side branches of the myosin filaments and adjacent actin filaments (see Huxley and Hanson, 1960). When the Ca pump has removed the Ca^{++} necessary for the maintenance of these forces and ATP and Mg^{++} are present, the actin and myosin filaments do not cross-link and can be drawn apart easily. This relaxed state is maintained as long as ATP and Mg^{++} are present, but the adenosine triphosphatase activity of the actomyosin system is suppressed. In this state, which is that of skeletal muscle immediately after death, the muscle is soft, plastic, and highly extensible.

When ATP is washed out of muscle model systems they become rigid and relatively inextensible in whatever state of shortening or tension they happen to be at the time. This rigidity is similar to that of rigor mortis in postmortem muscle and has been ascribed to cross linking between the actin and myosin filaments in the absence of ATP. The nature of the cross linkages in rigor is thought to be different from that in contraction (Davies, 1963).

PHYSICAL CHANGES IN POSTMORTEM MUSCLE

The increase in hardness of muscle postmortem, measured with a sclerometer (Mangold, 1922) or penetrometer, has been used to follow the development of rigor mortis (Erdös, 1943; Marsh, 1952), as also has the decrease in torsional elasticity (Nemitz, Partmann, and Scharra, 1960). The physical criterion most commonly used, however, is the decrease in the ability of the muscle to extend under load. This decrease is followed by recording the length changes in muscle strips in which the fibers run longitudinally, when the strips are subjected to periodic loading and unloading (Bate-Smith and Bendall, 1949; de Fremery and Pool, 1960; Briskey, Sayre, and Cassens, 1962). The increase in length obtained at each loading cycle is referred to hereafter as "extension."

Kymograph records obtained in this way normally show two more or less distinct phases. During the first, there is virtually no change in extension, and this delay phase may last for several hours after death. It is followed by the onset phase, during which the extension decreases continuously. When there is no further change in extension the muscle is considered to be in full rigor.

Any shortening of the test strips during the period of examination is also reflected in the kymograph records. This will be referred to as kymograph shortening, to distinguish it from the shortening of unrestrained muscle discussed later. Kymograph shortening, when it occurs, coincides in time with the decrease in extension (Bendall, 1951; Lawrie, 1953; Marsh, 1954; de Fremery and Pool, 1960) and is greater at 37 C than at 17 C (Bendall, 1951; Marsh, 1954).

METABOLISM OF ATP IN POSTMORTEM MUSCLE

On the basis of hardness or extension changes, stiffening of postmortem muscle has been associated with decrease in ATP content in rabbit muscle (Erdös, 1943; Bate-Smith and Bendall, 1947; Bendall, 1951), whale muscle (Marsh, 1952), horse muscle (Lawrie, 1953), beef muscle (Marsh, 1954; Howard and Lawrie, 1956, 1957), chicken muscle (de Fremery and Pool, 1960), and pig muscle (Lawrie, 1960; Bendall, Hallund, and Wismer-Pederson, 1963). Hence factors which influence the rate of disappearance of ATP could be expected to influence the time course of the postmortem stiffening.

Muscle contains other adenosine triphosphatases in addition to myofibrillar adenosine triphosphatase. Bendall (1960) has concluded that the slow splitting of ATP during the normal process of rigor is attributable entirely to one or more sarcoplasmic adenosine triphosphatases.

Under the anaerobic conditions obtaining in muscle following circulatory failure, ATP is resynthesized by the transfer of high energy phosphate from creatine phosphate to ADP, and by glycolysis. When ATP is dephosphorylated more rapidly than it is resynthesized by these means, myokinase catalyzes the conversion of ADP to ATP and AMP, and the AMP is deaminated to IMP at about the same rate as it is formed.

INTERRELATIONS BETWEEN PHYSICAL AND CHEMICAL CHANGES

Since acid-labile P arises mainly from ATP, it is commonly used as an estimate of ATP concentration. Also, fall in pH has been shown to be linearly related to lactic acid production in rabbit muscle (Bate-Smith and Bendall, 1949, 1956; Bendall, 1960) and is generally preferred as a measure of glycolysis.

The usual time course of the postmortem changes in muscles of a number of animal species is as illustrated in Figure 14.1. The main features of these changes are that (1) from the start the pH and the creatine phosphate concentration fall; (2) acid-labile P remains virtually constant until the creatine phosphate content has been greatly reduced (the P of creatine

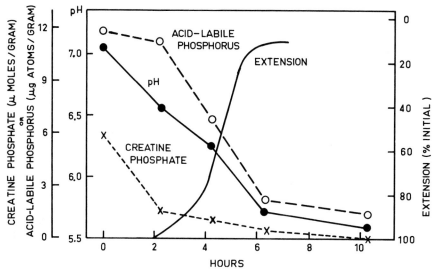

Fig. 14.1. — Chemical and physical changes in beef sternomandibularis muscle held at 37 C. Extension changes were recorded on an apparatus similar to that described by Bate-Smith and Bendall (1949) using a load of about 60 g/cm² and a loading-unloading cycle of 8 min on and 8 min off. Zero time: 1 hr and 45 min postmortem.

phosphate is not included in the term acid-labile P); and (3) the maximum rate of decrease of extension is not attained until the acid-labile P has decreased appreciably.

Hence it appears that, until the creatine phosphate reserve has been depleted, ATP is resynthesized as rapidly as it is dephosphorylated, and that extension changes are closely associated with loss of ATP which itself depends on loss of creatine phosphate.

Rapid loss of extension has been reported to begin when the ATP level has fallen to about 30% of its initial level in horse muscle (Lawrie, 1953) and chicken muscle (de Fremery and Pool, 1960); to about 25% and 50% in rabbit muscle at 17 C and 37 C respectively (Bendall and Davey, 1957); and to about 67% in beef muscle (Howard and Lawrie, 1957). Two different values, 87% (Lawrie, 1960) and 30% (Bendall et al., 1963), have been reported for pig muscle.

The relation of the completion of the physical changes to the fall in pH and to ATP disappearance is considered later.

FACTORS AFFECTING THE TIME COURSE OF RIGOR MORTIS

The foregoing suggests that the time course of the rigor process is influenced by the relative activities of the enzyme systems involved in the dephosphorylation and rephosphorylation of ATP. This appears to be of particular importance in the pig, since in corresponding muscles from different individuals the rates of fall of pH, creatine phosphate, and ATP may vary widely (see Bendall et al., 1963).

In addition, the duration of the rigor process depends to some extent on the creatine phosphate, ATP, and glycogen levels in the muscle at the time of death (see Bendall, 1960). The creatine phosphate and ATP levels may be reduced if struggling occurs at death, and the glycogen level is lowered by antemortem starvation, exhausting exercise, or other physiological stresses.

Another factor of considerable importance is temperature. Its effects on the postmortem changes in mammalian and chicken muscle are discussed below.

EFFECTS OF TEMPERATURE ON POSTMORTEM PHYSICAL CHANGES

Evidence has been obtained with muscles from a number of different species that the rigor process is completed more slowly the lower the temperature (Bate-Smith and Bendall, 1949; Bendall, 1951; de Fremery and Pool, 1960; Briskey et al., 1962). However, kymograph records have been obtained at temperatures below 7 C only with rabbit muscle (Bate-Smith and Bendall, 1949; Bendall, 1960).

The shortening of unrestrained, excised muscle at temperatures ranging from 0 C to 43 C has been studied by Locker and Hagyard (1963). They found that beef sternomandibularis muscle shortened more at 0 C or 2 C than at any other temperature, minimum shortening occurring in the region of 14 C to 19 C. At temperatures below this range shortening commenced immediately. It was most rapid at 0 C, and at 0 C and 2 C approached 50% of the initial length. A similar effect was observed consistently with beef longissimus dorsi muscle, less consistently with beef psoas muscle, but not at all with the corresponding rabbit muscles. The shortening of rabbit psoas muscle was least at the lowest temperature (2 C).

Kymograph records obtained with beef sternomandibularis muscle at temperatures from 5 C to 37 C conformed to the "normal" pattern described previously, with shortening occurring only during the onset phase. However, a markedly different pattern was consistently obtained at 1 C. At this temperature, kymograph shortening started immediately and a considerable amount had occurred before the onset phase became clearly defined (Cassens and Newbold, 1966b). In contrast, kymograph records obtained with rabbit psoas muscle at 1 C were of the same general type as those obtained with all muscles at temperatures of 5 C and above.

In the beef muscle there was an appreciable amount of kymograph shortening at 37 C, a small amount at 15 C, and virtually none at 5 C. On the other hand unrestrained strips began to shorten immediately at 5 C, and at this temperature shortened more than at 15 C but less than at 37 C. Hence it appears that shortening is more easily overcome by a load at 5 C than at 15 C.

At each temperature the times to completion of the extension changes and kymograph shortening corresponded closely, the average times from the start (about 1 hr and 45 min postmortem) being about 14 hr at 1 C, 20 hr at 5 C, 19 hr at 15 C, and 7 hr at 37 C. The onset phase commenced sooner at 1 C than at 5 C or 15 C. Hence it appears that in this muscle, while rigor takes longer to develop fully the lower the temperature in the range 5 C to 37 C, it commences earlier and becomes fully developed sooner at 1 C than at 5 C or 15 C.

EFFECTS OF TEMPERATURE ON POSTMORTEM CHEMICAL CHANGES

The chemical events that have been followed during the development of rigor include changes in pH and in the creatine phosphate and ATP concentrations. Except in chicken muscle, these have been found to occur most slowly at the lowest temperatures investigated. With beef (Marsh, 1954) and sheep muscles (Marsh and Thompson, 1958), the lowest temperature was 7 C, whereas with rabbit (Bendall, 1960) and chicken muscles (de Fremery and Pool, 1960) it was 0 C. The rate of disappearance of ATP from chicken muscle was found to be faster at 0 C than at temperatures in the range 10 C to 30 C.

Recently the studies on beef muscle have been extended, using the sternomandibularis muscle, to include temperatures down to 1 C (Cassens and Newbold, 1966a, c). It was found that in the range 5 C to 37 C the pH fell more slowly the lower the temperature. However, at 1 C the pH fell faster for the first few hours than at 5 C and closely matched the rate at 15 C; during this time the pH fell to about 6.5. The ultimate pH was reached in about 24 hr at 15 C, but at 1 C and 5 C was not reached until 48–72 hr postmortem. It was significantly higher at 1 C and 5 C than at 15 C or above, indicating less lactic acid production at the lower temperatures.

While the creatine phosphate and ATP levels fell more slowly at 15 C than at 37 C, no difference between the rates at 1 C and 15 C was apparent. At the latter two temperatures, ATP (measured as acid-labile P) had fallen to a low level by 24 hr postmortem. Although muscles from both species have not been examined at exactly the same temperatures, these findings suggest that beef sternomandibularis muscle behaves differently from rabbit psoas muscle. In the latter, changes in pH, creatine phosphate, and ATP are reported to take place 1.3 times more slowly at 0 C than at 17 C (Bendall, 1960).

Using enzymic methods for measuring concentrations of the individual phosphates, it has been found that, in the beef muscle, glucose-1-phosphate, fructose-1,6-diphosphate, and triose phosphate, which are acid labile, are present in only comparatively small amounts at any time, and that ATP concentration is close to that calculated from the acid-labile P value (Scopes and Newbold, unpublished observations). Usually traces of ATP (about 0.2 μmoles/g) remained even after the ultimate pH was reached. At all temperatures, the ADP concentration, initially about 0.9 μmoles/g, increased as the ATP level started to fall, but later decreased to a fairly consistent level of about 0.3 μmoles/g, which may represent actin-bound ADP (see also Bendall and Davey, 1957).

As mentioned above, the hexose diphosphate and triose phosphate concentrations were very low. Hence alkali-labile P may be considered to arise mainly from hexose-6-phosphate. This has been confirmed using enzymic methods (Scopes and Newbold, unpublished observations). The initial hexose-6-phosphate concentrations were variable, the sums of the glucose-6-phosphate and fructose-6-phosphate concentrations averaging about 3 μmoles/g. During the development of rigor at 37 C only small, erratic changes in concentration were noted. However, at 1 C and 15 C there was a gradual increase in the levels of these intermediates; at 1 C the increase was greater, and the level reached a maximum of as much as 10 μmoles/g at 14–16 hr postmortem. The ratio of glucose-6-phosphate to fructose-6-phosphate was consistently around 4, indicating that at all times there was sufficient enzymic isomerization to maintain an effective equilibrium.

Hence it appears that whether the hexose-6-phosphate concentration increases, decreases, or remains constant depends on the relative activities of the enzymes phosphorylase and phosphofructokinase, the balance between the activities of these being partly dependent on such factors as temperature and pH.

The presence of hexose-6-phosphate after glycolysis has ceased indicates that loss of phosphofructokinase activity is responsible for the cessation, as suggested by Bate-Smith and Bendall (1949). Apparently phosphorylase, too, is virtually inactive at this stage (Newbold and Lee, 1965).

INTERRELATIONS OF PHYSICAL AND CHEMICAL EVENTS
IN BEEF STERNOMANDIBULARIS AT 1 C

Typical chemical and physical changes in beef sternomandibularis at 1 C are illustrated in Figure 14.2. A notable feature is the shape of the curves pertaining to kymograph shortening and extension. In contrast to the pattern at 37 C, marked changes in the length of the test strip had taken place before any distinct change in the acid-labile P level had occurred, and there were also some changes in extension in this time. The physical changes were completed by the time the pH had fallen to about 6.2 and the acid-labile P to about 40% of its initial value. There-

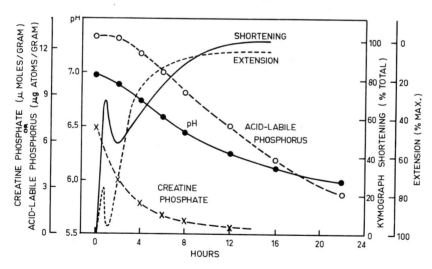

Fig. 14.2. — Chemical and physical changes in beef sternomandibularis muscle held at 1 C (average of four muscles). Kymograph records were obtained as in Fig. 14.1. Mean ultimate pH, 5.78. Mean total shortening, about 35% of the initial length.

after, the acid-labile P continued to fall and reached its final residual level about 24 hr postmortem, but the ultimate pH was not reached until 48 hr or more postmortem.

At 1 C, as at 37 C (see Fig. 14.1), the acid-labile P level remained virtually unchanged until much of the creatine phosphate had disappeared. It is of interest to note that at 1 C the completion of the physical changes and the attainment of the maximum hexose-6-phosphate concentration occurred at about the same time, but this was not so at 15 C. At 37 C on average the hexose-6-phosphate concentration changed little during the glycolytic period.

Whereas the relationships between the chemical and extension changes are similar at 0 C and 17 C in rabbit psoas muscle (Bendall, 1960) it is clear that there are marked differences between some of these relationships at 1 C and at 15 C in beef sternomandibularis muscle.

THAW RIGOR

Thaw rigor is the rigor that sets in after muscle frozen prerigor is thawed, and its characteristics have been studied mainly in muscle strips thawed at 16 C to 20 C. In these, a very pronounced shortening sets in almost immediately, and the usual postmortem chemical changes take place at a greatly accelerated rate. Bendall (1960) has noted that considerable thaw-shortening occurs in rabbit muscle before the ATP level has fallen significantly, and that after shortening has proceeded rapidly for a few minutes there is a temporary increase in the length of loaded strips, followed by further relatively slow shortening. These two features are illustrated in Figure 14.3, which presents similar results obtained with beef sternomandibularis muscle.

CONCLUSION

No clear-cut explanation can yet be given of the behavior of beef sternomandibularis muscle at 1 C. However, it is evident that the changes in length and their relation to ATP concentration resemble more closely those in thaw rigor than those in "normal" rigor, in which kymograph shortening (when it occurs) and changes in extension take place only after the ATP level has started to fall. It may well be that the underlying reasons for the effect observed with the beef muscle at 1 C and for thaw rigor are the same.

The total adenosine triphosphatase activity (calculated from the rates of change of pH, creatine phosphate, and ATP) is considerably greater in thaw rigor than in "normal" rigor at the same temperature, and Bendall (1960) has calculated that an appreciable amount of the total activity in thaw rigor is contributed by actomyosin adenosine triphosphatase. He has

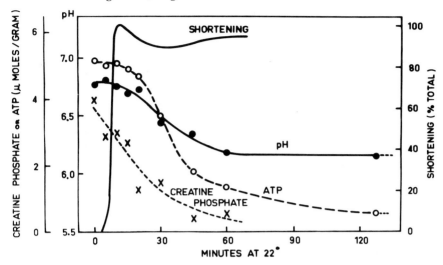

Fig. *14.3.*— Chemical and physical changes in beef sternomandibularis muscle frozen about 2 hr postmortem and thawed 24 hr later at 22 C. The strip used for recording length changes was initially about 0.4 cm² in cross section and remained under a load of 25 g throughout. ATP was measured enzymatically. Total shortening, about 50% of the initial length.

also offered a possible interpretation of thaw-shortening in terms of known effects of Ca⁺⁺ concentration on actomyosin adenosine triphosphatase activity and contraction. Although with the beef muscle the rigor pattern at 1 C differed markedly from the "normal" pattern obtained at 15 C, there was no obvious difference between the total adenosine triphosphatase activities at these two temperatures. It may be, however, that the actomyosin adenosine triphosphatase was more active and the other adenosine triphosphatases correspondingly less active at the lower temperature.

The difference in behavior at 1 C between beef sternomandibularis and rabbit psoas muscles may reflect a difference in the abilities of these muscles, when exposed to this temperature, to maintain the Ca⁺⁺ concentration below that needed to stimulate actomyosin adenosine triphosphatase.

In his studies on rabbit muscle, Erdös (1943) found that the full development of rigor was coincident with the complete loss of ATP. With few exceptions, data since published indicate that for the muscles and conditions used the change in extension was not complete until the *p*H was at or near its ultimate value and the ATP content had been reduced to a low level (see Fig. 14.1). Where ATP concentrations were measured in terms of acid-labile P (sometimes adjusted as described by Bailey and Marsh, 1952) it is possible that, owing to the presence of other acid-labile phosphates, the true ATP level at the time of completion of the extension changes was lower than indicated (see Bendall and Davey, 1957). Using more specific methods, it was found that in rabbit muscle most of the ATP disappeared as rigor was completed, but that occasionally as much as 0.7 μmoles/g survived at room temperature for a further 10–12 hr (Bendall and Davey, 1957). Mention has already been made of the finding that postmortem stiffening, as measured by kymograph shortening or change in extension, reached completion in beef sternomandibularis muscle at 1 C while there was still an appreciable amount of ATP present (Fig. 14.2). This also appears to have been the case in the pig muscles examined at 37 C by Lawrie (1960). Hence it seems that the interactions between the contractile proteins responsible for postmortem stiffening are not necessarily dependent on the loss of most of the ATP.

The relationship between pH fall and the completion of the extension changes noted above does not appear to be invariable: as has been pointed out earlier, the extension changes were completed in beef sternomandibularis muscles at 1 C before the pH had fallen below about 6.2 (Fig. 14.2), but the ultimate pH was about 5.8.

Finally, it is of interest to note that many published data show a close coincidence between the completion of the physical changes and the virtually complete disappearance of creatine phosphate. This is also apparent in thaw rigor (see Fig. 14.3; also Bendall, 1960: Fig. 10). Indeed, in beef sternomandibularis muscle at 1 C (see Fig. 14.2) and in the pig longissimus dorsi muscles examined by Lawrie (1960) this coincidence is closer than that between the completion of the physical changes and the reduction of ATP to a low level. This aspect merits closer investigation.

References

Bailey, K., and B. B. Marsh. 1952. The effects of sulfhydryl reagents on hydrolysis in muscle homogenates. *Biochim. Biophys. Acta* 9:133.

Bate-Smith, E. C., and J. R. Bendall. 1947. Rigor mortis and adenosinetriphosphate. *J. Physiol.* 106:177.

———. 1949. Factors determining the time course of rigor mortis. *J. Physiol.* 110:47.

———. 1956. Changes in muscle after death. *Brit. Med. Bull.* 12:230.

Bendall, J. R. 1951. The shortening of rabbit muscles during rigor mortis: its relation to the breakdown of adenosine triphosphate and creatine phosphate and to muscular contraction. *J. Physiol.* 114:71.

———. 1960. Post-mortem changes in muscle, p. 227. *In* G. H. Bourne (ed.), *The Structure and Function of Muscle*, Vol. 3. Academic Press, New York.

Bendall, J. R., and C. L. Davey. 1957. Ammonia liberation during rigor mortis and its relation to changes in the adenine and inosine nucleotides of rabbit muscle. *Biochim. Biophys. Acta* 26:93.

Bendall, J. R., O. Hallund, and J. Wismer-Pedersen. 1963. Postmortem changes in the muscles of Landrace pigs. *J. Food Sci.* 28:156.

Briskey, E. J., R. N. Sayre, and R. G. Cassens. 1962. Development and application of an apparatus for continuous measurement of muscle extensibility and elasticity before and during rigor mortis. *J. Food Sci.* 27:560.

Cassens, R. G., and R. P. Newbold. 1966a. Effects of temperature on post-mortem metabolism in beef muscle. *J. Sci. Food Agr.* (In press.)

————. 1966b. Effect of temperature on the time course of rigor mortis in ox muscle. Submitted to *J. Food Sci.*

————. 1966c. Temperature dependence of pH changes in ox muscle postmortem. Submitted to *J. Food Sci.*

Davies, R. E. 1963. A molecular theory of muscle contraction: calcium-dependent contractions with hydrogen bond formation plus ATP-dependent extensions of part of the myosin-actin cross-bridges. *Nature* 199:1068.

De Fremery, D., and M. F. Pool. 1960. Biochemistry of chicken muscle as related to rigor mortis and tenderization. *Food Res.* 25:73.

Erdös, T. 1943. Rigor, contracture and adenosinetriphosphoric acid. *Stud. Inst. Med. Chem.* (Univ. Szeged) 3:51. (*Chem. Abstr.* 41[1947]:130ld.)

Hanson, J., and H. E. Huxley. 1955. The structural basis of contraction in striated muscle. *Symp. Soc. Exp. Biol.*, No. 9, p. 228.

Hasselbach, W. 1964. Relaxing factor and the relaxation of muscle. *Progr. Biophys. Mol. Biol.* 14:167.

Howard, A., and R. A. Lawrie. 1956. Studies on beef quality. Part 2. Physiological and biochemical effects of various pre-slaughter treatments. CSIRO (Australia) Div. Food Preserv. Tech., Paper No. 2.

————. 1957. Studies on beef quality. Part 5. Further observations on biochemical and physiological responses to pre-slaughter treatments. CSIRO (Australia) Div. Food Preserv. Tech., Paper No. 4.

Huxley, H. E., and J. Hanson. 1960. The molecular basis of contraction in cross-striated muscles, p. 183. *In* G. H. Bourne (ed.), *The Structure and Function of Muscle*, Vol. 1. Academic Press, New York.

Lawrie, R. A. 1953. The onset of rigor mortis in various muscles of the draught horse. *J. Physiol.* 121:275.

————. 1960. Post mortem glycolysis in normal and exudative longissimus dorsi muscles of the pig in relation to so-called white muscle disease. *J. Comp. Pathol. Therap.* 70:273.

Locker, R. H., and C. J. Hagyard. 1963. A cold shortening effect in beef muscles. *J. Sci. Food Agr.* 14:787.

Mangold, E. 1922. Untersuchungen über Muskelhärte. Pt. I. *Arch. Ges. Physiol.* 196:200.

Marsh, B. B. 1952. Observations on rigor mortis in whale muscle. *Biochim. Biophys. Acta* 9:127.

————. 1954. Rigor mortis in beef. *J. Sci. Food Agr.* 2:70.

Marsh, B. B., and J. F. Thompson. 1958. Rigor mortis and thaw rigor in lamb. *J. Sci. Food Agr.* 7:417.

Nemitz, G., W. Partmann, and D. Scharra. 1960. Eine neue Methode zur Messung der Totenstarre. *Z. Lebensm. Untersuch. Forsch.* 112:261.

Newbold, R. P., and C. A. Lee. 1965. Post-mortem glycolysis in skeletal muscle. The extent of glycolysis in diluted preparations of mammalian muscle. *Biochem. J.* 97:1.

Weber, H. H., and H. Portzehl. 1954. The transference of the muscle energy in the contraction cycle. *Progr. Biophys. and Biophys. Chem.* 4:60.

Chapter 15

Relaxing Factor in Muscle

B. B. MARSH

The relaxing factor in muscle was first detected in a food investigation laboratory, and the observations leading to its detection were made during the course of a project designed to improve the quality of whale meat for human food. With such an applied origin, the relaxing factor seems a most appropriate topic for discussion in a book which seeks to remove the hypothetical barrier separating muscle research and meat science. Bearing in mind the wide interests embraced by prospective readers of this book and the complexity of muscular contraction and relaxation, I propose to introduce the subject gently by describing in some detail the original observations which led to the postulation of a relaxing factor. The current situation in relaxation research will then be discussed in fairly general terms, and finally (and speculatively) an attempt will be made to relate our knowledge of the factor to present-day meat science.

DETECTION OF THE RELAXING FACTOR

In 1947 a scientific team from the Low Temperature Research Station, Cambridge, England, accompanied the whaling factory-ship *Balaena* to the Antarctic to study the utilization of whale meat for human consumption. Among the biochemical observations made (Marsh, 1952a) was one concerning the water-retaining ability of whale meat; it was found that fresh whale muscle is almost always either dry, glistening, and firm, or wet, dull, and disrupted. It was established that those muscles with a pH (at the time of visual observation) higher than 6.3 were always dry, whereas only wet muscles were observed if the pH was below 6.1. In the pH range 6.1–6.3, both wet and dry muscles were found. In almost all cases the ultimate pH was in the range 5.5–5.9. It was further shown that the rapid phase of decomposition of ATP commenced at about pH 6.2, and it was concluded that the onset of rigor mortis, and with it the rapid disappearance of ATP, were responsible for a large decrease in water-holding capacity. Furthermore the decrease was found to be greater the higher the temperature of the muscle during rigor onset — an observation pertinent, I understand, to the current problem of watery pork.

To the well-established influence of declining pH on fluid retention by muscle (Empey, 1933), we were able, therefore, to add two new effects: the extent and the rate of ATP decomposition. Apart from their interest in meat quality investigations, these observations also appeared to be related to the then current views on muscular contraction. The striking contraction-like synaeresis or shrinkage caused by ATP addition to actomyosin gels or threads (Szent-Györgyi, 1947) was at that time taken by some to support a theory that the *presence* of ATP caused contraction while its decomposition occurred during relaxation. Our whale meat observations, on the other hand, suggested that the presence of ATP permitted a high fluid retention and relaxed state, while its enzymic decomposition coincided with synaeresis and shortening. This apparent contradiction was further investigated (Marsh, 1952b) at the Low Temperature Research Station, Cambridge, under the general supervision of the late Dr. K. Bailey, and with the active interest of Drs. J. R. Bendall, R. A. Lawrie, and E. C. Bate-Smith.

With a supply of prerigor whale meat no longer available, it soon became obvious that this had been an ideal experimental material. Its actual water-holding capacity did not much exceed the amount of water it was required to bind in the prerigor state; consequently the combined effects of declining pH and falling ATP content resulted in appreciable fluid exudation. In the muscles of other species the capacity to bind water appears to exceed considerably the amount to be bound, and as a result little or no obvious fluid release occurs with normal postmortem processes. It was partly for this reason that the muscle homogenate was selected as an experimental material, for with this we could, in effect, fully saturate the fluid-binding mechanism of the muscle, after which any decline in water-holding capacity could be followed fairly easily. A second reason for using the homogenate — and one equally applicable today — was that, while retaining physiological completeness and a considerable degree of fibrillar organization, it permitted the ready addition of reagents, removal of certain components, and observation of the effects of such treatments. Used in conjunction with a centrifuge modified to permit continuous visual observation of the spinning tube (Marsh, 1955), the homogenate becomes a versatile and extremely useful material for any study concerned with fluid retention.

Using fresh rabbit muscle homogenates prepared in isotonic (0.16 M) KCl, we confirmed and extended the earlier whale-meat observations. A "rapid phase" of declining fluid retention occurred some minutes after homogenizing and the start of centrifuging (Fig. 15.1). This may be com-

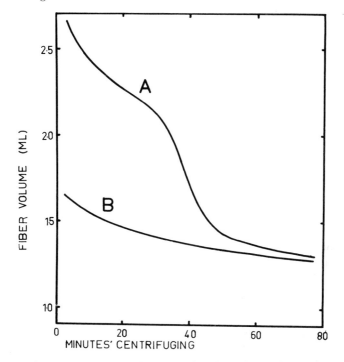

Fig. 15.1. — Volume of fibers as a function of centrifuging time. A: fresh rabbit muscle; B: rabbit muscle in rigor.

pared with the rapid phase of onset of rigor mortis (Bate-Smith, 1949), and, like it, is sandwiched between steady states: in the one case, of high and low fluid retentions and, in the other, of high and low extensibilities. An observation of some later significance was made at this time. The replacement of part of the KCl by phosphates or bicarbonates of Na or Mg did not much affect the three-phase picture, but the addition of Ca++ (1–2 mM) eliminated entirely the usual pattern, which was replaced by an immediate volume decrease of about 50%.

To test directly our supposition that the rapid shrinkage was due to ATP decomposition, ATP was added back to the shrunken system. The result of this addition was usually very satisfactory: the fiber pieces imbibed water and increased their volume relative to that of the same fragments before ATP addition. After a delay of up to 5 min in this swollen state, a rapid shrinkage occurred, the volume returning to about its earlier low value. This response to ATP was almost always observed in those homogenates prepared on the day of slaughter, and in somewhat more than half of those made after the excised muscles had been stored at 0 C until

24 hr postmortem. It clearly established the disappearance of ATP as the cause of the rapid phase of declining fluid retention.

In some trials involving ATP addition, however, a totally different effect was observed. An immediate, rapid, and large shrinkage or synaeresis occurred, and even before the first observation could be made in the centrifuge the fiber volume had declined to 60%–90% of that of the same fibers before ATP addition. This synaeresis proved quite irreversible regardless of the nature of later additions or treatments. In contrast to the reversible fiber swelling, this irreversible shrinkage bore a marked similarity to the well-established synaeresis of actomyosin gels or glycerol-treated fibers on which theories of muscular contraction were at that time based.

Our homogenate was capable, therefore, of responding to ATP addition in either of two very different ways (Fig. 15.2), and it became a matter of some importance to determine the reason for the difference. Further studies established that the swelling effect could be converted to the shrinkage phenomenon by three methods: (1) aging the muscle or the homogenate for two or three days at 0 C to 5 C; (2) adding Ca^{++} (1–2 mM); (3) washing the fiber pieces in isotonic KCl solution and discarding the bulk of the liquid phase before ATP addition (Fig. 15.3).

It was thus possible to postulate the existence in fresh muscle of a relatively unstable, Ca-sensitive factor, removable by homogenization and washing, in the presence of which ATP produced a reversible swelling-shrinkage effect comparable to relaxation-contraction, but in the absence of which ATP caused only an irreversible and large synaeresis of the type already well characterized by Szent-Györgyi and others.

Further experiments revealed the relatively high heat- and acid-lability of the factor (2 min at 60 C, or brief exposure to pH 3.6). Microscope observation showed that the swelling effect was accompanied by fiber lengthening, and synaeresis by immediate and very considerable shortening.

In the last few days available for completion of the study, a vital clue was obtained to account for the powerful effect exerted by the factor. In its presence ATP was found to be split enzymically at only 10% to 20% of the rate observed in its absence. It was concluded that the relaxing factor was some sort of physiological inhibitor, suppressing the vigorous, energy-producing, enzyme splitting of ATP during rest, yet being rapidly inactivated by Ca^{++} to allow a tenfold increase in energy output through enhanced adenosine triphosphatase activity when the occasion demanded it.

RELAXATION: THE CURRENT VIEW

Let us now consider our present-day knowledge of the relaxing factor, skipping over a decade of intense activity in the field of contraction and

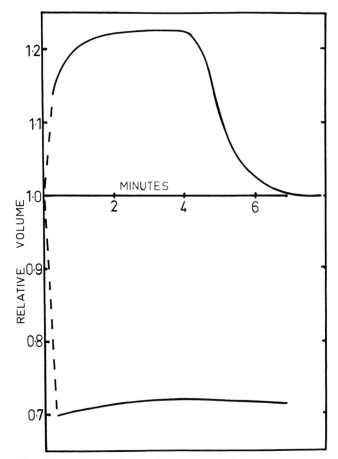

Fig. 15.2. — Volume of fiber fragments (relative to their volume before ATP addition) as a function of centrifuging time. *Broken line*: supposed volume changes during the first few seconds when visual observation was impractical. *Solid line*: volume changes during period of continuous visual observation.

relaxation (summarized in three recent review articles: Gergely, 1964; Hasselbach, 1964; Huxley and Huxley, 1964).

In general terms it may first be said that the conclusions of the original study have been confirmed. A relaxing factor does exist; it is relatively unstable; it is partly protein in composition; its activity is related to the concentration of Ca^{++}; its functioning is accompanied by greatly reduced myofibrillar adenosine triphosphatase activity. Confirmation, extension, and (in some aspects) correction of the earlier results have been accompanied, however, by tremendous advances in detailed knowledge. The

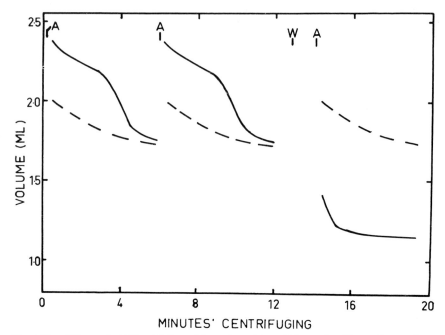

Fig. 15.3. — Effects of ATP additions (*A*) and washing (*W*) on the fiber volume of a homogenate prepared from rabbit muscle in rigor. *Broken line*: no ATP addition. *Solid line*: ATP added.

painstaking quantitative approach of recent years has overshadowed completely the inelegant qualitative methods used in the initial stages of factor detection.

In no aspect is this more apparent than in that of the actual physical nature of the factor. In the years immediately following its first detection, the factor was successively identified with several known enzymes and a number of glycolytic intermediates. Following the entry of Ebashi and his group to the field in 1955, and extension of their results by Portzehl in 1957, however, it became clear that the factor was not soluble but particulate in nature. This discovery enabled the biochemist to achieve very considerable purification and concentration by differential centrifuging techniques. It also revealed to the physiologist the possibility of identifying the factor with structural elements of muscle, and encouraged still greater use of the electron miscroscope.

Histology

To understand the role of the factor, it is first necessary to appreciate certain aspects of the fine structure of muscle, a field in which great advances have been made in recent years. The relaxing factor is now identified with the components known collectively as the sarcoplasmic reticulum. This is the counterpart in muscle of the endoplasmic reticulum of other cells, and is a closed membranous system separating the interfibrillar spaces into two phases. We may conveniently consider the sarcoplasmic reticulum to consist of two principal components, the longitudinal (or L) and the transverse tubular (or T) systems. It is from the physical breakdown of one or both of these that the particulate relaxing factor is derived.

The L system occupies most of the interfibrillar space, and although its sacs are interconnected laterally, the continuity of the system is interrupted longitudinally, usually at the level of the Z line or the A–I junction. This part of the structure, then, runs *across* the fiber and surrounds the fibrils without interruption for long stretches; it is continuous around sarcomeres which are adjacent side-by-side, but not directly connected around end-to-end sarcomeres, that is, around sarcomeres of the same fibril. The T system, on the other hand, occurs usually *only* at Z-line level or A–I junctions. It is best regarded as a series of invaginations of the sarcolemma, a sort of continuation of the fiber sheath, in the form of tubules, into the body of the fiber. Small structures probably bridge the narrow gap separating the L system and the T system.

The reader must visualize a most complex three-dimensional and three-component picture: first the fibrils, longitudinally continuous but laterally not connected; then the L system, laterally continuous but usually interrupted longitudinally once in each sarcomere length; and finally the T system, a network of transverse tubules, their inner linings continuous with the sarcolemma. Several recent papers (e.g., Franzini-Armstrong, in Gergely, 1964) include electron micrographs on which these interpretations are based.

Physiology

Interesting as is this picture of muscle structure, it is made even more so by recent physiological experiments. It was found that micro-application of Ca^{++} to the A band elicited a shortening in only half an I band, whereas application to the Z line caused shortening of the half I bands on both sides of it. Earlier work had shown that electrical activation produced symmetrical effects in adjacent half I bands if applied at the Z line, and the combined observations suggest that this electrical activation is due to the symmetrical release of Ca at the Z line. The presence of the invaginating tubules of the T system at just this position — the level of the Z line — indicates that the T system is probably the path along which the influence of membrane depolarization is transmitted inward. In other words, there is strong evidence that the tubules, opening to the sarcolemmal surface at those points where localized stimulation causes a contraction, are the route by which a stimulus is carried rapidly into the body of the fiber.

Biochemistry

Histological and physiological aspects, then, appear at present to be in complete and rather beautiful harmony. What of the biochemical picture, of the actual molecular or ionic mechanism by which Ca^{++} is released at one stage of the contraction-relaxation cycle and recaptured at another? Can we, in fact, postulate such a mechanism, bearing in mind the speed with which it must be able to function, the absorptive capacity for all the Ca which must be removed to permit relaxation, and the relatively very low resting metabolism of relaxed muscle? It is perhaps in this biochemical field that most remains to be done despite the great efforts of the past decade. As a result of the work of A. Weber, Hasselbach, Ebashi, Gergely, and others, however, the picture is becoming clearer.

The basic facts appear plain. If the contractile protein of muscle — actomyosin — contains bound Ca, it contracts with ATP; if part of this Ca is removed, it relaxes with ATP. It is the function of the relaxing factor to control the amount of bound Ca in actomyosin, and this it does by regulating the concentration of Ca^{++} in the environment. If pCa is 7 or more (i.e., if the concentration of Ca^{++} is 10^{-7} M or less), then myofibrillar activity in the form of synaeresis, adenosine triphosphatase activity, and contraction is maximally inhibited. If pCa increases to 6, however, the inhibitory mechanism does not operate and myofibrillar activity is high. It should be noted that this modern concept of the role of Ca differs greatly from our first ideas; it was earlier suggested that released Ca^{++} inhibited the factor and allowed contraction, and that Ca uptake (tacitly presumed to be due to a mechanism not directly involving the factor) permitted relaxation. The current view, in contrast, indicates that it is the factor itself which controls the level of Ca^{++}, and that this regulation of ionic Ca is alone sufficient to account for the relaxing effect.

The lowering of the concentration of Ca^{++} to the required 10^{-7} M or less has been shown to be well within the ability of the vesicles of the sarcoplasmic reticulum. Concerning the actual amount of Ca removed, as distinct from the reduction in its concentration, recent experiments of A. Weber indicate that the minimal amount of reticular protein present in muscle could bind twice as much Ca as would be necessary to induce relaxation.

The *rate* of uptake of Ca by the reticulum has not, as yet, been proven adequate to account for the known speed of relaxation; in fact there is a considerable discrepancy between the required rate in intact muscle and the observed rate in reconstructed systems. However, this appears to present no insuperable objection to the over-all conclusion, for we cannot assume that fragmentation of the sarcoplasmic reticulum has necessarily left its Ca-binding ability intact. Furthermore, certain practical difficulties have prevented measurements until the vesicles were 60% Ca-saturated, and it is quite possible that the initial rate of uptake might have been much higher.

There are other discrepancies, too, which are so far unresolved. We would expect the adenosine triphosphatase activity of maximally inhibited myofibrils to be equal to that of myosin alone, since in resting muscle there should be no interaction between actin and myosin. In fact the activity is somewhat higher than that of myosin. This raises yet another disparity, for even the adenosine triphosphatase activity of myosin alone exceeds that of resting muscle. In other words the relaxing factor, even when fully operative, has not yet been proven capable of reducing adenosine triphosphatase activity to that of resting muscle. These discrepancies might perhaps be due to imperfections of technique, to the relative lack of organization in reconstituted systems, or to the presence in intact muscle of as yet unsuspected relaxing mechanisms. It is quite possible that the transphosphorylating enzymes — myokinase, creatine phosphokinase — earlier claimed to be the relaxing factor itself, may have a significant effect on Ca uptake or on the configuration of actomyosin by their ability to control the level of ADP in muscle.

Finally in this section we must consider the nature of this rapid uptake and release of Ca by the particles of the sarcoplasmic reticulum. Hasselbach's term "Ca pump" to describe the sarcotubular elements responsible for the effect is an apt one; Ca is accumulated against a concentration gradient within the vesicles, and energy must be supplied, in the form of limited ATP splitting, to enable this gradient to be overcome. Some of the absorbed Ca combines with lipoprotein material of the vesicular membranes, but the bulk of it appears to pass inside the vesicles where it resides as a soluble Ca salt. Here it remains as long as the gradient can be maintained. The mean concentration of Ca within the vesicles may be more than 500 times the concentration outside; the attainment of such a gradient requires a very active Ca-transporting mechanism in the membranes. The only substrate present to supply energy to the vesicles is ATP, and it has indeed been found that, simultaneously with the commencement of Ca accumulation, ATP splitting by a so-called "extra adenosine triphosphatase" commences. This enzyme is Ca-activated, and when the declining Ca^{++} concentration outside approaches 10^{-8} M, its activity ceases. The splitting of ATP by the myofibrillar enzyme drops immediately to that characteristic of the relaxed or resting state because of the withdrawal of Ca. Meanwhile the splitting of ATP by the vesicles also returns to a low rate; the Ca-activated "extra adenosine triphosphatase" has become inoperative, but yet another adenosine triphosphatase, not dependent on Ca for its activity, maintains a low energy supply by limited ATP dephosphorylation.

We thus have a most interesting, though very complex, situation in which contraction, relaxation, and maintenance of the relaxed state are all dependent on adenosine triphosphatase activity, but by different enzymes. In contraction, ATP is split by the Ca-activated myofibrillar actomyosin to provide energy for the contractile machinery. In relaxation, it is decomposed by the Ca-activated "extra adenosine triphosphatase" of the sarcoplasmic reticulum to provide energy for "pumping." In the fully relaxed state, it is broken down by the Ca-insensitive adenosine triphosphatase to provide energy merely for the maintenance of a low-Ca environment.

The relaxing factor is seen, therefore, to be infinitely more complicated than was originally conceived. We now see it to be a structure rather than a substance, yet one which so permeates the fiber that it is ideally placed to perform its function, the capture and release of Ca^{++}. But not only is it a structure; it is also a very efficient machine — a sarcotubular pump, in Hasselbach's terminology — with its own energy suppliers in the form of adenosine triphosphatases to create, maintain, or erase a steep concentration gradient across its bounding membrane.

RELAXING FACTOR AND MEAT RESEARCH

The relaxing factor originated in meat studies, and it is to meat research that this chapter returns in conclusion. What has our knowledge of the factor contributed to meat science, and what clues does it provide to a greater understanding of present and future meat problems?

To the meat scientist the onset of rigor mortis is of prime importance, for the effects of this process are sometimes seen in many aspects of meat quality — wet whale meat, dark-cutting beef, and watery pork, for instance. The principal contribution of relaxing factor research, I feel, is a simple one: a fuller comprehension of this rigor process. The potentially most active adenosine triphosphatase of muscle, actomyosin, remains suppressed by relaxing factor during rigor onset, and the prolonged time-course of the process is accounted for rationally. Indeed, it seems no exaggeration to suggest the possibility of partial factor inactivation in any condition characterized by accelerated ATP decomposition, increased shortening, or unusually rapid lactic acid production.

A consideration of two interesting effects, thaw rigor and cold shortening, may serve to illustrate this generalization. They are selected, not because they are necessarily the best examples, but simply because they have occupied my attention recently.

Thaw rigor is the sometimes quite spectacular shortening which accompanies the thawing of isolated strips of muscle earlier frozen in a prerigor condition. Although known for nearly a century, and long considered a useful system for studies of muscular contraction, this effect has only recently become of some significance in the meat industry; for with the development of faster freezing techniques, prerigor freezing is now commercially possible. Major problems involving thaw rigor were first encountered when whale meat for human consumption was frozen rapidly (Sharp and Marsh, 1953); so the effect is a good example of a phenomenon interesting both to the meat scientist and to the muscle physiologist.

Thaw rigor has been ably reviewed by Bendall (1960), whose explanation postulates the occurrence of an extensive salt "flux" on thawing, with release of Ca and temporary inactivation of the relaxing factor. If thawing is not very rapid the salt imbalance persists and the factor remains inactivated; in this case the onset of rigor occurs while the muscle is in a highly contracted state. If, on the other hand, thawing is almost instantaneous, the salt balance quickly equilibrates, the released Ca is recaptured, normal factor activity is restored, and relaxation sets in. This theory is supported by the finding that spontaneous relaxation does indeed occur in thaw rigor if conditions favor very rapid thawing.

Locker and Hagyard (1963) discovered a "cold shortening" effect which promises to be as interesting, from the viewpoints of both the muscle biochemist and the meat scientist, as thaw rigor. Appreciable shortening, sometimes exceeding 60% of the initial length, follows the exposure of fresh, excised beef muscles to temperatures in the region of 0 C to 10 C, the rate and extent being greater with lower temperature in this range and with less delay after slaughter. The effect is being, or has been, investigated in New Zealand, Australia, and the United States, and already it has been established that appreciable toughening may result from the shortening (Marsh, 1964).

An explanation, both of the phenomenon itself and of the consequent toughening, still appears to be some distance away. I would like to suggest, however — and here I enter the realm of pure speculation — that cold shortening is due to the same basic cause as thaw rigor — the inactivation of relaxing factor by Ca^{++} release, this being the result of a salt "flux." This concept immediately suggests the possibility that the hypothetical salt "flux" is due, not to thawing, but rather to the exposure of muscles to temperatures just above freezing point, whether approached from above (cold shortening) or from below (thaw rigor). Such a salt "flux" could probably be explained in terms of the relative rates of diffusive and chemical processes, for it is well recognized that the temperature coefficient of diffusion is considerably lower than that of chemical reaction. Examples have long been known in which the exposure of a biological system to a lower temperature causes an ion-leakage across the bounding membrane, with a subsequent recapture when the temperature is raised.

This chapter has covered superficially a lot of ground, ranging from extremely basic research to very applied investigations. In steering the somewhat erratic course from meat to muscle and back to meat, I have tried to demolish the imaginary fence separating the fields of meat and muscle research. There is, in fact, as the title of this book implies, only one field.

References

Bate-Smith, E. C., and J. R. Bendall. 1949. Factors determining the time course of rigor mortis. *J. Physiol.* 110:47.

Bendall, J. R. 1960. Post mortem changes in muscle, p. 227. *In* G. H. Bourne (ed.), *The Structure and Function of Muscle*, Vol. 3. Academic Press, New York.

Empey, W. A. 1933. Studies on the refrigeration of meat. Conditions determining the amount of "drip" from frozen and thawed muscles. *J. Soc. Chem. Ind.* 52:230T.

Gergely, J. (chairman). 1964. Physiology symposium on the relaxing factor of muscle. *Fed. Proc.* 23:885.

Hasselbach, W. 1964. Relaxing factor and the relaxation of muscle. *Progr. Biophys. Mol. Biol.* 14:167.

Huxley, A. F., and H. E. Huxley (organizers). 1964. A discussion on the physical and chemical basis of muscular contraction. *Proc. Roy. Soc.* (London), B, 160:433.

Locker, R. H., and C. J. Hagyard. 1963. A cold shortening effect in beef muscles. *J. Sci. Food Agr.* 14:787.

Marsh, B. B. 1952a. Observations on rigor mortis in whale muscle. *Biochim. Biophys. Acta* 9:127.

———. 1952b. The effects of adenosine triphosphate on the fibre volume of a muscle homogenate. *Biochim. Biophys. Acta* 9:247.

———. 1955. A centrifuge permitting continuous observation of the spinning tube. *J. Sci. Instrum.* 32:205.

———. 1964. Meat quality and rigor mortis. *In* D. E. Tribe (ed.), *Carcass Composition and Appraisal of Meat Animals.* CSIRO, Australia.

Sharp, J. G., and B. B. Marsh. 1953. Whale-meat; production and preservation. *Spec. Rep. Food Invest. Board* (London), No. 58.

Szent-Györgyi, A. 1947. *The Chemistry of Muscular Contraction.* Academic Press, New York.

Chapter 16

Lysosomes: Enzymes and Catabolic Reactions

A. L. TAPPEL

Present knowledge of lysosomes is generally well covered in reviews. The main summaries of this field appear in the 1963 *Ciba Symposium on Lysosomes*. De Duve (1963) presents the development of knowledge of lysosomes and gives the broad perspective of their function. Novikoff (1961, 1963) and Novikoff, Essner, and Quintana (1964) have described in detail the involvement of lysosomes in cellular physiology and pathology as determined by histochemical and electron microscopy methods. Several reviews cover lysosomes and their involvement in catabolism. Straus (1963) discusses lysosomes and phagosomes of kidney and liver and their role in removal and catabolism of foreign proteins. In studies of muscle catabolism, the regressing tails of tadpoles during metamorphosis have been the source of considerable information on the role of lysosomes (Weber, 1963). Another advance in lysosomes and catabolism has been the study of Cohn, Hirsch, and Wiener (1963) on the lysosomes of phagocytic cells and their involvement in degradation of bacteria. Dingle (1963) and Weissman (1964) describe the labilization and stabilization of lysosomal membranes.

Important groups of enzymes have been localized in lysosomes. Protein catabolism in the lysosome is apparently initiated by enzymes of the cathepsin group; cathepsins have been reviewed by Fruton (1960). The main function of the lysosomal glycosidases, β-glucuronidase, β-galactosidase, a-mannosidase and β-N-acetyl glucosaminidase, is apparently the catabolism of mucopolysaccharides. Levvy and Marsh (1959, 1960) and Fishman (1961) summarize information on glucuronidase. Lysosomal acid phosphatases have broad specificity (Schmidt, 1961) and can catalyze hydrolysis of most of the cell's phosphate compounds. Although the physiological function of the aryl sulfatases has not been defined, they are one of the easily measured lysosomal enzymes; Roy (1960) reviews our knowledge of sulfatases. Lysosomes contain ribonuclease and deoxyribonucleases

which initiate the catabolism of RNA and DNA respectively; ribonucleases are reviewed by Anfinsen and White (1961).

MUSCLE LYSOSOMES

All animal tissues appear to contain lysosomes. Studies of muscle lysosomes have been limited largely to muscle regression and atrophy.
Muscle has generally low activity of lysosomal enzymes and has a relatively low rate of catabolism. Specific activities of lysosomal enzymes in selected animal tissues are tabulated in Table 16.1. The reader is referred
to the original papers (Zalkin *el al.*, 1962; Tappel *et al.*, 1962; Shibko *et al.*,

TABLE 16.1
Lysosomal enzymes in animal tissues

Tissue homogenate	Specific activities (mμ moles product/min per mg N)					
	Cath- epsin	Acid ribonu- clease	β- glucu- ronidase	Aryl sulfatase	Acid phos- phatase	β- galac- tosidase
Rabbit leg muscle	.1	8.3	...	0	...	0.2
Chicken pectoral muscle	.21	5.0	1.6	0	...	...
Mouse leg muscle	.8	42	4.2	1.1	...	...
Pigeon breast muscle	.2	43	0	0	...	0
Rabbit liver	1.1	33	...	4.9	...	31
Pigeon liver	.9	37	126	9.8	12	5.2
Sheep liver	3.6	113	201	82	25	95
Sheep spleen	.6	170	640	19	10	7.8
Sheep lung macrophages	12	248	497	181	59	2730

1963) for details of methods. It can be readily seen from these data that
skeletal muscle has low specific activity of the lysosomal enzymes compared
to organs such as liver and spleen. Phagocytic cells have the highest specific
activity of lysosomal enzymes. Another biochemical criterion for lysosomes
in muscle is the evidence that a portion of these lysosomal enzymes are
bound and can be released by treatment with Triton X-100 detergent. In
studies of the acid hydrolases of bovine heart muscle, Romero *et al.* (1962)
and Sottocasa *et al.* (1961) found cathepsins, glucuronidase, and galactosi-
dase which were particle bound and releasable with Triton. These studies
provide evidence that lysosomes occur in heart muscle. A problem involved
in measuring lysosomal enzymes in muscle is that the amount of lysosome
activity associated with phagocytic cells within the muscle is unknown.
From Table 16.1 it can be seen that a small amount of phagocytes in
muscle could account for all of the lysosomal enzyme activity found there.
In an electron microscope study of denervation atrophy in skeletal mus-

cle fibers in rat leg, Pellegrino and Franzini (1963) observed lysosomes in the fibers undergoing degeneration. In the first phase of atrophy a degenerative autolytic process occurs in areas of the fibers. It reaches a maximum in two weeks and accounts for a gross weight loss of 50%. Large lysosomes are seen especially at this two-week maximum. Lysosomes are formed during the process of atrophy, and they appear larger and more heavily loaded as the rate of degeneration increases. This increase in lysosomes inside the fibers could account for part of the increases in β-glucuronidase and acid phosphatase which were found. Macrophages containing lysosomes were occasionally present around the atrophying fibers.

LYSOSOMES IN MUSCLE PATHOLOGY

We have studied the involvement of lysosomal enzymes in muscular dystrophies which are characterized by a general degeneration of the muscle by hydrolytic and catabolic processes. Both genetic and nutritional dystrophies have been studied. In genetic muscular dystrophy of mice and chickens the pattern of inheritance of muscular dystrophy has been shown to follow an autosomal recessive gene (Asmundson and Julian, 1956; Stevens, Russell, and Southard, 1957). Three cases of nutritional dystrophy have been studied: the vitamin E deficient rabbit (Zalkin *el al.*, 1962), the vitamin E and methionine deficient chick (Desai *et al.*, 1964), and a similar type of dystrophy, the white muscle disease of lambs on Se deficient diets (Tappel, Sawant, and Shibko, 1963). Results are summarized in Table 16.2. Since the increases in lysosomal enzymes are the highest that have been recorded, it is convenient to express the results as the ratios of specific ac-

TABLE 16.2
Increased lysosomal enzymes in muscle pathologies

	Ratio of specific activity in pathology to specific activity of control						
		Genetically dystrophic chickens (pectoral muscles)		Nutritional dystrophic chickens (pectoral muscles)	Vitamin E deficient MD rabbit (leg muscles)		Bruised chicken muscle (leg)
Enzyme	Genetically dystrophic mouse (leg muscles)	5 weeks	16 months		Avg, exp 1	Max, exp 2	
Acid phosphatase	. . .	5.7	. . .	1.4	. . .	. . .	2.5
Cathepsin	2.4	5.9	3.2	1.6	15	25	9.2
Aryl sulfatase	3.3	0*	. . .	0*	∞	∞	. . .
β-glucuronidase	2.6	3.4	6.2	7.6	. . .	47	2.8
β-galactosidase	. . .	3.0	. . .	2.0	61	52	3.3
Acid ribonuclease	2.3	1.9	7.3	3.8	11	22	1.6

* Aryl sulfatase activity was zero in chicken pectoral muscle.

tivities in the dystrophies to the specific activities in the controls. Generally, all the increases are statistically significant. The reader is referred to the original publications for details.

Table 16.2 shows large increases in the lysosomal enzymes in the muscles of the genetically dystrophic mouse and chick. In the genetically dystrophic animal it is apparent that the relationship between genes and increased lysosomal enzymes is not a simple one (Tappel et al., 1962). The primary effect might be synthesis of an abnormal protein resulting in cell damage or death and subsequent macrophage invasion and increase in lysosomal enzymes. In previous work on genetically dystrophic chickens, muscle tissue was obtained from chickens 14–16 months old, and there was a possibility that the large increases of lysosomal enzymes reported (Tappel et al., 1962) occurred at a late stage of the development of the dystrophy. This problem was reinvestigated using chicks 4–6 weeks old, when the first clinical symptoms are observed. The methods used for assay were similar to those described previously. As shown in Table 16.2 there was a marked increase in the activity of enzymes in the dystrophic chicks. From the results of this study we consider that the earliest hydrolytic degenerative changes observed in the muscle are due to increased lysosomal enzymes in the tissue.

In the vitamin E deficient rabbit the increases in lysosomal enzymes were spectacular, and these increases were correlated with the excretion of tissue breakdown products in the urine and the observed histological changes (Zalkin et al., 1962). The first indication of breakdown of muscle constituents, as measured by an increase in the urinary creatine and amino acids, occurred concurrently with the first observed increase in lysosomal enzymes. All measured biochemical changes continued to increase during the course of the dystrophy and closely correlated with the observed histological scores. Vitamin E deficiency causes lipid peroxidation damage of the cell and its subcellular constituents, including lysosomes. Rupture of the lysosomes and release of lysosomal enzymes would cause further damage to the cell. Cell death and tissue damage would be followed by an invasion of macrophages and other phagocytic cells with increase in lysosomal enzymes, catabolism of the muscle, and muscle dystrophy. Studies have been made of the role of lysosomal enzymes in the nutritional dystrophy induced in chicks maintained on a diet low in vitamin E and sulfur amino acids (Desai et al., 1964). Chicks maintained on a vitamin E and methionine deficient diet had significantly large increases in the lysosomal enzymes, as shown in Table 16.2. This dystrophy is known to be associated with the infiltration of macrophages, leucocytes, and lymphocytes.

The increases in lysosomal enzymes reported here can be correlated with observed changes in rate of tissue turnover reported by other workers.

Dinning, Sime, and Day (1956) showed that vitamin E deficiency in rabbits led to marked increase of incorporation of ^{32}P into nucleic acid in muscle, spleen, kidney, liver, small intestine, and bone marrow. All these tissues, with the exception of muscle tissue, are major sites for the reticuloendothelial system, which is known to be rich in phagocytic cells and lysosomal enzymes. We have been able to demonstrate significant increases in the lysosomal enzymes of liver in addition to the muscle tissue in this dystrophy. The detailed studies of leg muscle of the vitamin E deficient rabbit allow correlation of incorporation or turnover values and activity of lysosomal enzymes. Dinning *et al.* (1955, 1956) found increased incorporation as follows: ^{32}P into nucleic acid, 6-fold; and formate ^{14}C into nucleic acid and RNA, 8-fold and 5-fold, respectively. We found ribonuclease increased 11-fold. Dinning found increased incorporation of formate ^{14}C into protein, 6-fold. We found cathepsin increased 15-fold. Thus, these increased incorporations appear to derive from increases in hydrolysis and synthesis. In the case of mice with hereditary muscular dystrophy, Simon, Gross, and Lesell (1962) showed that increase in protein catabolism was restricted to the muscle and not observed in the liver. Results obtained with lysosomal enzymes showed that no increases were observed in liver although highly significant increases were observed in the muscle. Further, the decreased half-life of leg muscle protein from 30 days for control to 10 days for dystrophic (Simon *et al.*, 1962) correlates with the 2-fold increase in cathepsin (Weinstock, Epstein, and Milhorat, 1958; Tappel *et al.*, 1962). For the nutritional muscular dystrophy in the chick the increases in inorganic phosphates and changes in the permeability of muscle observed by Calvert, Monroe, and Scott (1961) can be related to increases in lysosomal enzymes.

Another example of lysosomal enzyme involvement as a result of tissue damage has been described by Hamdy, May, and Powers (1961), studying bruised chicken muscle. Among the characteristic biochemical changes occurring during the course of the healing of the bruise they reported increases in proteolytic activity. As it has been previously demonstrated that one of the histological changes in the bruised tissue is an invasion of the damaged tissue by lymphocytes, monocytes, and neutrophils (Rickenbacker, 1959), the biochemical changes observed appear to be the result of tissue damage followed by invasion of phagocytic leucocytes with concomitant increase of lysosomal enzymes. In collaboration with Prof. M. Hamdy, we have assayed bruised tissue for lysosomal enzymes (Tappel *et al.*, 1963), and the results in Table 16.2 show significant increases in activity of the enzymes studied. Recently, Hamdy, Brown, and McRorie (1965) have studied more extensively the increases of ribonuclease, deoxyribonuclease, β-glucuronidase, and β-galactosidase, and their relationship to the condition of the bruise.

CATABOLISM

Lysosomes have the enzymic equipment for the full range of intracellular digestion. Autophagic vacuoles in liver and phagosomes of kidney are good examples of lysosomes in the digestive stage. Since intracellular digestion of mitochondria and endoplasmic reticulum is well known, these form interesting models for studies of over-all catabolism by lysosomes (Tappel et al., 1963; Sawant, Desai, and Tappel, 1964). One of the first events in lysosome disorganization of mitochondria is the uncoupling of oxidative phosphorylation. Along with the loss of oxidative phosphorylation, there is swelling of mitochondria and activation of adenosine triphosphatase. An uncoupling factor is present in the lysosomal membrane which is nonenzymic, heat-labile, and nondialyzable.

One of the most important catabolic reactions is the hydrolysis of proteins to peptides and amino acids by the cathepsin group of proteases. Some peptides and amino acids accumulate inside the lysosome but most diffuse out, or are otherwise released. The concentration of amino acids in liver lysosomes was found to be five times that in liver mitochondria (Tappel et al., 1965). The peptides coming from action of lysosomal proteases will be hydrolyzed further by the peptidases located in the cytoplasm of the cell. Metals, probably resulting from the hydrolysis of metalloproteins, accumulate in liver lysosomes so that the concentration of Fe, Cu, Mn, and Zn in lysosomes is higher than in the mitochondria. Lysosome action will disorganize membranes, such as the mitochondrial membrane, apparently by partial hydrolysis of membrane proteins. The phospholipids of the membrane are hydrolyzed to a lesser degree and their accumulation in lysosomes is seen as myelin whorls in electron micrographs. The nucleic acids, RNA and DNA, are hydrolyzed by ribonuclease and deoxyribonucleases to nucleotide products. Acid phosphatase will hydrolyze off the phosphate groups of the nucleotides. The glycosidases of lysosomes hydrolyze polysaccharides and glycosides. β-glucuronidase, β-N-acetyl glucosaminidase, and β-galactosidase appear to be important enzymes in this mucopolysaccharide catabolism. Phosphatases hydrolyze the major phosphate compounds of the cell, especially nucleotide phosphates. Flavin adenine dinucleotide (FAD) is hydrolyzed by a liver lysosomal enzyme recently found by Prof. H. Ragab in our laboratory. This FAD pyrophosphatase, which has been found only in liver lysosomes, hydrolyzes FAD to flavin mononucleotide and adenosine monophosphate. Flavin mononucleotide and AMP are further hydrolyzed by acid phosphatase. Liver lysosomes accumulate flavin compounds so that the concentration of total flavin is about the same as that of mitochondria. Flavins are seen as a predominant feature of fluorescent spectra of liver and kidney lysosomes. This accumulation of oxidized flavin mononucleotide and riboflavin in the lysosome may account for the autofluorescence of lysosomes (Novikoff, 1961) from liver and kidney of rats.

PURIFIED LYSOSOMES

Limitations in fractionation techniques have largely limited biochemical studies to the lysosomes of phagocytic cells (Cohn et al., 1963), kidney lysosomes, and liver lysosomes. Our recent experience with liver and kidney lysosomes will be briefly summarized. Liver lysosomes form a heterogeneous group of particles with a wide range of size and density, such that they fractionate centrifugally with the light mitochondria and the heavy microsomes. For unknown reasons, but ascribed by de Duve to its digestive properties in the cell, the lysosome size and density are variable. This makes the preparation of purified lysosomes according to a rigid fractionation scheme rather difficult. Extending the fractionation methods previously reported (Tappel et al., 1963), Prof. H. Ragab in our laboratory made large numbers of preparations of lysosomes of up to 92% purity. Averages of 30 liver lysosome preparations are given in Table 16.3. For

TABLE 16.3
Enzyme activities of rat liver lysosomes

Enzyme	Specific activity (mμ moles product/min per mg N)		
	Homogenate	Lysosomes	Other fractions
Acid phosphatase	32	673	....
Cathepsin	2.3	177	....
Aryl sulfatase	1.0	149	....
Glucose-6-phosphatase	87	24	(Microsomal) 434
Glutamic dehydrogenase	87	36	(Mitochondrial) 449

each new group of animals or new source of animals, it is advisable that preliminary preparations be done to determine the optimum conditions for preparation of purest lysosomes. As with any fractionation procedure of this type, a continuous evaluation of the different fractions as well as the final purified fraction was necessary. The increase in specific activity of a group of lysosomal enzymes was considered the most suitable index for following the concentration of lysosomal particles in the various fractions. In the final purified fraction, acid phosphatase showed 15–20-fold increase in specific activity over the homogenate; cathepsin, 45–65-fold; and aryl sulfatase, 146–156-fold. These results agree generally with results reported by Beaufay, van Campenhout, and de Duve (1959) and Sawant et al. (1964).

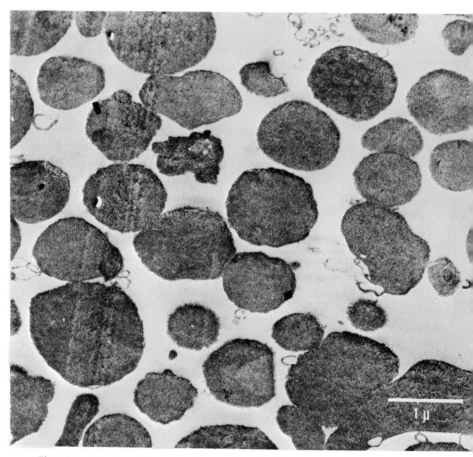

Fig. 16.1. — Electron microscope picture of section through isolated rat kidney lysosomes. × 21,000.

Kidney lysosomes were first isolated from rats by Straus (1956), who showed that their enzymic composition was similar to the lysosomes of liver. In further studies of kidney lysosomes, Shibko and Tappel (1965) described a method for centrifugal fractionation of lysosomes and their detailed enzymic composition. An electron microscope picture of a section through isolated rat kidney lysosomes is shown in Figure 16.1. Because of their large size, kidney lysosomes can be readily separated from contaminating organelles and can be isolated with much less technical difficulty than liver lysosomes. Enzyme analysis of kidney lysosomes is given in Table 16.4. Both glutamic dehydrogenase activity and electron micrographs showed that the lysosome preparations had only 5% mitochondrial contamination. Whereas the glucose-6-phosphatase activity indicates

TABLE 16.4
Enzyme activities of rat kidney lysosomes

Enzyme	Specific activity (mμ moles product/min per mg N)		
	Homogenate	Lysosomes	Other fractions
Protein (% total homogenate)	100	0.4	....
Acid phosphatase			
Glycerol phosphate	53	847	....
Nitrophenol phosphate	52	507	....
Cathepsin (hemoglobin)	11	65	....
Cathepsins A, B, C		4.3, 0.6, 0	....
Aryl sulfatase	1.5	52	....
β-glucuronidase	16	966	....
β-galactosidase	3.8	68	....
Acid ribonuclease	7.9	140	....
Glucose-6-phosphatase	31	23	(Microsomal) 284
Glutamic dehydrogenase	17	11	(Mitochondrial) 180

some microsomal contamination, in electron microscopy microsomal fragments were seldom seen. Increased specific activity of enzymes in the lysosomes showed considerable variation — from 14 times that of homogenate for acid phosphatase, ribonuclease, and β-galactosidase to 30 and 60 times for sulfatase and β-glucuronidase, respectively. Because of the importance of protein catabolism by kidney lysosomes the distribution of cathepsins was analyzed. Cathepsin A was the major activity, with a smaller activity of B and none of C. Kidney lysosomes were found to have membrane stability similar to that described for macrophage lysosomes.

CATHEPSINS

Most of the proteolytic activity in muscle resides in the catheptic enzymes of the lysosomes of phagocytic cells and the lysosomes of muscle fibers. As indicated in Table 16.1, the cathepsin activity of muscle measured by hemoglobin hydrolysis at pH 3.8 is low as compared to organ tissue and phagocytic cells. Another comparison of activities is found in the measurements of cathepsins in rat tissues by Bouma and Gruber (1964). Comparing the activity of cathepsins, with spleen arbitrarily set at 100, they recorded activities of 20, 204, and 30 for liver and the low activities of <5, 8, and 11 for heart and <5, <5, and <5 for skeletal muscle for cathepsins B, C, and D, respectively. Liver and kidney have some of the highest catheptic activity found in animal tissues. As seen in Tables 16.3 and 16.4, liver and kidney lysosomes have a high specific catheptic activity.

Knowledge of cathepsins has been reviewed by Fruton (1960), and the review of proteolytic enzymes by Whitaker (1961) gives good comparisons of the animal tissue enzymes and methods of measuring proteolytic enzymes. Catheptic enzymes have not been subjected to detailed study commensurate with their importance in protein catabolism and the catabolic muscle pathologies. Similar deficiencies in information apply to the role of cathepsins in postmortem tenderization of meats. Although there is ample evidence for some proteolytic activity during the tenderization of meats, definitive studies of proteolytic changes in myofibrillar proteins require use of the more modern techniques of product fractionation and identification. Postmortem proteolytic changes in meats have been reviewed by Whitaker (1959, 1964). The most dramatic proteolytic changes in meats can be found in radiation-sterilized raw meats held at room temperature and above for long periods. The meat becomes mushy, and the hydrolysis is so extensive that free amino acids accumulate to concentrations exceeding the solubility of tyrosine which crystallizes in the meat (Drake *et al.*, 1957).

In recent investigations of cathepsins of bovine muscle, Landmann (1963) demonstrated cathepsin A, and Bodwell and Pearson (1964) demonstrated cathepsins B and C. Whitaker (1964) reports 900-fold fractionation of chicken skeletal muscle cathepsins A and B. In the continuing development of automated analysis of lysosomal enzymes, we reported (Tappel, 1964) the automation of hemoglobin hydrolyzing cathepsins. Auto analyzer programs have been developed which measure amino acid and peptide hydrolysis products either by a combined biuret-phenol reaction or a spectrophotofluorometric measurement of tryptophan. Although these tech-

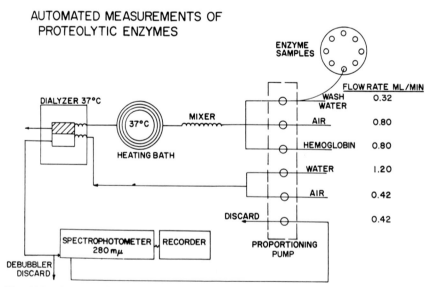

Fig. 16.2. — Program from automated measurements of proteolytic enzymes.

niques achieve the highest sensitivities, we find that an automated method measuring hydrolysis products by their UV absorbancy is one of the most useful methods. This automated program for analysis of enzyme samples is shown in Figure 16.2. These programs are used flexibly in research; for example, kinetic parameters can be varied, and the enzyme reaction rate versus these parameters can be recorded directly. Substrate concentration, pH, inhibitor and activator concentrations can be varied by use of gradient machines. Temperature changes can be programed for the heating bath reactor.

ACKNOWLEDGMENTS

This investigation was supported by Public Health Service Research Grant No. AM-05609 from the National Institute of Arthritis and Metabolic Diseases and project WM-33 of the U.S. Department of Agriculture.

References

Anfinsen, C. B., and F. H. White. 1961. The ribonucleases: occurrence, structure and properties, p. 95. *In* P. D. Boyer, H. Lardy, and K. Myrbäck (eds.), *The Enzymes*, Vol. 5. Academic Press, New York.

Asmundson, V. S., and L. M. Julian. 1956. Inherited muscular abnormality in the domestic fowl. *J. Hered.* 47:248.

Beaufay, H., E. van Campenhout, and C. de Duve. 1959. Tissue fractionation studies. XI. Influence of various hepatotoxic treatments on the state of some bound enzymes in rat liver. *Biochem. J.* 73:617.

Bodwell, C. E., and A. M. Pearson. 1964. The activity of partially purified bovine catheptic enzymes on various natural and synthetic substrates. *J. Food Sci.* 29:602.

Bouma, J. M. W., and M. Gruber. 1964. The distribution of cathepsin B and C in rat tissues. *Biochim. Biophys. Acta* 89:545.

Calvert, C. C., R. A. Monroe, and M. L. Scott. 1961. Studies on phosphorus metabolism in dystrophic chicks. *J. Nutr.* 73:355.

Cohn, Z. A., J. G. Hirsch, and E. Wiener. 1963. The cytoplasmic granules of phagocytic cells and the degradation of bacteria, p. 126. *In* A. V. S. de Reuck and M. P. Cameron (eds.), *Lysosomes*. Little, Brown & Co., Boston.

De Duve, C. 1963. The lysosome concept, p. 1. *In* A. V. S. de Reuck and M. P. Cameron, (eds.), *Lysosomes*. Little, Brown & Co., Boston.

Desai, I. D., C. C. Calvert, M. L. Scott, and A. L. Tappel. 1964. Peroxidation and lysosomes in nutritional muscular dystrophy of chicks. *Proc. Soc. Exp. Biol. Med.* 115:462.

Dingle, J. T. 1963. Action of vitamin A on the stability of lysosomes *in vivo* and *in vitro*, p. 384. *In* A. V. S. de Reuck and M. P. Cameron (eds.), *Lysosomes*. Little, Brown & Co., Boston.

Dinning, J. S., J. T. Sime, and P. L. Day. 1955. The influence of vitamin E deficiency on the metabolism of sodium formate C¹⁴ and glycine-1-C¹⁴ by the rabbit. *J. Biol. Chem.* 217:205.

————. 1956. An increased incorporation of phosphorus-32 into nucleic acids by vitamin E deficient rabbits. *J. Biol. Chem.* 222:215.

Drake, M. P., J. W. Giffee, Jr., R. Ryer III, and H. Harriman. 1957. Proteolytic enzyme activity in irradiation-sterilized meat. *Science 125:23.*

Fishman, W. H. 1961. β-glucuronidase, p. 124. *In* W. H. Fishman, *Chemistry of Drug Metabolism.* Charles C. Thomas, Springfield, Ill.

Fruton, J. S. 1960. Cathepsins, p. 233. *In* P. D. Boyer, H. Lardy, and K. Myrbäck (eds.), *The Enzymes* (2d ed), Vol. 4. Academic Press, New York.

Hamdy, M. K., W. E. Brown, and R. A. McRorie. 1965. Lysosomal enzymes in traumatized tissue. (Abstr.) *Fed. Proc. 24:616.*

Hamdy, M. K., K. N. May, and J. J. Powers. 1961. Some biochemical and physical changes occurring in experimentally inflicted poultry bruises. *Proc. Soc. Exp. Biol. Med. 108:185.*

Landmann, W. A. 1963. Enzymes and their influence on meat tenderness. *Proc. Campbell Soup Co. Meat Tenderness Symposium* (Camden, N.J.), p. 87.

Levvy, G. A., and C. A. Marsh. 1959. Preparation and properties of β-glucuronidase. *Advance. Carbohydrate Chem. 14:381.*

————. 1960. β-glucuronidase, p. 397. *In* P. D. Boyer, H. Lardy, and K. Myrbäck (eds.), *The Enzymes* (2d ed.), Vol. 4, Academic Press, New York.

Novikoff, A. B. 1961. Lysosomes and related particles, p. 423. *In* J. Brachet and A. E. Mirsky (eds.), *The Cell,* Vol. 2. Academic Press, New York.

————. 1963. Lysosomes in the physiology and pathology of cells: contributions of staining methods, p. 36. *In* A. V. S. de Reuck and M. P. Cameron (eds.), *Lysosomes.* Little, Brown & Co., Boston.

Novikoff, A. B., E. Essner, and N. Quintana. 1964. Golgi apparatus and lysosomes. *Fed. Proc. 23:1010.*

Pellegrino, C., and C. Franzini. 1963. An electron microscope study of denervation atrophy in red and white skeletal muscle fibers. *J. Cell Biol. 17:327.*

Rickenbacker, J. E. 1959. Biochemical problems in determining the age of bruised animal tissue. U.S. Farmers Coop. Service, *Service Rep. 42.*

Romero, D., N. Stagni, G. L. Sottacasa, and B. de Bernard. 1962. Studies upon acid hydrolases of beef heart muscle. IV. β-Galactosidase activity associated to beef heart sarcosomes. *Ital. J. Biochem. 11:300.*

Roy, A. B. 1960. The synthesis and hydrolysis of sulfate esters. *Advance. Enzymol.* 22:205.

Sawant, P. L., I. D. Desai, and A. L. Tappel. 1964. Digestive capacity of purified lysosomes. *Biochim. Biophys. Acta 85:93.*

Schmidt, G. 1961. Nonspecific acid phosphomonoesterases, p. 37. *In* P. D. Boyer, H. Lardy, and K. Myrbäck (eds.), *The Enzymes* (2d ed), Vol. 5. Academic Press, New York.

Shibko, S., K. A. Caldwell, P. L. Sawant, and A. L. Tappel. 1963. Distribution of lysosomal enzymes in animal tissues. *J. Cell. Comp. Physiol. 61:85.*

Shibko, S., and A. L. Tappel. 1965. Kidney lysosomes: isolation and properties. *Biochem. J. 95:*731.

Simon, E. J., G. S. Gross, and I. M. Lesell. 1962. Turnover of muscle and liver proteins in mice with hereditary muscular dystrophy. *Arch. Biochem. 96:*41.

Sottocasa, G. L., N. Stagni, R. Cremese, and G. Giudici. 1961. Studies upon acid hydrolases of beef heart muscle. II. The behavior of β-glucuronidase and cathepsins in sarcosome suspensions treated with increasing concentrations of Triton X-100. *G. Biochim. 10:*538.

Stevens, L. C., E. S. Russell, and J. L. Southard. 1957. Evidence on inheritance of muscular dystrophy in an inbred strain of mice using ovarian transplantation. *Proc. Soc. Exp. Biol. 95:*161.

Straus, W. 1956. Concentration of acid phosphatase, ribonuclease, desoxyribonuclease, β-glucuronidase, and cathepsin in "droplets" isolated from the kidney cells of normal rats. *J. Biophys. Biochem. Cytol. 2:*513.

――――. 1963. Comparative observations on lysosomes and phagosomes in kidney and liver of rats after administration of horse-radish peroxidase, p. 151. *In* A. V. S. de Reuck and M. P. Cameron (eds.), *Lysosomes.* Little Brown & Co., Boston.

Tappel, A. L. 1964. Automated multiple analysis of hydrolytic enzymes. Technicon Int. Symp. (New York), Paper 32.

Tappel, A. L., P. L. Sawant, and S. Shibko. 1963. Lysosomes: distribution in animals, hydrolytic capacity and other properties, p. 78. *In* A. V. S. de Reuck and M. P. Cameron (eds.), *Lysosomes.* Little, Brown & Co., Boston.

Tappel, A. L., S. Shibko, M. Stein, and J. P. Susz. 1965. Studies on the composition of lysosomes. *J. Food Sci. 30:*498.

Tappel, A. L., H. Zalkin, K. A. Caldwell, I. D. Desai, and S. Shibko. 1962. Increased lysosomal enzymes in genetic muscular dystrophy. *Arch. Biochem. Biophys. 96:*340.

Weber, R. 1963. Behavior and properties of acid hydrolases in regressing tails of tadpoles during spontaneous and induced metamorphosis *in vitro*, p. 282. *In* A. V. S. de Reuck and M. P. Cameron (eds.), *Lysosomes.* Little, Brown & Co., Boston.

Weinstock, I. M., S. Epstein, and A. T. Milhorat. 1958. Enzyme studies in muscular dystrophy. III. In hereditary muscular dystrophy in mice. *Proc. Soc. Exp. Biol. Med. 99:*272.

Weissman, G. 1964. Labilization and stabilization of lysosomes. *Fed. Proc. 23:*1038.

Whitaker, J. R. 1959. Chemical changes associated with aging of meat with emphasis on the proteins. *Advance. Food Res. 9:*1.

――――. 1961. Proteolytic enzymes. *Wallerstein Lab. Commun. 24:*4.

――――. 1964. Post-mortem proteolytic changes affecting myofibrillar proteins. *Proc. 17th Reciprocal Meat Conf.* (Madison, Wis.), p. 153.

Zalkin, H., A. L. Tappel, K. A. Caldwell, S. Shibko, I. D. Desai, and T. A. Holliday. 1962. Increased lysosomal enzymes in muscular dystrophy of vitamin E-deficient rabbits. *J. Biol. Chem. 237:*2678.

Chapter 17

Summary and Discussion of Part III

PANEL MEMBERS: E. J. BRISKEY, *Chairman*
J. R. BENDALL
R. E. DAVIES
D. DE FREMERY
R. L. FISCHER

Briskey: In considering the behavior of muscle postmortem, one is at the outset faced with immense biological variation in physical and biochemical reactions. These variations range from virtually no change in acidity, stiffening, color, and gross morphology to a sudden drop of approximately 2 *p*H units within a few minutes after death, as has been observed in some porcine muscle. In the latter case there is a low ATP/ADP ratio at death, an accelerated breakdown of ATP, and a concomitant development of rigidity. There is also a drastic change to a pale, white color, and not only does the muscle become soft and exudative, but it and its fibers separate from each other and their attachments, as if the connective tissue structure had been destroyed. The development of a putrid, sour odor also usually accompanies the severe development of this condition and frequently prevails 30–45 min after death. The pale, soft, exudative condition merits emphasis here as one of the best examples of postmortem change affecting muscle as a food; it serves also to illustrate many of the basic points mentioned in the chapters of Part III. The postmortem changes, which have been described by Dr. Cassens, are not limited to porcine muscle but may be manifested in a pale, soft, exudative condition in bovine muscle as well as halibut — the latter referred to as "chalky halibut" (Tomlinson, Geiger, and Dollinger, 1965).

The opposite extreme in postmortem behavior of muscle is one in which there is virtually no postmortem change in acidity — a condition long observed in certain bovine muscle (dark-cutting) and also frequently observed in other species. Severe stiffening may or may not accompany either extreme in postmortem behavior. One can (except in the case of some whale muscle) describe the postmortem behavior of muscle from all animals used for food as customarily falling somewhere between these extremes.

Since these postmortem changes are initiated simultaneously with exsanguination and circulatory failure, one cannot and should not disregard the physiology of the animal in relation to the postmortem behavior of the muscle. This area was ably discussed by Dr. Lawrie in Chapter 9; however, it is worth while to recall the observation of Forrest *et al.* (1966*b*) that certain porcine animals, exposed to a warm environment, show almost total loss of venous oxygen, and upon exsanguination exhibit a violent rate of glycolysis.

One is constantly faced with the fact that rigor mortis is not an all-or-none proposition. It may be occurring at different rates in different fibers, myofibrils, and even in different sarcomeres; and even after this fact is rationalized, there is the additional task of estimating how closely the changes in an excised strip parallel the changes in the intact muscle. Muscles with a relatively rapid to an extremely rapid glycolytic rate show a wide variation in the actual time before the onset of rigor mortis — a fact which may be of great relevance to the severity of the pale, soft, exudative muscle development. The duration of the delay phase not only coincides in time with rigorometer shortening but also appears to be related to the sarcomere shortening of the intact muscle (Sink *et al.*, 1965). The fact that red muscle generally has a longer sarcomere than white muscle (when categorized on the basis of red fiber content) is interesting, especially since red muscle is usually considered to have a shorter delay phase than white muscle. Is the postmortem shortening of red muscle also highly influenced by tension, or are the sarcomeres inherently longer due to the nature or type of contraction which these muscles undergo? Postmortem shortening of the myofibril and the molecular alteration associated with this shortening may have a marked influence on the use of muscle as a food.

When rate of glycolysis is extremely rapid and rigor development occurs within a few minutes postmortem, the postrigor sarcomeres (contraction state) are usually extremely short. Occasionally, however, the postrigor sarcomeres are relatively long: Could these long sarcomeres be due to sufficient resynthesis of ATP to bring about an artificial relaxation more nearly approximating the resting length? Is there, in fact, a resolution of rigor? Is water-binding of an intact muscle proportional to extent of contraction or relaxation? This is undoubtedly a factor in the process described by Dr. Marsh, in which when ATP was added back to a muscle homogenate the imbibition of H_2O and the fiber volume were increased. Could sufficient ATP resynthesis be a feature of the occasional sudden loss in stiffening at rigor onset? While, as Dr. Newbold pointed out, the rate

of disappearance of ATP could be expected to influence the time course
of the postmortem stiffening, what additional factors influence the severity
of stiffening as well as the duration of rigidity? Do muscles which show
severe hardening during rigor onset terminate their postmortem changes
in a more highly contracted state? Under these conditions, is there tension
developed prior to rigor onset and is ATP splitting during violent glycolysis attributable to myofibrillar adenosine triphosphatases, as is thought
to be the case with thaw rigor? Why does the loss of extension and ATP
concentration vary so widely among species?

The postmortem change in muscle temperature is perhaps one of the
largest single alterations occurring postmortem. It is therefore of considerable importance to understand the behavior of muscle as it undergoes
changes in temperature. These changes in temperature are particularly
important since it is during this time that rigor mortis occurs. It is also
pertinent that most exposed carcass muscles, which will be ultimately used
for food, are subjected to conditions which are conducive to a cold
contracture. How far can the postmortem changes progress before the
characteristic cold shortening and thaw rigor effects are lost?

The total explanation for contraction and relaxation in muscle is perhaps one of the most basic questions not completely understood in muscle biochemistry today. Studies of these phenomena in postmortem muscle
are of great importance, not only for the basic information which they
might reveal but also in the consideration of muscle as a food.

Dr. Marsh has suggested a partial relaxing factor inactivation in conditions characterized by accelerated ATP decomposition, such as occur in
thaw rigor and cold shortening. ATP decomposition is invariably rapid
in porcine muscle with a rapid pH decline. Could nervous stimulation
cause the release of Ca^{++} and in turn cause a partial factor inhibition,
activate the myofibrillar adenosine triphosphatases, and be a major contributing factor to the rapid glycolytic rate in certain muscles postmortem?

Bendall and Wismer-Pedersen (1962) postulated that when the pH declines rapidly the sarcoplasmic proteins denature and precipitate on myofibrillar proteins, appear as irregular bands, and lower the extractability
of fibrillar proteins — without any detectable alteration in the fibrillar protein per se. Voyle (1963, personal communication) has indicated that in a
case of an adrenaline-treated animal the bands formed; however, extractability of sarcoplasmic and myofibrillar protein remained high. While unquestionably the irregular band situation seems to be in need of further
study, there is reason to believe that they are associated in some way with a
strong contraction. One point is certain, and that is that sarcoplasmic
proteins are particularly susceptible to postmortem denaturation. Many
times these muscles, frequently within 30 min postmortem, develop pale,

soft characteristics, the fibers lose their integrity, and a putrid odor develops. Is it reasonable to believe that these changes are due only to alterations in sarcoplasmic protein?

How widespread are lysosomes in muscles of animals of different species? Norman (1965) has shown numerous occasions of degeneration and regeneration in porcine muscle; some of the muscles were pale, soft, and exudative, and some were quite normal in visual appearance. Could lysosomes be important in this respect? Are the lysosomes susceptible to nervous stimulation, heat, adrenaline, and other antemortem factors? Can the immediate rupturing of lysosomes, by low pH and high temperature, be a factor influencing the effect of postmortem alterations on the changes in the tissue, even in normal muscle? Can this have a significant effect on the use of muscle as a food?

All of these points serve to illustrate that only the investigation of basic biochemical alterations in postmortem muscle can be expected to shed light on properties influencing its use as a food.

DISCUSSION

De Fremery: What is the postmortem stability of lysosomes in muscle and how is that stability affected by accelerated glycolysis? Do lysosomes exert an effect on the tenderization process?

Tappel: The stability of lysosomes is in general very low. The labile membrane is probably hydrolyzed by catheptic enzymes as the pH falls. This has been observed, particularly by de Duve's laboratory (de Duve, 1963) and represents the only knowledge in the field at present. If one wishes to isolate liver lysosomes, very fresh liver is a prerequisite. Our attempts to isolate lysosomes from sheep liver obtained from a near-by abattoir were unsuccessful because they had apparently already ruptured and leaked their enzymes. During long-term storage of meat, particularly irradiation-sterilized meat, there are tremendous autolytic reactions involving great protein breakdown, and this could only come from the catheptic enzymes. This phenomenon is probably related to the tenderization process.

Davies: What causes the apparent increase in the lysosomal enzymes after death?

Tappel: There is no known increase in enzymes, only an increase in activity related to the release of lysosomal enzymes.

Allen: Why is the unit membrane structure of lysosomes so susceptible to disruption?

Tappel: Most single unit membranes are labile. The red blood cell membrane appears to be as labile as the lysosomal membrane.

Bendall: What natural process is supposed to be responsible for the release of catabolic enzymes from the lysosomes?

Tappel: Digestive action of lysosomal enzymes takes place mainly within lysosomes.

De Fremery: Dr. Cassens, you mentioned that accelerated glycolysis damages mitochondria. Have you made any observations on other subcellular particles, particularly lysosomes?

Cassens: No, we did not observe any lysosomes in the studies which I reported. However, Dr. Tappel's presentation makes it apparent that lysosomes are very labile to the postmortem environment, especially to the drastic pH fall and high temperature associated with the development of PSE muscle. The possible role of lysosomal enzymes in PSE muscle could be very interesting (see Summary, Part III).

Allen: Do you have any other information in addition to the presence of FAD pyrophosphatase in liver, that lysosomal enzyme contents differ between tissues or lysosomes of the same tissue?

Tappel: All lysosomes have a similar complement of hydrolytic enzymes; proteases, nucleases, glycosidases, and acid phosphatases. Beyond this they have enzymes related to specific functions, for example, the lysozyme of leucocyte lysosomes.

Andrews: Has any work been done on the influence of intravenous injection of foreign protein (such as papain) antemortem on the rupture of lysosomal membranes?

Tappel: Proteolytic enzymes and increased proteolytic activity can cause rupture of lysosomal membranes. The effects of papain injection are not known.

Gould: Do you have any information on the stability of lysosomal enzymes in animal or fish muscle during periods of storage — frozen or other — for more than a month or two? And, if they remain stable at frozen storage temperatures, do they function at those temperatures, either to the detriment or to the benefit of flavor and texture?

Tappel: The lysosomal membrane is very labile and ruptures shortly after death (< 1 hr). Important desirable texture and flavor changes may be related to catheptic hydrolysis of proteins and nuclease breakdown of nucleic acids.

Fischer: In genetic dystrophy of mouse and chicken, you suggested the possible synthesis of an abnormal muscle protein. Has anyone reported such a finding?

Tappel: This hypothesis follows the known gene-to-protein relationship.

Fischer: Have cooked muscles from dystrophic and nondystrophic chickens or rabbits ever been compared?

Tappel: Professor Peterson (University of California, Davis) has investigated some of the biochemical changes in dystrophic chicken; and, as I recall, there was actually more flavor in the dystrophic muscle, probably because of released amino acids. I do not think that this is a practical point because the muscles have either gone into a hypertrophic condition, or have atrophied with subsequent fatty infiltration.

Fischer: Are the dystrophic muscles tender?

Tappel: I am not aware of any objective tenderness measurement on these muscles.

Bendall: Would Dr. Tappel please explain whether the proteolytic activity during dystrophic and atrophic changes in muscle is due to a real increase in the intrinsic lysosome content of the muscle, or to the invasion by phagocytes, or both?

Tappel: Increase in proteolytic activity is mainly due to lysosomes of invading phagocytes.

Bendall: Does Dr. Tappel think that the catheptic activity of muscle, as measured by the hemoglobin method at pH 3.8, is sufficient to explain the turnover of the sarcoplasmic and myofibrillar proteins in the living muscle at pH 7.3?

Tappel: Present knowledge is in accord with this hypothesis.

Bendall: The tenderization of muscle during conditioning is generally assumed to be due to the breakdown of connective tissue proteins. Is there any evidence that the cathepsins of muscle are able to break down these proteins, particularly native collagen, at the pH of about 5.5 obtained in postrigor muscle?

Tappel: This undoubtedly occurs because the family of catheptic enzymes have a broad capacity for protein hydrolysis.

Morse: In vitamin E deficient muscle dystrophy, is high catabolic rate confined to area of dystrophy in legs or is it body-wide?

Tappel: Catabolic processes are greatest in legs of vitamin E deficient rabbits, and this is related to low vitamin E in leg muscles and greater lipid peroxidation damage.

Carlin: Would the proportion of cathepsins be higher in lysosomes of muscle cells than in other cells?

Tappel: Comparative measurements do indicate higher cathepsins based on other lysosomal enzymes. More studies of lysosomal enzymes of muscle are urgently needed.

Whitaker: What approaches would you recommend for the evaluation of cathepsin action in postrigor tenderization?

Tappel: I would recommend quantitative studies of hydrolysis of myosin, actin, actomyosin, etc., by specific cathepsins and mixtures of cathepsins, as well as studies of the mechanical strength of muscle fibers after various degrees of catheptic hydrolysis.

Mozersky: Could you provide a reference source for the automatic equipment for enzyme analysis?

Tappel: Tappel, 1964.

Bendall: It has been reported that rabbit psoas major muscle does not show the cold shortening effect. However, we have been able to show the effect very well in the red semitendinosus muscle of the rabbit. It does not shorten quite as much as the bovine sternomandibularis, but it will show the reversibility effect. If the muscle is cooled to 1 C it will shorten. Then if the temperature is raised to 15–18 C the muscle will lengthen again. This cycle may be repeated as long as rigor has not occurred and as long as sufficient ATP remains in the muscle.

Carpenter: In the studies of cold shortening–stretch length, do the tenderness-toughness values react in the same manner in "normal" muscle as in PSE muscle? Also, is "rest length" of the sarcomere related to the amount of cold shortening that will occur?

Cassens: Cold shortening has not been studied in porcine muscle to my knowledge. Different muscles have different sarcomere lengths; this is probably controlled in part by strains induced in the carcass. For example, the psoas major (highly stretched) will shorten markedly if detached prerigor, while the longissimus dorsi shortens very little when detached, indicating a large difference in inherent stretch. Since most cold shortening studies are done on muscle detached from the carcass, the sarcomere length of these isolated pieces would be the most important consideration, and this sarcomere length could be quite different from "rest length" of muscles attached to the carcass. I do not know if the sarcomere length of prerigor detached muscle varies greatly.

Bendall: I agree with Dr. Marsh that the most likely explanation of the cold shortening effect is an upset of the ionic balance at the plasma membrane, followed by partial release of Ca^{++} by the sarcotubules. But there is a very great quantitative difference between cold shortening and thaw contracture. With a thin piece of muscle the latter is complete in 10 sec and develops a great deal of force, whereas the former takes minutes for completion and develops very little force.

Marsh: I agree that there is a quantitative difference between cold shortening and thaw contracture, but not such a great difference as the comment suggests. Thin strips of muscle cold-shorten more slowly than comparably-sized strips thaw-shorten, but the process is still much more rapid than the shortening which accompanies rigor at 37 C. Similarly, although force development is less in cold shortening than in thaw rigor, it is greater than in rigor at 37 C. Both in rate and in force development, the cold shortening effect is intermediate between high temperature rigor and thaw contracture. We must also bear in mind the probable cell damage caused by ice crystal formation in thaw rigor experiments, and this might well accelerate still further the changes already speeded by ionic imbalance.

Bendall: Dr. Marsh is quite right to emphasize the discrepancy between the lowest adenosine triphosphatase activity observed in artificial systems, in the virtual absence of Ca^{++}, and the much lower activity of the intact resting muscle. The adenosine triphosphatase activity of fibrils, for instance, can rarely be reduced below 6% of the rest rate, whereas Professor A. V. Hill assures me that the resting rate in intact muscle is less than .0025% of the maximal rate.

King: What effect does cutting the muscle from the carcass have on cold shortening as compared to leaving that muscle in the carcass?

Marsh: Dr. Locker (Meat Industry Research Institute of New Zealand) found that 20%–30% shortening occurred during chilling in an ox psoas major muscle when one end of it had been cut shortly after death. Compared with its uncut sister muscle, the cut muscle had a shorter mean sarcomere length and was noticeably tougher after cooking. In addition to this direct experiment, many of our investigations have involved paired muscles, one of which was clamped prerigor at rest length while the other shortened by 50%–65% of its initial length.

King: Can one demonstrate cold shortening below 0 C by bathing a muscle in a glycerol-based cooling solution?

Marsh: This has not been attempted.

Sayre: Is the sarcomere length constant along a fiber?

Cassens: Sarcomere length can vary among fibers or along the length of the same fiber. Shortening of muscle attached to the rigid skeleton may perhaps be accomplished by shortening in localized parts of a fiber.

Lawrie: If the normal white rabbit muscle is able to show the phenomenon of thaw rigor, why does it not show cold shortening if the mechanisms are the same?

Marsh: I have no answer to that question.

De Fremery: Is there any explanation for cold shortening and the acceleration of ATP and *p*H changes in beef and chicken muscle as the temperature is lowered towards 0 C?

Newbold: As I mentioned in my paper, the underlying reasons for both thaw shortening and cold shortening could well be the same. According to current theory, muscle contraction depends on the release of Ca^{++}. Hence thaw shortening very likely reflects the release of Ca^{++} during thawing (Bendall, 1960), and cold shortening reflects the release of Ca $^{++}$ upon exposure of muscle to sufficiently low temperatures. These ions are probably released from the tubules of the sarcoplasmic reticulum, but why the Ca pump should not be able to maintain the Ca $^{++}$ concentration below that needed for contraction, in either case, is not clear. The thaw rigor process is characterized not only by the almost immediate commencement of rapid shortening but also by greatly increased adenosine triphosphatase activity. In addition, both the rate of fall of pH and the rate of disappearance of ATP are faster than in "normal" rigor. The more rapid fall in pH reflects increased rates of phosphorolysis of glycogen and phosphorylation of fructose-6-phosphate, catalyzed by phosphorylase and phosphofructokinase, respectively. Each of these reactions plays a major role in the regulation of glycolysis (Helmreich and Cori, 1965). The increase in the rate of phosphorolysis of glycogen is probably brought about by an increase in the amount of phosphorylase present in the a form. Like contraction and the increased adenosine triphosphatase activity this may also be attributable to the release of Ca $^{++}$. These ions are known to stimulate phosphorylase b kinase, the enzyme which catalyzes the conversion of phosphorylase b to phosphorylase a. The increase in the rate of phosphorylation of fructose-6-phosphate may be a consequence of the increase in the rate of phosphorolysis of glycogen. Although the rate of glycolysis and hence of ATP resynthesis is increased, ATP disappears more rapidly than in normal rigor; that is, adenosine triphosphatase activity is stimulated more than is the glycolytic resynthesis of ATP. Since thaw shortening and the increased rates of the ATP and pH changes in thaw rigor may all be consequences of the release of Ca $^{++}$, increased rates of the chemical changes might also be expected in cold-shortened muscle.

Bendall: A 60% shortening can occur during cold shortening, and this results in a curious corrugated appearance on the outside of the muscle. Possibly these are the fibers which have not shortened, and which have therefore been pulled passively into folds. Has Dr. Newbold or Dr. Marsh made any measurements on the tenderness of this cold-shortened muscle?

Newbold: Dr. Bendall's comment about cold shortening occurring in rabbit semitendinosus but not psoas major emphasizes the fact that the cold shortening phenomenon is apparently quite specific. We need to know more about species and muscles which show this phenomenon. Dr. Marsh has observed cold shortening in some ovine muscles, and Dr. Cook (University of Sydney) has noticed the effect in chicken breast muscle.

Experiments in my laboratory have not included a tenderness evaluation of cold-shortened muscle.

Marsh: We have made numerous estimations of muscle tenderness in relation to extent of cold shortening, and I can confirm that the extent of cold shortening has a very pronounced effect on muscle tenderness. Most of our work has been done on bovine muscle, but we have also done some work on ovine muscle. It is not at all unusual for us to get, in terms of shear force measurements, a toughening of 400%–600% with shortening of an appropriate extent. The question of how much shortening relates to how much toughening is something we are presently examining more carefully. It is not a simple linear relation. Some degree of shortening can take place with no toughening at all, but from a certain point onwards toughening doubles as the muscle shortens an additional 3%, 4%, or 5%. I think this rules out any possibility that this toughening might be a result of connective tissue folding, fiber sheath thickening, or anything of that nature.

Bendall: The sternomandibularis has a large amount of collagen. Can cold shortening produce the same change in toughness in the longissimus dorsi?

Marsh: With ovine longissimus dorsi, we produced a sixfold increase in toughness as a result of cold shortening. The effect is, in fact, greater in the longissimus dorsi than in the sternomandibularis because there is less background "connective tissue type" of toughness. Therefore the "actomyosin type" of toughness is apparently very much greater in the cold-shortened longissimus dorsi muscle.

Cassens: Our work has likewise indicated that various methods which cause muscles to shorten result in a substantial increase in toughness, while stretching makes the muscle more tender.

Kauffman: Does physiological age play a role in contraction? If so, can this explain part of the age-tenderness relationship?

Marsh: We have noticed cold shortening of varying magnitudes with bovine animals as young as six months and as old as ten years, but we have not found any major difference due to age. In the older animals, connective tissue perhaps contributes to a greater extent to what we call "background toughness."

Bendall: What is the effect of the age of the animal upon "background toughness"? Conflicting results have appeared in the literature.

Marsh: We find 40%–80% more background toughness in a ten-year-old bull than in a six-month-old steer, but this is negligible in relation to the degree of toughening caused by cold shortening. Consequently we are concerned with "actomyosin toughening," which is much greater and, I might say, much more interesting.

Bendall: What are the histological characteristics of cold-shortened muscles? What proportion of folded fibers are present?

Marsh: Dr. Locker has done our histological work, and he has not detected a great deal of macrofolding (visible to the eye) within these cold-shortened sternomandibularis muscles. On the outside there is occasionally some degree of folding, but on the inside of the muscle the fibers are remarkably uniform, showing very little of this folding and twisting. In other words, we do get the impression that within — and this is where we are taking our samples for toughness estimations — a fairly uniform product exists. Outside samples are slightly suspect from this point of view because the outside will be cold-shortened much more rapidly than the interior and we cannot assume that a uniform rate of cooling has occurred throughout the sample. Since rate of cooling is of the utmost importance in determining the extent of shortening and subsequent toughening, it is imperative that samples be taken from the interior portions of the muscles.

Fischer: What happens to the membranes surrounding muscle fibers when contraction occurs?

Cassens: With ordinary histological preparations of contracted muscle, one can sometimes see the cell membrane assume a "puckered" appearance. That is, it is attached tightly to the cell contents at the level of the Z line but has swollen away from the cell contents between the Z lines. This phenomenon is usually seen in highly contracted muscles and often when a reversal of striation has occurred. In cross section (Herring, Cassens, and Briskey, 1965b) it has been demonstrated that fiber size increases markedly with contraction. This means that fewer, but larger, fibers are present per unit area. However, no measurements of fiber wall thickness were made, nor are possible configurational changes known. Change in the sarcoplasmic reticulum with contraction is another interesting aspect for investigation.

Bendall: One should remember that only a minority of the fibers ever actively shorten during rigor, and that the rest are pulled passively into folds. These folded fibers would present a greater area of cell wall to the chewing surfaces of the teeth, and so indeed would the shortened fibers or portions of fibers, which are necessarily thicker and in which the cell wall must also have been forced into folds. In any case, this picture is an oversimplification, because changes must also have occurred in the conformation of the connective tissue of the endomysial, perimysial, and epimysial layers of the shortened muscle.

De Fremery: Is there any relationship between rigor nodes and muscle tenderness?

Cassens: I do not know of any specific studies in this regard, but rigor nodes are very likely the result of a strong local contraction, and the relationship between contraction and tenderness has been thoroughly discussed at this symposium. It has been well documented that an association exists between muscle contraction and increased toughness.

We have studied the structure of so-called contraction clots (Cassens, Briskey, and Hoekstra, 1963a, 1963b) and found that a tangled mass of filamentous material composed the dense contraction clot area. Z lines had apparently undergone some change and there also appeared to be an absence of membranous sarcoplasmic components in these areas. We are presently studying the reversibility of the contraction clot.

Other references pertaining to this subject are as follows: Cheney, 1939; Ramsbottom and Strandine, 1949; Innerfield et al., 1963.

Davies: I have been very interested in the fact that the toughness of muscle increases tremendously as shortening occurs. This is apparently especially evident with extreme shortening when presumably there are no I bands. Perhaps it is the actual presence of actomyosin that makes the muscle tough. If an isolated frog sartorius is stretched until there is no overlap of the thin and thick filaments, and is kept under these conditions until the ATP has disappeared, Miss K. Minihan and I have found that when tension is released, the muscle never goes into rigor mortis as ordinarily understood. It never becomes stiff. It remains soft and flexible, and if you examine it with a microscope all the fibers appear rather wavy. In this case, there is virtually no actomyosin formed, because as soon as the ends of the actin filaments make contact with the ends of the myosin filaments, there will be only one or two links formed. There will then be a minimum amount of actomyosin because the links can never be broken. In this case you should get meat of extreme tenderness. This should be technically easy to accomplish.

Has anyone stretched muscle to such an extent that there is no overlap of the A–I filaments, and kept it under these conditions until the ATP has disappeared and then tested its tenderness?

Cassens: We have not examined sufficient numbers microscopically to make a firm statement regarding extent of filament overlap (Herring, Cassens, and Briskey, 1965a). However, the bovine psoas major (very tender) has a sarcomere length of about 3.6 microns and must, therefore, be approaching the region of a minimum of filament overlap.

Davies: If no overlap exists between the A and I filaments, it should be very easy to shear the whole sarcomere with your teeth or with an objective measuring device. The I filaments are apparently more tender than the mixed actin-myosin filaments.

Marsh: I do not think that stretching excessively will tenderize to a reciprocal extent that shortening toughens. At some time in stretching one must reach a baseline tenderness which may be due largely to connective tissue and individual filaments. From 20% shortening back to

0% shortening we find no further tenderization. If we go beyond that into lengthening, I would not expect any major change. If bull sterno-mandibularis muscles (supposedly very tough) are not allowed to shorten by more than 10% or 15% postmortem, they will not, in fact, be very tough.

Davies: It appears, therefore, that one should prevent extreme shortening and perhaps stretch the muscle if possible in order to produce tender meat.

Marsh: The important thing is to prevent extreme shortening, rather than to attempt to lengthen. From the theoretical point of view, it is of most interest to find out what happens when we force a lengthening on the muscle, but from the meat industry point of view it is of paramount importance to prevent the excessive shortening.

Davies: What is the biochemical cause of PSE muscle?

Briskey: The animals which are destined to be PSE have low oxygen levels; their muscles contain high levels of lactic acid and glucose and low levels of creatine phosphate (many times completely absent) and ATP. Such animals also appear to have some deficiency in adrenal hormone production. These circumstances are accompanied by an extremely rapid rate of anaerobic glycolysis, and result in the development of rigor mortis at a low pH. Sarcoplasmic and myofibrillar proteins are also rendered insoluble (0.6 M KCl or 1.1 M KI) under these circumstances. These changes are followed by what might be considered to be a general disruption of the tissue (see Summary, Part III; also Briskey, 1964; Briskey *et al.*, 1966).

Davies: Can PSE muscle be prevented by cooling the animal before death or rapid chilling of the carcass postmortem?

Briskey: The environment of the animal immediately prior to exsanguination is extremely important in influencing postmortem changes in the muscle. A change from a warm to a cold environment has a marked influence on postmortem glycolytic rate and greatly reduces the incidence of PSE muscle (Kastenschmidt, Briskey, and Hoekstra, 1964; Kastenschmidt *et al.*, 1965). Rapid postmortem chilling can also effectively prevent the development of PSE muscle (Borchert and Briskey, 1964, 1965).

Thomas: How does pale, soft, exudative muscle differ from normal muscle in its response to freezing and thawing?

Briskey: The characteristics of the muscle appear to have more influence than freezing and thawing technique on the quantity of exudation in the frozen and thawed muscle. The PSE muscle may have considerably greater quantities of exudation. For more detail on this question see Sayre, Kiernat, and Briskey, 1964.

Birmingham: Has the heritability of PSE muscle ever been determined?

Cassens: A heritability study involving 150 animals (E. C. Allen *et al.*, in preparation, University of Wisconsin) revealed very low heritability estimates for pale, soft, exudative muscle. However, more recent observations with Poland China animals indicates that the offspring of certain sires have a much higher incidence of PSE muscle than the offspring of other sires. These observations suggest a definite predisposition to the development of PSE muscle.

Bendall: Would measurement of *p*H immediately after slaughter be as useful as electrical stimulation for predicting the time course of rigor mortis?

Cassens: Although *p*H is definitely a factor, one often finds two muscles with the same *p*H but different electrical stimulation properties (Forrest *et al.*, 1966*a*).

Bendall: We should bear in mind that porcine muscle is not exceptional in showing exudation after rigor at high temperature and low *p*H. Rabbit, bovine, and whale muscle all behave the same way during rigor at 38 C, if there is sufficient glycogen present for the *p*H to fall below 5.8, whale being far worse than all the rest.

Fischer: Can other metal ions, such as Sr^{++}, substitute for Ca^{++} in the contraction and relaxation of muscle?

Marsh: Several workers have investigated the effects of metal ions, particularly Mn^{++} and Zn^{++} on either isolated enzymes of muscle or on model systems, but I am not aware of any metal substitution studies in muscle itself.

Bendall: Does Dr. Marsh think the Ca pump in relaxed muscle is ever truly resting? Is it not more likely that the adenosine triphosphatase of the pump is operating slowly all of the time against the co-diffusion-gradient? Could not this low activity explain the low rate of splitting of ATP in resting muscle?

Marsh: Dr. Bendall's question implies that there is no need to postulate a Ca-insensitive adenosine triphosphatase to provide a very low energy supply for maintenance of the relaxed state, and that the Ca gradient could be maintained by slow operation of the pump adenosine triphosphatase. Provided this latter enzyme can be shown to be still operative in the virtual absence of Ca^{++}, but at only about one-eighth of its Ca-activated rate, the scheme appears reasonable, and certainly simplifies the picture by eliminating one enzyme.

Sutton: Is there any direct evidence for the localization of Ca in the sarcoplasmic reticulum?

Marsh: Hasselbach (1964*a*) has demonstrated a considerable and rapid decrease in the free Ca concentration of a solution to which only relaxing vesicles, ATP, and Mg have been added. Technical difficulties have prevented the direct determination of Ca within the vesicles, but its disappearance from the solution can mean only one thing: it has been taken up by the vesicles, the only particles present.

Allen: Is the removal of Ca^{++} by the sarcoplasmic reticulum a physical entrapping or chemical binding process?

Marsh: Hasselbach (1964*b*) has said, "As to the physico-chemical state of the calcium accumulated, about 0.2 micro-mole/mg. of nitrogen combines with the lipoprotein structures of the vesicular membranes, and the main part is stored inside the vesicles, presumably as a soluble calcium salt."

De Fremery: How is "active Ca^{++}" released to initiate muscle contraction?

Marsh: This question could be answered rather vaguely by reference to depolarization of the fiber membrane, propagation to the interior along the tubules of the sarcoplasmic reticulum, and consequent Ca^{++} release along the excitation path. However Dr. de Fremery is probably more interested in the chemical release mechanism than in the supposed physiological sequence. Unfortunately no answer can be given until more is known of the nature of Ca binding within the vesicles. When the inactivation of Ca is better understood, we may be able to discuss its release.

De Fremery: Do perfusions of ionic Ca (or, conversely, Ca-chelators) accelerate (or delay) the onset of rigor mortis?

Marsh: Howard and Lawrie (1956) have shown that the intravenous injection of Ca borogluconate into steers before slaughter caused a significant acceleration of rigor onset in both longissimus dorsi and psoas major muscles. In a single steer injected preslaughter with the Ca-chelator "Versene," indirect evidence suggested that lowering of the serum Ca^{++} had diminished adenosine triphosphatase activity and delayed rigor onset.

Fischer: Would introduction of chelating agents into muscle prevent thaw rigor and the cold shortening effect?

Marsh: This is a question we are considering at present. If Ca release is in fact involved in these phenomena, we would expect chelating agents to have an appreciable effect. The principal problem will be to ensure that the agents do actually reach the active sites, and at a rate sufficient to forestall any effects of free metal ions.

Davies: Could contraction be reversed by pyrophosphate or by a high ionic strength?

Marsh: I assume that "contraction" here refers to the contraction-like effect observed while centrifuging homogenates. Pyrophosphate did not reverse the effect, but if added with ATP to a system containing the relaxing factor, it did prevent the reswollen particles from shrinking right back to their original low volume. Increased ionic strength had no significant effect up to about 0.25 M, but observations at higher KCl concentrations were prevented by the practical difficulty of increasingly obscure boundaries.

Hamm: Dr. Marsh mentioned the fact that adding ATP to aged muscle caused synaeresis of the system. We have generally found this to be true in bovine longissimus dorsi, but in some cases aged muscle did not contract after the addition of 1.5×10^{-3} M ATP. There was no synaeresis and also probably no adenosine triphosphatase activity. Perhaps there was some activity of the relaxing factor; however, after adding Ca^{++} there was still no adenosine triphosphatase activity and no contractibility. The same was observed with GTP. Do you have any explanation for this unusual finding?

Marsh: I can offer no real explanation for your observations. If you find that there is no adenosine triphosphatase activity even after the addition of Ca, I can only suggest that for some reason or other your actomyosin has been, if not denatured, at least completely ruined as an enzyme by some process or processes unknown. I cannot really imagine any situation where with the addition of Ca, you would not get any adenosine triphosphatase activity.

Hamm: One can prevent thaw rigor and also normal rigor by adding NaCl (1%–2%) to the muscle or to the muscle homogenate before the ATP has reached a critical level. Water-holding capacity can be maintained by this method. After thawing, ATP is broken down in the same way as in absence of NaCl, but apparently there is no association of actin and myosin in terms of specific viscosity and adenosine triphosphatase.

Marsh: The NaCl effect is very interesting. Nevertheless, even if actin and myosin associations are completely suppressed there would still be some adenosine triphosphatase activity in the muscle. There are a number of adenosine triphosphatases present which eventually could carry on significant splitting of ATP. Also the addition of NaCl (1%–2%) might, in addition to keeping the actin and myosin separated, have an effect on the ionic balance as far as release of Ca, etc., is concerned. Consequently NaCl may affect the separation of both fibrillar proteins and also alter the ionic balance within the tissue, influencing its release of Ca.

Quass: Dr. Marsh mentioned that adenosine triphosphatase activity of maximally inhibited myofibrils should be equal to that of myosin alone, since there should be no interaction between myosin and actin in resting muscle. I would agree that the adenosine triphosphatase activity of maximally inhibited myofibrils should be equal to that of resting muscle, since they are somewhat synonymous. Why would you not expect both of them to be somewhat greater than myosin alone, since it is difficult to visualize, even in resting muscle, that there would be no interaction between myosin and actin?

Marsh: I cannot see the difficulty of visualizing a resting state in which there is no interaction between myosin and actin. The sliding filament theory of contraction is based on just this absence of interaction. Furthermore, the large extensibility of prerigor muscle can be explained only in terms of interdigitating filaments able to slide freely past each other when a load is applied.

Fischer: What type of curve do you obtain during centrifugation of an aged muscle homogenate without the addition of ATP? Does the shape of this curve have any relationship to texture in the cooked muscle?

Marsh: Centrifugation of an aged muscle homogenate always results in a smooth curve tending toward linearity with increased centrifuging time — the sort of packing curve we would expect, in fact, with any reasonably compressible material. Although several factors are known to affect the shape of this curve (for instance the degree of homogenization or the rate at which ATP had disappeared from the muscle), no study has been made of the shape in relation to texture.

Quass: You mentioned that recent data show a close coincidence between the completion of the physical changes associated with postmortem stiffening and the virtually complete disappearance of creatine phosphate instead of ATP. Would you comment on this with respect to the theory that there are two "compartments" for the utilization of phosphate in muscle, one for maintenance of body metabolism and one for contraction?

Newbold: The finding of appreciable amounts of ATP in muscle at the time the physical changes are completed supports the view that ATP is present in different "compartments." Presumably, since this "residual" ATP does not "plasticize" the muscle, it is not present in the contraction (rigor) compartment, nor does it diffuse into this compartment. It seems likely that creatine phosphate, though not necessarily located entirely in this compartment, can readily diffuse into it.

Greaser: What part of the H^+ build-up postmortem can be explained by the increase in lactic acid, and what other sources may contribute to the increase in acidity after death?

Newbold: This whole question is a very complex one. There is no doubt that the increase in acidity after death can be accounted for largely in terms of lactate production. A small part of the total acidity change may be attributable to other reactions but it is difficult to assess how much. For example, H^+ are released or taken up in many of the transphosphorylations and dephosphorylations that occur in muscle postmortem. In addition, ammonia is produced when AMP is broken down to IMP. The net contribution by these reactions to the total acidity will depend on the pH.

One observation of interest in relation to this question is that of Bate-Smith and Bendall (1956), who reported that during the breakdown of creatine phosphate and ATP in muscle which, at the time of death, contained normal amounts of these substances but no glycogen, the pH did not change from its initial value.

Fischer: In chicken muscle the pH was reported to decrease faster at 0 C than at slightly higher temperatures. In beef sternomandibularis muscle the pH fell faster at 1 C for the first few hours, although the ultimate pH was not reached until 48–72 hr later, while at 15 C it was reached in 24 hr. Is there an explanation for this?

Newbold: Consideration of the concentrations of phosphorylated intermediates in beef sternomandibularis during postmortem glycolysis leads to the conclusion that the phosphofructokinase step is rate-limiting at all times and temperatures. It follows that the rate of fall of pH reflects very closely the rate of the reaction catalyzed by phosphofructokinase. Why, for the first few hours, the rate of phosphorylation of fructose-6-phosphate is faster at 1 C than at slightly higher temperatures is not clear, but it may be a consequence of an increase in the rate of phosphorolysis of glycogen. When the pH falls below about 6.5, the rate at which fructose-6-phosphate is phosphorylated decreases more at 1 C than at 15 C, for example. I will not speculate on the reason for this, but the ultimate pH is reached sooner at 15 C than at 1 C as a result.

Fischer: Is the IMP that is formed by the deamination of AMP bound to muscle proteins or is it free?

Newbold: The concentration of IMP when the ATP has virtually all disappeared is about 5–6 μmoles/g. Only a small amount of this, if any, could be expected to be bound to the muscle proteins. In a study of the bound nucleotide of the isolated myofibril, Perry (1952) was unable to detect the presence of any bound IMP.

Herring: Is the state of muscular contraction related to the rapidity of development and extent of rigidity occurring with the phenomenon of rigor mortis?

Newbold: We have not made a critical examination of this point, but the results of our studies on the effect of temperature on both the shortening of beef sternomandibularis and the time course of rigor mortis in this muscle suggest (1) that there is no relation between either the duration of the onset phase, or the time taken for rigor to develop fully, and kymograph shortening or unrestrained shortening, and (2) that there may be a relation between the duration of the delay phase and unrestrained shortening. Such a relation has recently been demonstrated by Sink *et al.* (1965), who have shown that in pig longissimus dorsi there is a close correlation between mean sarcomere length after 24 hr at 4 C and the duration of the delay phase at 37 C, greater shortening being associated with shorter duration of the delay phase.

I know of only one study in which shortening and final extensibility have been compared. This was reported by Marsh (1953), who found that in beef longissimus dorsi at temperatures ranging from 7 C to 37 C, kymograph shortening was directly related to final extensibility.

Goll: I am intrigued by your slide showing a kymograph picture of muscle passing into rigor. This picture shows shortening occurring simultaneously with loss in extensibility. I interpret this to indicate that the sliding of filaments is occurring concomitantly with the formation of inextensible linkages between these filaments, at least in terms of today's concepts of contraction and rigor. I find it difficult to reconcile these two events in terms of molecular events and would like to hear your ideas about how this can occur.

Newbold: The net result of changes in a very large number of sarcomeres is recorded on the kymograph. Not all the sarcomeres will either contract or go into rigor at the same time. Contraction of some of the sarcomeres concomitantly with the development of rigor in others would lead to simultaneous shortening and loss of extensibility in the test strip.

Bendall: Is Dr. Newbold sure that the extensibility changes were really complete during rigor at 1 C as early as Figure 14.2 suggests? We have also found a large extension change at this time, but there is a further slow decrease later on, which seems to parallel the loss of ATP.

Newbold: There was always some uncertainty in determining from the kymograph records just when shortening and the change in extension had reached completion. The writing arm of the kymograph provided about an eightfold magnification of the length changes in the test strip, which was alternately loaded and unloaded every 8 min. When the extension changes were judged to have reached completion at 1 C, shortening had stopped and the downward movement of the pen during the 8 min the muscle was under load amounted, in most instances, to about 2 mm. This was equivalent to 5%, or less, of the maximum extension observed at any time during the period of examination. There was no measurable change in extension during the next 8–10 hr. On a few occasions the kymograph records were continued for a further 24–48 hr; during this time the extension, measured as the distance moved by the pen, decreased by less than 0.5 mm, if at all.

De Fremery: Is there any evidence that periodic loading and unloading of muscle strips (as in kymograph experiments) affects the physical or chemical properties of the test strips?

Newbold: I can say little about the effect of loading and unloading on the physical changes in muscle except to note that, at least at 5 C and 15 C, the over-all shortening in loaded and unloaded strips is appreciably less than that in unrestrained strips. We are currently investigating the possibility that loading and unloading influences the chemical changes, and preliminary work has suggested that some of these changes may take place more slowly in loaded and unloaded strips than in unrestrained strips. It is of interest to note, in this connection, that Howard and Bouton in our Brisbane Laboratories have recently shown that both the pH and the ATP level fall more slowly in restrained or stretched strips than in strips that are allowed to shorten during the onset of rigor.

Henrickson: Thaw rigor occurs as a result of freezing prior to rigor. Is rigor mortis restricted by heat? Is there any disadvantage to heating to a temperature of 155 F before meat has proceeded through rigor?

Newbold: During slow heating the rigor changes would take place more rapidly as the temperature of the meat rose, and by the time cooking was complete the muscle would be in rigor. Presumably, however, if the temperature were raised quickly enough the changes associated with the onset of rigor would be prevented. Meat cooked soon after slaughter has been reported to be more tender than that cooked in the same way immediately on completion of the rigor changes. The tenderness of ox sternomandibularis cooked rapidly at various times after slaughter has been examined by Marsh (1963). He found that (1) this muscle was remarkably tender if cooked within 1–2 hr postmortem, (2) there was a rapid increase in toughness as the interval between slaughter and cooking increased, and (3) when the pH at the start of cooking was 6.4 or lower the cooked muscle was four times as tough as when the pH at the start of cooking was 7.1 or higher.

De Fremery: Should relaxation be considered the "normal" state of muscle, maintained in a condition of high potential energy by the sarcoplasmic reticulum and "extra adenosine triphosphatase," until its status quo is somehow upset by Ca release?

Marsh: We must watch our terminology here, clearly distinguishing between "relaxation" and "the relaxed state." The former is a definite process brought about by the Ca pump, while the latter is a static condition accompanied only by the maintenance of a concentration gradient. It is the relaxed state, rather than relaxation, which should be considered the "normal" state of muscle.

Fischer: How does thaw rigor affect the flavor of cooked meat?

Marsh: We have not set up a specific experiment to detect an effect of thaw rigor on flavor. At present I can see no strong reason to expect a direct influence.

Price: What is the possibility that the observed tenderization of bovine, avian, and porcine muscle with postmortem aging (storage) is a result of continuation of physiological and biochemical changes associated with the rigor mortis process rather than direct proteolytic enzyme action? Also, what role do microorganisms play in tenderization?

Marsh: Physiological and biochemical changes associated with the rigor process cease with the full onset of rigor, and I cannot see that these could be concerned directly with postrigor tenderization. On the other hand it is becoming increasingly obvious that direct proteolytic enzyme action cannot explain tenderization adequately, and a wider view must be taken of the structure resulting from rigor onset, particularly the configuration of actomyosin. Thus, although the changes leading to rigor onset are unlikely to be involved postrigor, the structural results of these changes may well be of great importance in tenderization.

Although many microorganisms can undoubtedly tenderize meat — often with undesirable side-effects — it certainly does not follow that tenderization is due to the presence of microorganisms.

De Fremery: Should rigor mortis be characterized as an inactivation of the relaxing factor, or as the lack of an ATP-synthesizing apparatus?

Marsh: I agree entirely with Dr. Bendall's (1960) published views of the rigor process: it is the inability of ATP-synthesizing mechanisms to maintain the ATP level which leads to rigor mortis. Only when we turn to thaw rigor or abnormally rapid rigor do we need to consider factor inactivation.

Solberg: I would like to have Dr. Marsh's comments and hypotheses with respect to the reactions which take place in the postrigor state (rigor resolution), since it appears that there is a very rapid return to a state of tenderness which does not seem to permit any return of extensibility to the muscle.

Marsh: I can advance no hypotheses and make few comments here. Extensibility measurements give no indication of a change following rigor onset, but on the other hand penetrometer measurements do, the peak resistance-to-penetration values being followed quite soon by a return to low readings. Within the meat industry, too, there is a recognition of rigor "passing off," and it seems very unlikely that this could be due to massive bacterial proliferation. I am prepared to believe, therefore, that there is a resolution of rigor, that it is not a reversal of earlier changes, and that it is not due to microorganisms.

References

Bate-Smith, E. C., and J. R. Bendall. 1956. Changes in muscle after death. *Brit. Med. Bull.* 12:230.

Bendall, J. R. 1960. Post mortem changes in muscle, p. 227. *In* G. H. Bourne (ed.), *The Structure and Function of Muscle*, Vol. 3. Academic Press, New York.

Bendall, J. R., and J. Wismer-Pedersen. 1962. Some properties of the fibrillar proteins of normal and watery pork muscle. *J. Food Sci.* 27:144.

Borchert, L. L., and E. J. Briskey. 1964. Prevention of pale, soft, exudative porcine muscle through partial freezing with liquid nitrogen post-mortem. *J. Food Sci.* 29:203.

———. 1965. Protein solubility and associated properties of porcine muscle as influenced by partial freezing with liquid nitrogen. *J. Food Sci.* 30:38.

Briskey, E. J. 1964. Etiological status and associated studies of pale, soft, exudative porcine musculature. *Advance. Food Res.* 13:89.

Briskey, E. J., L. L. Kastenschmidt, J. C. Forrest, G. R. Beecher, M. D. Judge, R. G. Cassens, and W. G. Hoekstra. 1966. Biochemical aspects of post-mortem changes in porcine muscle. *J. Agr. Food Chem.* (In press.)

Cassens, R. G., E. J. Briskey, and W. G. Hoekstra. 1963a. Electron microscopic observations of a dense irregularly banded material occurring in some porcine muscle fibers. *Nature* 198:1004.

———. 1963b. Similarity in the contracture bands occurring in thaw rigor of muscle and other violent treatments. *Biodynamica* 9:182.

Cheney, R. H. 1939. Microphysical changes induced in striated muscle after caffeine immersion. *Anat. Rec.* 73:129.

De Duve, C. 1963. The lysosome concept, p. 1. *In* A. V. S. de Reuck and M. P. Cameron (eds.), *Lysosomes.* Little, Brown & Co., Boston.

Forrest, J. C., M. D. Judge, J. D. Sink, W. G. Hoekstra, and E. J. Briskey. 1966. [Forrest *et al.*, 1966a]. Prediction of time course of rigor mortis through response of muscle tissue to electrical stimulation. *J. Food Sci.* (In press.)

Forrest, J. C., L. L. Kastenschmidt, M. D. Judge, W. G. Hoekstra, and E. J. Briskey. 1966 [Forrest *et al.*, 1966b] Oxygen debt in porcine animals. Submitted to *J. Appl. Physiol.*

Hasselbach, W. 1964a. Relaxing factor and the relaxation of muscle. *Progr. Biophys. Mol. Biol.* 14:167.

———. 1964b. Relaxation and the sarcotubular calcium pump. Physiology Symposium on the Relaxing Factor of Muscle. *Fed. Proc.* 23:909.

Helmreich, E., and C. F. Cori. 1965. Regulation of glycolysis in muscle. *Advance. Enzyme Regulation* 3:91.

Herring, H. K., R. G. Cassens, and E. J. Briskey. 1965a. Sarcomere length of free and restrained bovine muscles at low temperatures as related to tenderness. *J. Sci. Food Agr.* 16:379.

———. 1965b. Further studies on bovine tenderness as influenced by carcass position, sarcomere length and fiber diameter. *J. Food Sci.* 30:1049.

Howard, A., and R. A. Lawrie. 1956. Studies on beef quality. II. Physiological and biological effects of various pre-slaughter treatments. CSIRO (Australia) Div. Food Preserv. Transp. Tech., Paper 2, p. 18.

Innerfield, I., L. Cannavella, A. Mezzatesta, and R. Hochberg. 1963. Modification of kinin activity in injured tissue by oral kinases and proteases. *Proc. Soc. Exp. Biol. Med. 112*:189.

Kastenschmidt, L. L., G. R. Beecher, J. C. Forrest, W. G. Hoekstra, and E. J. Briskey. 1965. Porcine muscle properties. A. Alteration of glycolysis by artificially induced changes in ambient temperature. *J. Food Sci. 39*:565.

Kastenschmidt, L. L., E. J. Briskey, and W. G. Hoekstra. 1964. Prevention of pale, soft, exudative porcine muscle through regulation of ante-mortem environment. *J. Food Sci. 29*:210.

Marsh, B. B. 1953. Shortening and extensibility in rigor mortis. *Biochim. Biophys. Acta 12*:478.

———. 1964. Meat quality and rigor mortis. *In* D. E. Tribe (ed.), *Carcass Composition and Appraisal of Meat Animals.* CSIRO, Australia.

Norman, W. P. 1965. Pathological conditions in muscle. *Proc. 18th Reciprocal Meat Conf.* (Manhattan, Kansas). (In press.)

Perry, S. V. 1952. The bound nucleotide of the isolated myofibril. *Biochem J. 51*:495.

Ramsbottom, J. M., and E. J. Strandine. 1949. Initial physical and chemical changes in beef as related to tenderness. *J. Anim. Sci. 8*:398.

Sayre, R. N., B. Kiernat, and E. J. Briskey. 1964. Post-mortem physiological condition and ultimate classification as associated with fluid retention and related properties of porcine muscle. *J. Food Sci. 29*:175.

Sink, J. D., R. G. Cassens, W. G. Hoekstra, and E. J. Briskey. 1965. Rigor mortis pattern of skeletal muscle and sarcomere length of the myofibril. *Biochim. Biophys. Acta 102*:309.

Tappel, A. L. 1964. Automated multiple analysis of hydrolytic enzymes. Technicon Int. Symp. (New York), Paper 32.

Tomlinson, N., S. E. Geiger, and E. Dollinger. 1965. Chalkiness in halibut in relation to muscle pH and protein denaturation. *J. Fish. Res. Bd. Can. 22*:653.

PART IV

Molecular Biology of Myofibrillar Proteins

Chapter 18

Molecular Alterations in Myofibrillar Proteins

W. F. H. M. MOMMAERTS

As in many other subjects in physiological chemistry, the study of the composition of muscle began in a purely descriptive manner. The materials discovered in early explorations were not in the beginning properly understood with respect to their role in the tissue of their origin; many, in fact, arose secondarily in the course of the preparation. Thus, among the "extractives" of muscle, creatine and inosinic acid were discovered. It took many more years to learn that creatine, which is a rather inert substance, occurs in muscle in a labile phosphorylated form. This phosphorylated creatine is of great functional importance as a small but vital reservoir of transferable phosphate groups which aid in maintaining the quantity of ATP. Inosinic acid is present in only small amounts in muscle, although it is also the product of the autolytic decomposition of ATP. Still other extractives are even at this moment known only on a descriptive level; for example, we are not definitively informed about the functional role of carnosine and anserine, or of carnitine. In other words, functional biochemistry, after a century or more, is still not completed. A substance which plays an active part in the metabolism may undergo postmortem changes which represent an exaggerated expression of their normal physiological reactions, or may take part in postmortem reactions which go altogether beyond the normal range of vital processes.

Similar observations apply to the study of the protein constituents of muscle. Here, too, the original emphasis was upon cataloguing the inventory, although as early as in the work of Kühne (1864) much attention was given to some coagulative changes occurring after death. Out of these efforts came, in the course of a relatively straightforward historical development, our present knowledge of the muscle proteins. A few points in this development will be mentioned later. In recent years, we have arrived at a general understanding of the architecture of the muscle cell, which is summarized in Table 18.1 This table refers to structures and constituents playing a role in the contractile actvity of the muscle and the metabolism which supports this; it omits those structures, including the nuclei and the cytoplasmic reticulum with its ribosomes, which function in the maintenance and growth of the cells, but which we know less about in muscle than in other tissues where biosynthetic activities are more prominent. The classification in Table 18.1 is made from three

TABLE 18.1
Architecture of muscle cell

Structural component	Composition	Function
Sarcoplasm	Soluble enzymes	Glycolysis, anaerobic contraction
Mitochondria	Structure-bound enzymes for oxidation and phosphorylation	Aerobic steady-state activity, or oxidative restitution after oxygen debt
Fibrils	Actin and myosin	Contraction itself
Sarcotubular reticulum	Membranous tubular structures with concentrating activity toward Ca^{++}	Excitation-contraction coupling; on-off control of contractile activity
Cell membranes	Lipoprotein layers with variable ion permeability	Conduction of the excitatory state

Source: W. F. H. M. Mommaerts, "The muscle cell and its functional architecture," *Amer. J. Med. 35(1963)*:606.

different points of view: morphological, chemical, and functional. It will not be fully elaborated here; instead, selected problems will be discussed briefly, to show the multitude of phenomena currently under investigation in different laboratories.

The protein fraction representing the glycolytic enzymes was known as "myogen" during the earlier period of establishing the protein inventory. This fraction seems to consist wholly of enzymes: there is no indifferent protein. All, or most, of the protein is functionally active in one metabolic reaction or another. Still, since this material can be obtained as one preparative entity in aqueous solution, and its collective total solubility at low ionic strength exceeds the concentration in which this protein is found in muscle (Weber, 1934), it was held until recently that the enzymes of the myogen fraction occur in the sarcoplasm in a dissolved, and not otherwise organized, condition. The recognition of the general occurrence of membranous reticula in cytoplasm gives rise to the question whether this structural feature might not impose some differentiation upon the fluid sarcoplasm, and recent experiments by Amberson *et al.* (1964), on the distribution of enzymes in the press-juice obtained by ultracentrifugation of whole muscles, suggest that this is the case. Such a spatial organization of soluble enzymes might introduce new possibilities for the interpretation of the regulation of metabolism, in addition to the biochemical feedback control mechanisms that are currently receiving attention.

In the other cell fractions of Table 18.1, the presence of a morphological organization is much more evident. I shall pass briefly over the category of the mitochondria, which are the subject of such intensive research, not particular to muscle, but fully applicable to it. One special feature, though, deserves mention: the quantitative predominance of mitochondria among the constituents of muscle varies widely. To mention just two extremes among vertebrate muscles, there is the distinction between "white" and "red" muscle, although the correlation between the crucial physiological features in question, and the color of the muscle determined by the presence or absence of myoglobin, is not rigid. In typical red muscles — the heart being one of them — which in the body are at least moderately active over extended spans of time, the mitochondria are numerous, so that the oxidative phosphorylation can provide the conditions for a steady state of activity supported by metabolic energy provision. In typical white muscles, the mitochondria may be almost absent; thus, such muscles perform their most intense activity not in a steady state, but only to the degree that they can engage in an oxygen debt considerably extended by the use of anaerobic glycolytic metabolism. The importance of glycolysis for the conduct of muscular activity is shown dramatically by the symptoms of a muscle disease (Pearson, Rimer, and Mommaerts, 1961) in which phosphorylase, the starting enzyme for glycolytic metabolism, is absent. Since glycolysis cannot be initiated, intense muscular effort cannot be sustained.

Not much is known in any detail about the cell membranes. The other major extrafibrillar fraction, the sarcotubular system, is entirely specific for muscle, where it performs the inward conduction of the excitatory state from the cell membrane, and the cyclic activation and deactivation of the contractile fibrils. The morphological organization of this system is complex (Andersson-Cedergren, 1959; Franzini-Armstrong, 1964), and much remains to be learned about its mode of action. But one feature is prominent and is surely the key to its major function: isolated preparations of vesicular material derived from it can take up Ca^{++} when splitting ATP, and this property appears to explain (Ebashi, 1961) the relaxation caused by this preparation in contractile actomyosin systems under conditions where these require trace amounts of Ca. When oxalate is present at the same time, these vesicles can transport massive amounts of Ca, depositing it inside as Ca-oxalate, while concomitantly splitting an extra amount of ATP (Hasselbach and Makinose, 1961). Thus, apart from their importance to the physiological problem of excitation-contraction coupling, these isolated vesicles are of extraordinary interest for the study of active transport, because they may be the simplest system known for the study of such a phenomenon. Our current work on the fractionation of this material (Seraydarian and Mommaerts, 1965) aims at a decision as to which parts of the sarcotubular system are active in this regard.

Both in this system and in the contractile myofibrils, we meet a problem basic to physiology and defining, indeed, the field of molecular physiology: driven by a chemical reaction, the splitting of ATP in the final balance, work is performed which, by definition, is directed or vectorial in nature: the directional movement of a substance in the one case, the directional generation of mechanical force in the other. This causative link of a scalar process, as a chemical reaction would ordinarily be, to a process of higher tensorial rank poses problems of great fundamental importance, the explanation of which falls under the general heading of the anisotropy of the transforming structures (Mommaerts, 1965). The actual way in which this is accomplished in detail is, of course, the very heart of the biophysical problem, and neither for membrane transport nor for fibrillar contraction do we have any knowledge beyond the hypotheses of the moment. It would be in keeping with current lines of interest to invoke conformational changes in protein molecules in these mechanisms.

Certainly, molecular transformations, in a descriptive sense, are a striking property of the myofibrillar proteins which make up the contractile machinery. Some changes display themselves as postmortem alterations: while myosin is extractible from freshly minced muscle, with 0.5 KCl, for example, it turns insoluble when the mince is left to stand, and also in rigor mortis of intact muscle. During the continued extraction of fresh muscle, an interesting sequence occurs wherein myosin is extracted first, and actin later to form actomyosin. The experimental recognition of this sequence was basic to Szent-Györgyi's discovery of the contractility of actomyosin, the most important event in this field (see Banga et al., 1942).

While the developments following this discovery have been described adequately (Szent-Györgyi, 1951; Mommaerts, 1950), it may be helpful to give a brief listing of those molecular transformations or interactions that occur in or between the muscle proteins. Myosin is an adenosine triphosphatase, the activity of which is strongly influenced by the electrolyte medium. This activity and its ion dependence are strongly modified by its combination with actin. Actin can occur in a monomeric form and as a polymer which is a longitudinal array of doublets; actin and myosin in solution combine to form a complex in which about one myosin molecule combines with one doublet; this complex, when dissolved, dissociates into actin and myosin in the presence of ATP, as long as a sufficient quantity of ATP is present to saturate the one active site on the myosin molecule. When the actomyosin complex is precipitated it shows the contractile synaeresis phenomena with ATP, independent of how the actomyosin was formed. This suggests that it does not matter whether actin and myosin were combined and subsequently precipitated, or whether the myosin was precipitated as needle-shaped tactoids and then mixed with actin: in either case they show the same phenomena with the addition of ATP. Likewise, actomyosin isolated directly from myofibrils will show the same phenomena with the addition of ATP; however, actin and myosin independently show no contraction. (Some key references to the phenomena referred to are reviews by Kielley, 1964; Mommaerts, Abbott, and Brady, 1961; and Szent-Györgyi, 1960; and the following selected papers: Nanninga and Mommaerts, 1960; H. Huxley, 1963; Hanson and Lowy, 1963; Gergely, in preparation.)

Each of these interactions, as well as other related ones not singled out, poses interesting problems concerning chemical and physical mechanisms. One of these will be selected for closer scrutiny, namely, the molecular transformations of actin. This polymerization process is ordinarily initiated by salt (Straub, 1943) which, due to an elimination of electrostatic repulsions between the negatively charged G-actin molecules, allows collisions and so permits the interaction leading to polymerization to occur; this, at least, was the original simple view (Mommaerts, 1952), which may need elaboration. Nucleotides are involved in this process, because G-actin loses its activity when the associated ATP is removed (Straub and Feuer, 1950; Laki, Brown, and Clark, 1950). The authors just cited also noticed enzymatic changes in the nucleotides in polymerizing actin, although in impure actin one could not really decide whether these were due to salt activation of contaminating enzymes or to the polymerization process itself. After the purification of actin, however, it could be shown (Mommaerts, 1952) that a stoichiometric breakdown of ATP accompanies the polymerization process, in that for each molecule of actin monomer, one molecule of loosely bound ATP is converted to ADP and inorganic phosphate, and that the ADP becomes very tightly bound to the polymer although it is not entirely impossible to remove it. This led to the stoichiometrical equation for the polymerization reaction (Mommaerts, 1952):

$$n \text{ actin} + n \text{ ATP} \to (\text{actin})_n \text{-ADP}_n + n \text{ P}$$

which equation was of special interest because a single occurrence of a
$G \leftrightharpoons F$ cycle in muscle could account for the order of magnitude of chemical change that may be deduced to occur from the energetic magnitude
of a muscle twitch (Mommaerts, 1951). After more than a decade of
validity, however, this stoichiometric equation must now be regarded as
a limiting case. Several investigators, myself included, have observed
instances in which less than one molecule of nucleotide is dephosphorylated; and especially clear is the case in which no ATP is present at all,
but the reaction starts with the more labile G-actin-ADP; when this poly-
merizes (Grubhofer and Weber, 1961), the result is still F-actin-ADP, but
no nucleotide is dephosphorylated at all. Still more striking is the recent
success of Oosawa (1964), who, in the presence of sucrose as a stabilizer,
could obtain nucleotide-free actin, and this polymerized without any
nucleotide participation altogether. It is not certain whether this polymer
has the same structure as ADP-containing F-actin; it remains a significant
possibility that nucleotide is of importance for the lateral dimerization
involved in the double-stranded structure of the normal polymer, but at
any rate it is clear that nucleotides are not required for the major aspect
of the G-F transformation. On the other hand, nucleotide, optimally
ATP, protects G-actin from inactivation, and special precautions are
needed to keep the molecule in the native state without nucleotide.
Finally, it must be stated that in G-actin the nucleotide, while bound, can
be detached or exchanged for other nucleotides, while in F-actin this
exchange is very much slower.

How can these various, seemingly paradoxical facts be interpreted? The
following picture is tentative, but may serve as a guide in the understanding of current work.

Globular actin has an affinity for ATP, but is not an adenosine triphosphatase. During the polymerization process, when a monomer enters into
reaction with another or adds to an already existing polymer, it may undergo a conformational change. (Whether salt induces polymerization
merely by electrostatic screening, or whether its primary effect is upon
transconformation as well, is now an important question.) While in this
transient state, the actin molecule temporarily acquires adenosine triphosphatase activity and splits ATP if it comes in contact. The maximal extent
of the reaction (which may not occur at all if ADP is the associated nucleotide) is one mole per molecule. This limitation in its capacity is
probably due to the fact that it cannot rapidly acquire a new ATP molecule. Furthermore it may be subjected to an extreme degree of substrate inhibition by ADP, or it may form a polymer too rapidly to exert a different
response. On the other hand, when the transitional state is maintained by
disturbing the polymer, a progressing adenosine triphosphatase activity

results; this would be the explanation of the continued ATP splitting by actin in an ultrasonic field (Asakura, Taniguchi, and Oosawa, 1963).

This assumption of a conformational change, while fashionable, is not entirely arbitrary but does require some further discussion from a number of angles, factual as well as conceptional. Concepts like the theory of induced fit (Koshland, 1958) and the theory of allosteric transition (Monod, Changeux, and Jacob, 1963; Monod, Wyman, and Changeux, 1965) imply, respectively, that the conformation around the active site may mold itself to accommodate the substrate, or that as a part of metabolic control mechanism a regulatory substance when combining with an enzyme at one site may so modify the conformation as to affect the reactivity of the active site. The transformations proposed for actin resemble these postulated phenomena without exactly falling in either category.

On the factual side of this subject we are not as well off: current work with circular dichroism in the far ultraviolet (Mommaerts, in preparation) is somewhat complicated by the occurrence of higher-order phenomena in the polymer due to ordered gel-formations, but when these are eliminated it seems that no difference between G- and F-actin can be measured. But we must distinguish at least three kinds of conformational features: (1) specific steric arrangements around the active or interacting sites, determining the reactivity of these sites, but not involving the rearrangement of a helical structure, or at least not enough of it to express itself in circular dichroism; (2) a distinct change in the fraction of the protein molecule that is organized as a helix or other structure characterized by optically active transitions, and therefore revealed by the circular-dichroic spectrum; (3) gross changes in monomer-oligomer interaction, including, as the limit, massive polymerization phenomena as in actin, and binary associations as in actomyosin. In the modifications under consideration, as in allosteric transitions, each of these phenomena could occur. The results of the circular dichroism measurements, so far, only indicate that the effects in category 2 do not determine the difference between the beginning and end states of the G-F transition of actin, while they might still occur transiently; the effects in category 1 may well occur, and those in category 3 evidently do occur to an extreme degree. The phenomena in category 1 require other methods of investigation, and interesting indirect approaches are discussed by Szent-Györgyi, in Chapter 19, below.

The problem of the molecular events in muscle contraction are not, of course, limited to actin, but extend also to myosin and to myosin-actin interrelations. One most interesting aspect of this may fall within the limits of allosteric transitions in a broader sense. Actomyosin in certain states, especially in the form of isolated myofibrils, needs traces of Ca to be contractile and to display its maximal adenosine triphosphatase activity (A. Weber, Herz, and Reiss, 1964). This is physiologically important in that it may be the basis of the on-off control of contractile activity exerted by the excitation-contraction coupling mechanism. We have no detailed information about the molecular mechanism of this Ca effect, and no knowledge whether it involves changes in helical conformation or stability. Its counterpart does not occur in pure myosin; but when half of the freely reacting sulfhydryl groups of myosin are covered, its adenosine triphosphatase becomes strongly stimulated in the presence of Ca, inhibited in its absence (Kielley and Bradley, 1956). This, qualitatively, is much like the case of myofibrils, and the suggestion may be made that the selective substitution of sulfhydryl groups causes a change similar to that encountered in the combination with actin which also involves sulfhydryl groups of myosin. The question again arises of what the molecular nature of this change may be. So far, measurements of the circular dichroism of myosin (Mommaerts, in preparation) have shown no effects of partial or complete reaction of the sulfhydryl groups with p-mercuric benzoate, and one would thus eliminate the changes in helical structure under category 2. However, this has not yet been completely investigated with due reference to the presence or absence of Ca and ATP which may be required for the expression of an allosteric change, and this conclusion is therefore preliminary.

These first explorations are still far removed from the contractile mechanism itself, but clearly point the direction of future work. Evidently, as implied in the pioneer theory of A. F. Huxley (1957), a conformational transition of one of the active sites may be the ultimate basis of the specific directional movement of the myofibrillar constituents that is the contractile event. Thus, from a broad comparative and perhaps evolutionary viewpoint, we see that the steric changes which were first invoked by Koshland (1958) and by Monod et al. (1963, 1965) to explain the modification of catalytic action, and which have no other function than this in common enzymes, now assume additional significance in the case of contractile proteins (and presumably also in membrane transport constituents) as the basis for the chemo-mechanical transduction mechanism which converts the ordinarily scalar chemical reaction into a vectorial work process.

References

Amberson, W. R., A. C. Bauer, D. E. Philpot, and F. Roisen. 1964. Proteins and enzyme activities of press juices, obtained by ultracentrifugation of white, red, and heart muscles of the rabbit. *J. Cell. Comp. Physiol.* 63:7.

Andersson-Cedergren, E. 1959. Ultrastructure of motor end plate and sarcoplasmic components of mouse skeletal muscle fiber. *J. Ultrastruc. Res., Suppl. 1.*

Asakura, S., M. Taniguchi, and F. Oosawa. 1963. Mechano-chemical behavior of F actin. *J. Mol. Biol.* 7:55.

Banga, I., T. Erdös, M. Gerendas, W. F. H. M. Mommaerts, F. B. Straub, and A. Szent-Györgyi. 1942. Myosin and muscular contraction. *Stud. Inst. Med. Chem.* (Basel and New York).

Ebashi, S. 1961. Calcium binding activity of vesicular relaxing factor. *J. Biochem.* 50:236.

Franzini-Armstrong, C. 1964. Fine structure of sarcoplasmic reticulum and transverse tubular system in muscle fibers. *Fed. Proc.* 23:887.

Grubhofer, N., and H. H. Weber. 1961. On actin-nucleotide and the function and binding of nucleotide phosphate in G and F actin [in German]. *Z. Naturforsch (B) 16B*:435.

Hanson, J., and J. Lowy. 1963. The structure of F-actin and of actin filaments isolated from muscle. *J. Mol. Biol.* 6:46.

Hasselbach, W., and M. Makinose. 1961. Die calciumpumpe der, Erschlaffungsgrana des muskels und ihre abhangigkeit von der ATP-spaltung. *Biochem. Z.* 333:518.

Huxley, A. F. 1957. Muscle structure and theories of contraction. *Progr. Biophys. and Biophys. Chem.* 7:255.

Huxley, H. E. 1963. Electron microscope studies on the structure of natural and synthetic protein filaments from striated muscle. *J. Mol. Biol.* 7:281.

Kielley, W. W. 1964. The biochemistry of muscle. *Annu. Rev. Biochem.* 33:403.

Kielley, W. W., and L. B. Bradley. 1956. The relationship between sulfhydryl groups and the activation of myosin adenosinetriphosphatase. *J. Biol. Chem.* 218:653.

Koshland, D. E. 1958. Application of a theory of enzyme specificity to protein synthesis. *Proc. Nat. Acad. Sci.* 44:98.

Kühne, W. 1864. *Untersuchungen über das Protoplasma und die Contractilität.* Engelmann, Leipzig.

Laki, K., W. J. Brown, and A. Clark. 1950. The polymerization of proteins. Adenosine triphosphate and the polymerization of actin. *J. Gen. Physiol.* 33:437.

Mommaerts, W. F. H. M. 1950. *Muscular Contraction: A Topic in Molecular Physiology.* Interscience Publishers, New York.

———. 1951. Phosphate metabolism in the activity of skeletal and cardiac muscle, p. 551. *In* W. D. McElroy and B. Glass (eds.), *Symposium on Phosphate Metabolism*, Vol. 1. Johns Hopkins Univ., Baltimore.

———. 1952. The molecular transformations of actin. I. Globular actin. II. The polymerization process. III. The participation of nucleotides. *J. Biol. Chem.* 198:445, 459, 469.

———. 1963. The muscle cell and its functional architecture. *Amer. J. Med.* 35:606.

———. 1965. Energy transformations and structural organization of cytoplasm. *Fed. Proc.* 24:169.

Mommaerts, W. F. H. M., B. C. Abbott, and A. J. Brady. 1961. Major problems in muscle physiology. *Annu. Rev. Physiol.* 23:529.

Monod, J., J. Changeux, and F. Jacob. 1963. Allosteric proteins and cellular control systems. *J. Mol. Biol.* 6:306.

Monod, J., J. Wyman, and J. Changeux. 1965. On the nature of allosteric transitions: a plausible model. *J. Mol. Biol.* 12:88.

Nanninga, L. B., and W. F. H. M. Mommaerts. 1960a. Studies on the formation of an enzyme-substrate complex between myosin and adenosine triphosphate. *Proc. Nat. Acad. Sci.* 46:1155.

————. 1960b. Kinetic constants of the interaction between myosin and adenosinetriphosphate. *Proc. Nat. Acad. Sci.* 46:1166.

Oosawa, F. 1964. Paper No. VIII-S18, Symp. 6th Int. Congr. Biochem.

Pearson, C. M., D. G. Rimer, and W. F. H. M. Mommaerts. 1961. A metabolic myopathy due to absence of muscle phosphorylase. *Amer. J. Med.* 30:502.

Seraydarian, K., and W. F. H. M. Mommaerts, 1965. Density gradient separation of sarcotubular vesicles and other particulate constituents of rabbit muscle. *J. Cell Biol.* 26:641.

Straub, F. B. 1943. Actin II. *Stud. Inst. Med. Chem.* (Univ. Szeged) 3:23.

Straub, F. B., and G. Feuer. 1950 Adenosinetriphosphate — the functional group of actin. *Biochim. Biophys. Acta* 4:455.

Szent-Györgyi, A. 1951. *Chemistry of Muscular Contraction.* Academic Press, New York.

Szent-Györgyi, A. G. 1960. Proteins of the myofibril, p. 1. *In* G. H. Bourne (ed.), *The Structure and Function of Muscle*, Vol. 2. Academic Press, New York.

Weber, A., R. Herz, and I. Reiss. 1964. Role of calcium in contraction and relaxation of muscle. *Fed. Proc.* 23:896.

Weber, H. H. 1934. *Ergebn. Physiol.* 36:109.

Chapter 19

Nature of Actin - Myosin Complex and Contraction

A. G. SZENT-GYÖRGYI

It has been twenty-five years now since Albert Szent-Györgyi (see A. Szent-Györgyi, 1951, 1960) discovered that an actomyosin thread shortens when brought in contact with ATP. He immediately proposed that the shortening of actomyosin induced by ATP is the basis of contraction of muscle. He and his associates have also shown that the protein undergoing this reaction is a complex one and consists of two kinds, actin and myosin, and that the presence of both proteins is required for contraction. Contraction is thus the result of an interaction of actin, myosin, and ATP in the presence of a suitable ionic milieu. The suitable ionic milieu consists of the presence of Mg, traces of Ca, and, most important, low ionic strength at the neighborhood of physiological salt concentrations. At these ionic strengths actomyosin precipitates, and contraction can be observed only when actomyosin is in the precipitated or gel state. At higher ionic strength at which actomyosin is dissolved, ATP instead of inducing contraction will dissociate the two proteins from each other, preventing their interaction.

The scheme which Albert Szent-Györgyi originally proposed was somewhat as follows. In the resting state, interaction between actin and myosin is somehow prevented. The two proteins lie side by side, and the presence of ATP is necessary for the maintenance of the resting state, to keep them separated. There are two ways to establish interaction between actin and myosin. One of them is to deplete the ATP, and such depletion occurs in the rather unphysiological condition of death. It has been shown by Erdös and by Bate-Smith and Bendall that rigor mortis is due to the disappearance of ATP. Usually this is the state of these proteins in washed myofibrils or glycerol extracted fibers. Another way to establish a link between actin and myosin according to this scheme is the one that happens as a result of excitation. Once actomyosin is formed in excited muscle it will contract in the presence of ATP. ATP will be hydrolyzed to pay for the work which the muscle performed. Once excitation is over the original conditions will be re-established and muscle will return to its resting state.

This description is a simple one and does not go into details. It is still essentially correct and explains in a simple fashion and in general terms the mechanical properties of muscle in its three main states. At rest, muscle is soft, extensible, and capable of being stretched beyond its rest length. In other words, it has a low viscosity and a low elastic modulus. This is due to the fact that there are no cross linkages established between actin and myosin. In rigor mortis, the muscle cannot be stretched; it will rather tear than elongate, and it is harder. This is due to the cross linkages formed between actin and myosin since ATP has disappeared. The active-state muscle is also characterized by a high viscosity and by an increased elastic modulus which again could be explained by the formation of these cross linkages, but of course since ATP is present the muscle will contract.

This scheme does not discuss the actual mechanism of the shortening process and the reactions of actomyosin which are responsible for it. The question now, of course, is what alterations these proteins undergo during contraction. We have very little information at present to clarify this issue. To my mind there are two reasons for our ignorance, one of them being that contraction in vitro and in vivo can be demonstrated only when these proteins are out of solution. Thus one cannot use those techniques of physical chemistry which were designed to measure size, shape, and conformational changes in solution. The second reason for our ignorance is due to our prejudices. Up to about ten years ago no one had even considered the possibility that contraction of muscle at the molecular level is more complex than contraction of simple polymers. That is to say, it was natural to assume that when muscle shortens to half of its length, then either half of the constituent molecules will shorten to essentially zero length or each of the molecules will be shorter on the average by 50%. Thus one looked for a conformational change and alteration in the structure of such magnitude. In other words, one assumed that the changes in structure would be proportional to the extent of the shortening of muscle. Such a concept prevailed until about ten years ago when Hanson and Huxley (1955) proposed their sliding theory of contraction, which states that muscle contracts without an over-all permanent change in the lengths of the constituent molecules (see also A. F. Huxley, 1957; H. E. Huxley, 1960).

Let me first discuss some of the outstanding properties of actin and myosin, then describe briefly the important structural features of muscle which led to the formulation of the sliding theory of contraction. I will point out some of the chemical consequences of this theory and, finally, deal in somewhat more detail with recent efforts to find out what type of changes may happen during contraction at molecular level.

The simple observations already described tell us a number of things.

At first it is clear that muscle contraction is the result of interaction of two macromolecules. The elucidation of the nature of the interaction at the active sites of these two proteins is the central problem of muscle biochemistry. Secondly, contraction is driven by a phosphagen, ATP. The over-all reaction is certainly not a simple equilibrium between a contracted and relaxed state or between a short and the long state of the participating macromolecules. It is a cycle in which ATP is hydrolyzed and inorganic phosphate is liberated, and which consists of many steps even though some of the individual steps may be in equilibrium with each other. The system does not return into the relaxed state by retracing the steps which led to contraction; rather, it describes a full cycle. In this respect the behavior of muscle differs from the behavior of simple polymers.

Both actin and myosin have unique properties and structure which determine their contribution and participation in the structure of muscle and in its function. As stated in Chapter 18, actin can exist in both globular and fibrous form. The globular actin has a molecular weight of 60,000, and recent hydrodynamic measurements indicate that its shape approximates a sphere (Hayashi *et al.*, 1965). In fibrous actin these monomeric units aggregate very regularly into two strands which are wound around each other and form a helical structure (Hanson and Lowy, 1963). The length of fibrous actin even in vitro is of the order of microns, about the length it occupies in muscle. ATP and ADP are involved in the globular fibrous transformation of actin (a process discussed later in this chapter).

With myosin the situation is somewhat different, though not less interesting. More than ten years ago it was shown that the molecule can be fragmented with the aid of the proteolytic enzyme trypsin into two entirely different kinds of molecules. Light meromyosin, which has a very regular structure, consists of a fully coiled α-helix and has solubility properties similar to myosin. Light meromyosin does not combine with actin and has no adenosine triphosphatase activity. These functions are retained by the heavy meromyosin, which is water soluble and soluble at low ionic strengths, where myosin and light meromyosin precipitate. Evidence in the early experiments suggested that these two components of myosin are linked end to end and that the heavy meromyosin must be thicker than light meromyosin. Electron microscopic studies have since shown that the myosin has a tadpole shape with a head and tail (Rice, 1964; Zobel and Carlson, 1963; H. E. Huxley, 1963). The heavy meromyosin occupies the head and part of the tail, while the major portion of the tail consists of light meromyosin. The whole length of the molecule amounts to about 1600Å. This is a length which is considerably shorter than the units within the sarcomere, and a single myosin molecule cannot cover the length of the A band or the I band.

The essential observations on which the sliding theory of muscle contraction is based may be summarized as follows. There are two types of filaments present in muscle — thick ones having a diameter of 120 to 150 Å and thin ones with a diameter of about 60 to 80 Å. Myosin is present in the thick filaments while the thin filaments are made up almost entirely of actin. The thick filaments are about 1.5 microns long and occupy the A band region of the sarcomere. The thin filaments are about 1 micron long and extend from the Z band to the H band. During the physiological contraction of muscle or the ATP-induced contraction of washed myofibrils, the A band stays constant and the I band and H band lengths decrease. When the muscle is stretched the A band stays constant again, while the lengths of the I band and H band increase. Thus the length changes in muscle are reflected in the changes of the I band and the H band. The lengths of individual thin filaments and thick filaments do not change; what changes is their relative position to each other. Thus the unusual feature of muscle contraction is that length changes are accounted for by the sliding of macromolecular aggregates relative to each other, with no over-all length change in the macromolecular aggregates themselves. In the electron microscope, cross connections extending from the thick filaments towards the thin filaments can also be observed. It is proposed that these cross bridges represent the site of interaction between actin and myosin. In the state of rest this interaction is broken and muscle would be extensible because the filaments can move freely relative to each other. The increased resistance to stretch in rigor or during contraction of muscle arises from the fact that, at the cross bridges, links are established between the filaments containing the actin and the filaments containing myosin. The information derived from the chemical properties of the system and from the fine structure accord well.

H. E. Huxley (1963) was able to reconstitute filaments from purified myosin which were very similar in appearance to the thick filaments present in muscle. Moreover he was able to observe the intermediate aggregates in filament formation. He has found that in the aggregates the myosin molecules are laid down with opposite polarity, the tail ends lying next to each other towards the center, the heavy meromyosin ends being oriented away from the center. In the growing filaments the additional myosin molecules are laid down in a similar fashion. Thus a completed myosin filament has a polarity and a center of symmetry, and all the heads of the molecules are facing away from the center. Huxley has also shown polarity in actin filaments, using heavy meromyosin which is deposited on an actin filament in a fashion which indicates directionality. The simplest interpretation of these findings is that the light meromyosin makes up the shaft of the filament while the cross bridges are a part of the heavy meromyosin, and it is the heavy meromyosin portion which interacts with actin and carries the center for adenosine triphosphatase activity. There are somewhat over two hundred cross bridges extending from a thick filament. Muscle activity is the summation of reactions taking place at the cross bridges, and a cross bridge would be the site of a unit of activity. The cross bridge is where actomyosin is formed, where contraction is mediated, and where ATP is hydrolyzed.

As indicated above, the sliding filament theory states that the over-all lengths of the molecules and the aggregates made out of these molecules do not change permanently. If there is any structural or conformational change in the molecules these changes are only transitory. No proportionality between the extent of shortening and the extent of conformational change can be expected. The conformational change at any time may involve only a few of the many molecules present in the filaments, and the structural alteration could easily be restricted to a small region of the participating molecules. According to the sliding theory the conformation of actin and myosin will be very similar in a muscle shortened by 10% or by 60%. The extent of contraction rather depends on the number of cycles that the interacting sites have undergone. A larger contraction is the result of a greater number of cyclic reactions. A direct demonstration of any conformational change thus faces formidable difficulties.

There are perhaps two major mechanisms proposed as the means by which sliding may occur. In one type it is assumed that the cross bridges are not at right angle to the filaments, that they change their length in a cyclical fashion, and that this transient length change brings about the sliding of one of the filaments relative to another (Davies, 1963). In a different type of mechanism it is assumed that the over-all length of one of the filaments undergoes a small amount of periodic change. It is known that the periodicity associated with actin is different from the ones associated with myosin. Thus at any given time not all the myosin sites can combine with actin sites. If at the site of interaction there is a lengthening or shortening of the actin filament the result will be that new sites on the actin will be brought into an interaction with myosin sites. The whole cycle can repeat itself then at these new sites.

To approach these problems, a way to demonstrate transient conformational changes in actin or myosin, or in both, is required. One also would like to establish the cyclic nature of the structural alteration and to be able to distinguish those sites which have reacted from the ones which have not yet reacted. Actin is particularly suitable for such studies. In the monomeric globular form, actin contains ATP which is available to enzymes and readily exchanges with ATP of the medium. Polymerized actin contains ADP, and this ADP is well protected from enzymatic attack and does not exchange with free ATP or ADP of the medium. The availability and the nature of the bound nucleotides may be utilized to obtain information of the state of actin in various experimental conditions.

In the past twenty-five years several different authors proposed that a structural alteration in actin is a part of the contraction cycle. The alterations proposed were either depolymerization of fibrous actin into a globular form, or a transition of the helical form of actin into a linear one (Asakura, Taniguchi, and Oosawa, 1963). It is very likely that muscle at rest or washed myofibrils contain actin in the fibrous form. The bound ADP of muscle is not available for enzymatic attack (Perry, 1954); moreover, the thin filaments prepared from muscle, approximating conditions at rest, are indistinguishable from the filaments prepared of F-actin in vitro (Hanson and Lowy, 1963). Several attempts were made previous to our studies to find out whether or not the nucleotide bound to actin becomes available in contraction of myofibrils or superprecipitation of actomyosin. Two techniques were used. In one, the actin-bound nucleotide was labeled by incubating globular actin with radioactive ATP; the actin was polymerized then and combined with myosin. The resulting actomyosin was made to superprecipitate with ATP and the loss of actin-bound ADP was analyzed (Martonosi, Gouvea, and Gergely, 1960). In another study, myofibrils were incubated with isotopically labeled ATP and the extent of incorporation into actin was determined (Moos, 1964). These approaches met with limited success only, and the results were interpreted as denying any alterations of actin structure in contraction as measured by the increased availability of the ADP bound on actin.

Recently we (A. G. Szent-Györgyi, 1965; Szent-Györgyi and Prior, 1965) reinvestigated this problem, using similar techniques, and obtained more hopeful results. The ADP bound to actin and labeled, in this case, by tritium is not available for creatine kinase–phosphocreatine action even after actomyosin formation. The ADP remains tightly bound to actin even if ATP is present in great excess in the medium, provided that superprecipitation is inhibited by one means or another. If the actomyosin preparation is allowed to superprecipitate, up to one-half of the bound ADP is released into the medium, indicating that myosin in conditions favoring superprecipitation induced a change on actin which leads to the availability of the nucleotide for a release. We then demonstrated that the mechanism of the reaction is an exchange reaction. If one suspends an actomyosin preparation which contains ^{3}H-ADP as its bound nucleotide, into a medium containing ^{14}C-ATP, the loss in ^{3}H-ADP from actomyosin is compensated by a gain in ^{14}C-ADP throughout the whole course of the reaction. Only ADP is found in such a preparation as bound nucleotide. The reaction is then an exchange reaction, and the actin-bound ADP during superprecipitation exchanges with medium ATP which is then dephosphorylated to form ADP. If there is no ATP in the medium — only ADP or AMP — the reaction does not proceed. The exchange starts with a burst: when the first samples are taken, half a minute after addition of ATP, about 10%–20% of the ADP has exchanged. This is followed by a slower reaction, during which up to half of the total bound nucleotide can undergo an exchange reaction. We interpret the reaction the following way. In conditions of superprecipitation the myosin can induce a conformational change in actin which allows its bound nucleotide to undergo an exchange reaction. When actomyosin is formed, not all the sites on myosin can interact with sites on the actin because of steric limitations. The rapid burst of exchange represents those sites which can interact. The following reaction is essentially a similar type, but it is slower because time is required for the next site to be brought in contact — time for the previous cycle to be completed and for the next cycle on a new site to start.

With such techniques one may be able to get some information that the reaction is cyclic. At any point during the exchange reaction the sites containing ^{3}H-ADP are those which have not undergone an exchange yet, while the sites containing ^{14}C-ADP are those which have reacted at least once and, for that reason, contain newly incorporated ADP. The exchange reaction can be interrupted by centrifuging and washing the actomyosin suspension, and the preparation can be analyzed for reacted and unreacted sites. If the actomyosin preparation is resuspended in ATP the exchange reaction will proceed. If the medium in which actomyosin is resuspended contains nonradioactive ATP the removal of ^{3}H-ADP and ^{14}C-ADP, can be simultaneously followed. Since previously reacted and unreacted sites can be distinguished by this technique, one can determine how far the previous history of a site influences its reactivity, and whether or not the same site can undergo reaction more than once. It turns out that most of the ^{14}C-ADP and ^{3}H-ADP exchange with nonradioactive ATP at a comparable rate. Thus a site on actin can participate in the reaction more than once in superprecipitated actomyosin and the repetitive nature of the reaction can be directly demonstrated. The fact that unreacted sites and reacted sites behave in a similar fashion means that the structural change which allowed the exchange reaction is rapidly repaired. If the alteration in the conformation of the actin had persisted one would have expected a rapid selective removal of ADP of the reacted site. That did not happen. One can check for the reversibility of structural alteration at the reacted sites in a different fashion. As I mentioned, the ATP associated with G-actin is available for enzymatic attack. The ADP on F-actin is protected from such an action, and thus cannot participate in the coupled enzymatic system consisting of creatine kinase and phosphocreatine and does not lead to the liberation of creatine, in the presence of myosin. One can check with high accuracy and great sensitivity whether or not the ADP of the superprecipitated actomyosin will catalyze creatine liberation. The results show that 98% or more of the actin-bound ADP in superprecipitated actomyosin is protected, even though half of this ADP represents newly incorporated ADP.

We have also found an extensive incorporation of ADP into myofibrils when incubated with labeled ATP without any change in the concentration of over-all bound ADP content. The exchange reaction does proceed with myofibrils also, though at a slower rate.

It appears then that the chemical and structural changes operate in a cyclic fashion. Let us consider then how many steps make up such a cycle as that represented by the exchange. At first, binding between actin and myosin is established in the presence of ATP. In the second step, actin undergoes a conformational change, at the site where it interacts with myosin. This conformational change may involve a local breaking up of the actin structure or it may involve a conversion of the helical polymer into a linear one. In the third step, the available ADP is released in the medium. In the fourth step, ATP is incorporated from the medium into the actin. The fifth step would consist of the dephosphorylation of bound ATP. In the sixth step, the structural damage on actin is repaired, permitting it to return to its original conformation. Finally in the seventh step, the link between actin and myosin is broken.

There are, of course, alternative possibilities. However, all of them would have to include an opening up of the actin structure in the sense that its bound ADP becomes available. For instance, an alternative route to exchange would be a direct rephosphorylation of the actin-bound ADP. It may be that rephosphorylation is the dominating reaction in myofibrils and is the explanation of the relative slowness of the exchange when myofibrils are studied. The exchange reaction itself may not be part of the normal reaction sequence in this case. Such a scheme can be tested experimentally, and it may well be that test results would support speculations about the role of the actin-bound ADP in the energetics of muscular contraction.

The experiments I have described were made with techniques which were designed to check for a possible structural and conformational change in actin. The techniques do not detect changes in the myosin; thus these findings cannot and do not exclude such changes. At present we have no idea whether or not cyclic alterations on myosin are also part of the contraction cycle. The evidences which are described here indicate that cyclic and repetitive alterations do take place on actin and the changes on actin are part of the contraction cycle.

In summary, then, we know a great deal about the structure of the molecules participating in contraction. We have quite detailed information as to how the molecules aggregate in larger units into filaments and how these filaments make up the structure of striated muscle. The changes in the fine structure of muscle suggest that contraction is brought about by the interaction between two proteins which are present in different filaments. The active sites of actin and myosin present in the separate filaments have to be brought into close proximity for contraction, and in a single twitch of muscle many repetitive cycles at the interacting sites occur.

It is possible now to speculate what a single cycle may consist of, and at the present state the speculation will not necessarily be entirely divorced from experimental reality. The type of structure and reaction mechanism goes rather far in explaining some of the peculiarities of contraction of muscle, the changes in its mechanical properties, and its ability to govern the total rate of energy release according to the task it has to perform, where the molecules participating in contraction and responsible for rate of energy release set their activity according to the load the muscle lifts at the tendons. It also seems that the conformational change, which is very likely similar to the conformational changes in synthetic polymers, occurs only at restricted parts of the molecule and is part of the cycle which has to go on in a repetitive fashion even during a single twitch. Thus the apparent differences between muscle and synthetic polymers can be reconciled.

I have restricted my discussion to the interaction of actin and myosin during the contraction cycle. We know a great deal about how actin and myosin interaction may be controlled in living muscle and what the nature of the excitation-contraction coupling may be. This problem is discussed in Chapter 15 by Dr. Marsh, whose original discovery initiated this exciting development. There is a great deal left to be done. At present, rather detailed mechanisms can be proposed as to how muscle may contract, how activity can be controlled in such a marvelously precise fashion, how the change from activity to rest and from rest to activity can be brought about so rapidly. What is important is that the various schemes can be checked by fairly direct experiments and can be proven to be wrong in most instances. It is stimulating to see how structure and function in this cell are interwoven and inseparable and how information concerning the structure helps in the understanding of the chemical reaction and how chemistry helps in the interpretation of the function of the fine structures discovered. It may be taken as an example of a feedback mechanism in scientific investigation, and I only hope it turns out to be a positive and not a negative one.

ACKNOWLEDGMENTS

The author was the recipient of a USPHS Research Career Award from the National Cancer Institute (5-K6-CA-14,218). The experimental part discussed was supported by research grants from the National Science Foundation (NSF-G22004) and from the Division of General Medical Sciences, National Institute of Health USPHS (RG-9808).

References

Asakura, S., M. Taniguchi, and F. Oosawa. 1963. Mechano-chemical behavior of F-actin. *J. Mol. Biol.* 7:55.

Davies, R. E. 1963. A molecular theory of muscle contraction: calcium-dependent contractions with hydrogen bond formation plus ATP-dependent extensions of part of the myosin-actin cross-bridges. *Nature* 199:1068.

Hanson, J., and H. E. Huxley. 1955. The structural basis of contraction in striated muscle. *Symp. Soc. Exp. Biol.* 9:228.

Hanson, J., and J. Lowy. 1963. The structure of F-actin and of actin filaments isolated from muscle. *J. Mol. Biol.* 6:46.

Hayashi, T., R. J. Grant, L. B. Cohen, and E. E. Clark. 1965. Abstract of symposium on biological movement. Tokyo.

Huxley, A. F. 1957. Muscle structure and theories of contraction. *Progr. Biophys. and Biophys. Chem.* 7:255.

Huxley, H. E. 1960. Muscle cells, p. 365. *In* J. Brachet and A. E. Mirsky (eds.), *The Cell*, Vol. 4, Academic Press, New York.

——. 1963. Electron microscope studies on the structure of natural and synthetic protein filaments from striated muscle. *J. Mol. Biol.* 7:281.

Martonosi, A., M. A. Gouvea, and J. Gergely. 1960. Studies on actin III G-F transformation of actin and muscular contraction. *J. Biol. Chem.* 235:1707.

Moos, C. 1964. Incorporation of labeled ADP into myofibrils and actomyosin. *Fed. Proc.* 23:309.

Perry, S. V. 1954. Creatine phosphokinase and the enzymatic and contractile properties of the isolated myofibril. *Biochem. J.* 57:427.

Rice, R. V. 1964. Electron microscopy of macromolecules from myosin solutions, p. 41. *In* J. Gergely (ed.), *Biochemistry of Muscle Contraction*. Little, Brown & Co., Boston.

Szent-Györgyi, A. 1951. *Chemistry of Muscular Contraction* (2d ed.), Academic Press, New York.

——. 1960. Chapters in G. H. Bourne (ed.), *The Structure and Function of Muscle*, Vols. 1 and 2. Academic Press, New York.

Szent-Györgyi, A. G. 1965. Evidence for conformational changes in actin on contraction, p. 141. *In* W. M. Paul, E. E. Daniel, C. M. Kay, and G. Monckton (eds.), *Muscle*. Pergamon Press, London.

Szent-Györgyi, A. G., and G. Prior. 1965. Exchange of nucleotide bound to actin in superprecipitated actomyosin. *Fed. Proc. 24:*598.

Zobel, C. R., and F. D. Carlson. 1963. An electron microscopic investigation of myosin and some of its aggregates. *J. Mol. Biol. 7:*78.

Chapter 20

Summary and Discussion of Part IV

PANEL MEMBERS: J. R. WHITAKER, *Chairman*
A. ANGLEMIER
J. R. BENDALL
R. E. DAVIES
H. S. OLCOTT
A. M. PEARSON

Whitaker: Great progress has been made in the elucidation of muscle structure at the molecular level. The sarcoplasmic protein fraction (myogen) of muscle was originally thought to be homogeneous because of its uniform behavior on extraction. However, more recent work has shown that this myogen fraction is composed of more than 50 enzymes (Bailey, 1954). Phosphoglyceraldehyde dehydrogenase (10%), creatine phosphokinase (10%), phosphorylase (2%), and the aldolase-isomerase system (5%) make up 27% of the myogen fraction. This fraction comprises approximately 30% of the total muscle proteins.

Another protein fraction of muscle consists of the proteins of the granules (nuclei, mitochondria, microsomes, and lysosomes). The proteins of the granules are involved in the biosynthetic and degradative activities of the muscle. In mitochondria are located the components of oxidative phosphorylation where ATP is produced and in the microsomes protein synthesis takes place. The lysosomes contain various hydrolytic enzymes important in degradative activities.

Stroma proteins constitute another portion of muscle. These are the proteins which remain in the residue after prolonged extraction of a well-homogenized muscle with strong salt solutions. These proteins, some collagenous in nature, contribute to the structure of the sarcolemma and possibly to the Z membrane. Very little is known about this fraction.

The most important protein fraction of muscle consists of the myofibrillar proteins. These proteins are responsible for contraction. Contraction must be a molecular property of these proteins since, when properly arranged, they will undergo shortening to 20% of their original length in the absence of the other protein fractions of muscle. This fraction, approximately 60% of the total protein of the muscle, is composed largely of the proteins myosin (38%), actin (13%–15%), and tropomyosin (5%–10%).

The sliding filament theory, first advanced around 1953 by H. E. Huxley (see review, Huxley and Hanson, 1960), to explain the molecular organization of actin and myosin in the myofibril, has withstood the test of time very well (A. F. Huxley, 1964). By the use of the electron microscope, it has been shown that the myofibril itself is composed of thinner threads which are called filaments. There are apparently two types of filaments present (H. E. Huxley, 1953*a*, 1953*b*; Huxley and Hanson, 1954, 1957). From electron microscope observations of changes produced in the myofibrils as the result of differential extraction of the proteins, it has been concluded that the thick filaments of the A band contain the myosin of the sarcomere and the thin filaments extending from the Z lines to the border of the H zone contain the actin and perhaps the tropomyosin of the sarcomere. The arrangement of these filaments is responsible for the anisotropic and isotropic (dark and light) bands typical of striated muscle. During contraction, the actin filaments "slide" past the myosin filaments and into the H zone. Relaxation would involve the reverse process. This process, which permits shortening of the myofibril without shortening of either filament, must be due to the cyclic formation and breaking of weak bonds between the two constituent proteins of the contractile complex (actomyosin). Sulfhydryl groups on myosin appear to be involved, but the nature of the groups on actin is not known. Myosin and actin individually are noncontractile. Furthermore, it is F-actin rather than G-actin which combines with myosin to produce contraction. Professor Mommaerts, in Chapter 18, described some of the information available on the G- to F-actin conversion.

ATP must be involved directly or indirectly in the contraction-relaxation phenomenon. However, despite the many elegant hypotheses put forth (Davies, 1963; Szent-Györgyi and Johnson, 1964), much remains to be learned on the contraction process. ATP has two effects on models. It causes contraction and in addition it imparts that degree of plasticity and extensibility which is a prerequisite for both active and passive changes in length.

While there have been extensive developments in the physiology, physics, and biochemistry of muscle, there are many questions concerning muscle contraction and relaxation which have not been satisfactorily answered. Among these is the role of ATP in the contraction-relaxation phenomenon. What are the details of the interaction of ATP and actomyosin? How do actin and myosin combine during contraction? What is the role of tropomyosin? What mechanism permits the myofibrils to contract proportionally to the amount of work demanded from them? What is the exact role of Ca^{++} and Mg^{++} in this process? What role does the Marsh relaxing factor play under physiological conditions? What is the nature of the relaxation factor? These are only a very few of the many questions left unanswered.

In consideration of muscle as a food, one needs answers to the above questions and many more. After death, the flexible, soft, relaxed muscles become rigid, hard, and contracted (if the experiments are carried out around 37 C and the pH is above 6). The major chemical events in the development of rigor mortis have been extensively studied. They are (1) glycolysis, starting at death and continuing at a rate dependent on pH, substrate availability, product inhibition, and other as yet ill-defined factors; (2) decrease in pH due to formation of lactic acid; (3) fall of creatine phosphate to about 30% of the initial value by the time the pH reaches approximately 6.8; (4) decrease in ATP until it reaches a low level (20%–25%, depending upon the animal and muscle; at this point glycolysis is very slow; and at around 80% of the initial ATP value, the muscle suddenly loses its extensibility, becomes hard, and contracts); and (5) liberation of ammonia.

Rigor mortis at the molecular level would appear to involve the same events as those involved in the contraction process. There is formation of actomyosin. However, in rigor, the muscle stiffens, presumably due to loss of the plasticizing effect of ATP. Are there new, more stable, cross linkages formed between actin and myosin during rigor? ATP added after the formation of rigor does not appear to reverse the process. It must be kept in mind that the fall in pH during normal rigor is large and dramatic, changing from pH 7.0–7.2 to as low as pH 5.4. In the living, contracting muscle the decrease in pH is only a few hundredths of a unit. The isoelectric points of several of the myofibrillar proteins are around pH 5.4. Therefore, they begin to lose water of hydration. The combination of low pH and relatively high temperature must induce a large amount of protein denaturation. Very early in his work on muscle proteins, Bailey pointed out that denatured myosin behaves very much like the fibrous protein keratin with respect to its extensibility and X-ray diffraction characteristics.

The events leading to the softening of muscle after rigor mortis are very poorly understood. The softening is not analogous to the relaxation of living muscle. There is no evidence that actomyosin dissociates into actin and myosin on postmortem aging. During postmortem aging of muscles there is a reshuffling of the ionic constituents (Hamm, 1960) and a small increase in pH (Wierbicki et al., 1956). Both of these contribute to an increase in hydration of proteins. There is a rupture of the lysosomal membranes liberating the hydrolytic enzymes. These enzymes, particularly the protein-splitting enzymes (cathepsins), find an abundance of substrate and a pH at which they are active. Exactly how much the catheptic activity contributes to tenderization is not known at the present time.

DISCUSSION

Davies: Is it possible to effect an F-G actin transformation in muscle? Actin depolymerization might be of fundamental importance to the problem of tenderness. I raise this question in view of Dr. Marsh's comment on the "actomyosin toughness" in muscle. A possible method would be to wait until the ATP had disappeared, and then use ultrasonic treatment. This should transform F-actin to G-actin which could not repolymerize in the absence of ATP.

Mommaerts: Ultrasonic treatment might be used to depolymerize F-actin to G-actin. Freezing and thawing might also be used to effect the same actin depolymerization. The latter process, however, does not always work, for unexplained reasons. Freeze-drying depolymerizes actin but may not be practical for large pieces of meat. I do not know of any acceptable reagents that would readily depolymerize actin.

Szent-Györgyi: Ultrasonic treatment should be applied only to rigor muscle in which ATP has been depleted, because depolymerization is reversible in the presence of ATP.

Anglemier: Does water play a similar role in the polymerization of G-actin, as has been reported for the polymerization of A-protein of tobacco mosaic virus?

Mommaerts: There are undoubtedly common features in the polymerization phenomena exhibited by diverse proteins. However, we need further information on the specific mechanism of G-actin polymerization.

Davies: Has anyone had direct experience with sonification of meat?

Thomson: I have tried ultrasonic vibrations on the adductor muscle of the scallop (*Pecten gibbus* and *P. iradians*). A commercial single frequency probe sonicator was used in an attempt to make the bivalve relax its muscle and open. The probe was placed in the water in which the scallops were held and also placed in contact with the shell. No relaxation of the muscle (as evidenced by opening of the bivalve) occurred regardless of how the probe was oriented in relation to the surface of the shell. The shells became remarkably clean on the outside, and with prolonged sonification pieces of the shell began to chip off.

Wierbicki: Could irradiation of muscle as it goes into rigor mortis be used to dissociate actomyosin.

Szent-Györgyi: A recent report (Stephens, 1965) describes the use of ultraviolet irradiation for local inactivation of certain portions of the sarcomere. The results were, first of all, that the irradiation evidently leads to the depolymerization of actin, so that one could use it just like sonication to break up the actin-actin interaction. Secondly, irradiation inactivates the myosin adenosine triphosphatase and possibly the myosin-actin interaction. However, I think that the proposal of Dr. Wierbicki faces the difficult problem of penetration of ultraviolet light into the interior of muscle.

Wierbicki: We have been able to irradiate samples as large as six inches in diameter with a gamma source in one to two hours.

Pearson: Would anyone care to comment on the observation (Harmon, University of Illinois) that germ-free animals do not stiffen in the characteristic way during the development of rigor mortis?

Mommaerts: One should perhaps establish whether a rapid autolysis has occurred.

Briskey: Harmon (personal communication) has "observed this phenomenon only in the rat. All observations have been visual and pertain only to the question of rigidity. Germ-free rats definitely do not become rigid and, in fact, may remain limp and flexible for several days."

Davies: I have had experience with germ-free guinea pigs, and they entered into typical rigor mortis with associated stiffening. Therefore, the phenomenon apparently does not apply to all germ-free animals. It has been well established that when there is no ATP present, actin and myosin form a firm bond which is characteristic of rigor mortis.

Another point to be considered is the possible change in cell membrane fragility of germ-free animals. We have found extreme mechanical friability of the gastrointestinal tract of germ-free animals: it apparently needs constant attack by bacteria to maintain it in an elastic and strong state. If this is a general property of membranes from germ-free animals one might expect a rapid liberation of lysosomal enzymes and a subsequent rapid proteolysis. This may further Dr. Mommaerts' suggestion that the muscles may be, in effect, autolyzed before they destroy the ATP. If such circumstances existed, one would not observe rigor mortis because the actomyosin system would have been broken down before ATP depletion. No fundamental problem, concerning rigor mortis, would exist under these circumstances.

Nevertheless, this reported phenomenon in rats apparently does not exist in all animals and certainly requires immediate clarification.

Pearson: We have observed only one germ-free pig and in this case it did go into rigor mortis.

Ockerman: In work with germ-free mice we have noticed that they do follow a "normal rigor mortis" (rigid muscle) pattern. These mice were dispatched and observed under "germ-free" conditions.

Davies: What happens in rigor mortis to make myosin less soluble?

Mommaerts: This question was intensively debated in the 1940's. The work by Banga and Szent-Györgyi suggested that the presence of ATP during extraction was the main factor determining the dissociation of myosin from its links to actin, presumably the first step in dissolution. The work by Dubuisson, on the other hand, emphasized that this connection was not universal. The problem then received no further attention at this somewhat indefinite stage. According to some preliminary exploration on our part (1954), the relaxation factor plays a role in this problem, and this might conciliate conflicting views.

Sink: If actin and myosin are permitted to continue their association for a considerable length of time, do the cross bonds which were previously reversible now become irreversible?

Szent-Györgyi: During superprecipitation or extreme synaeresis, the protein content of muscle or even the actomyosin precipitate, will be extremely high. Even the centrifuged packed protein volume will go up to 30%, and that still includes the space between the particles. One can assume that nonspecific interactions, not simply the specific interactions between actin and myosin, will be established.

Davies: The glycerol extracted muscle would appear to be a model fc this phenomenon where the bond between the actin and myosin is made in the absence of ATP and can last for months and months, but be immediately broken upon the addition of ATP. I agree that when actin and myosin exist as a completely tangled mass, one might get other hydrophobic interactions which would make it difficult to dissociate. However, it appears that the glycerol extracted muscle presents strong evidence against the irreversibility of these bonds in intact tissue.

Szent-Györgyi: There is an additional unpublished observation, of pertinence, which I may mention. Myofibrils can be prepared very easily, with a Waring Blendor, from glycerinated muscle. However, if the glycerol-extracted muscle has first been made to contract or shorten slightly with ATP, a different situation exists. If the ATP were washed out and the muscle blended, myofibrils could not be separated. It almost appears as if cross bonds between fibrils had been established.

Bendall: I would like to make one additional point about glycerinated muscle. Recently I used some glycerinated fibers from a muscle which had been kept at $-10\,C$ for about two years. I was surprised to find that the muscle contracted in the presence of massive amounts of EGTA. The EGTA was certainly binding all of the free Ca, but the muscle continued to contract. Something seems to happen upon very long storage of glycerinated fibers which upsets the Ca-regulating machinery and the Ca sensitivity.

Lardy: Dr. Mommaerts said that there was no inosinic acid in living muscle or in muscle immediately postmortem. Is there none even in a fatigued muscle? If there is none, then what is the function of adenylic deaminase which is present in muscle?

Mommaerts: I should not say that there is none. There is very little, even if contractile activity is extensive as in the case of an iodoacetate poisoned anaerobic exhaustion series. When creatine phosphate is no longer present for the resynthesis of ATP, the ATP level begins to diminish. Initially ADP accumulates, followed by AMP. It would appear that you would need an extreme situation before anything other than the above would occur. Unfortunately, IMP, in small amounts, is more difficult to determine than other nucleotides and may require further study. However, it certainly does not occur in the early stages of nucleotide breakdown. One would certainly not expect it to appear in a twitch. I really do not know where these circumstances leave adenylic deaminase.

Lardy: Adenylic deaminase is bound to myosin, so it would appear logical that it had some function in relation with myosin.

Mommaerts: There is definitely a gap in our knowledge on this issue. Additionally we do not know enough about ammonia formation in muscle.

Bendall: One can follow the release of ammonia during the development of rigor mortis. Nevertheless more information is still needed on changes in IMP, IDP, and ITP. There is generally not very much IDP and ITP produced, but a considerable amount of IMP; this, of course, unlike the case with living muscle, occurs on a very extended time scale (Bendall and Davey, 1957).

Davies: There certainly is IMP in normal resting muscle, but it is in very small amounts (much less than one IMP per myosin molecule). Ordinary contraction produces no measurable change; and only, as Dr. Bendall says, when rigor mortis develops do you get inosine. ATP is changed to ADP and then myokinase uses up the ADP until only AMP remains, which then rapidly forms IMP. Eventually the IMP will degenerate to inosine. IMP does not seem to have any great significance in muscle, and perhaps the great value of the inosine deaminase is to get rid of AMP, because if it accumulated in muscle, both AMP and ADP could inhibit many crucial enzymes.

Lardy: Is not the allosteric regulation of phosphorylase by AMP a physiologically significant event?

Davies: The role of the AMP mechanism in stepping up glycolysis is quite normal and physiological. The IMP reaction seems to be important when the AMP level has elevated to slightly over 0.1 M, in order to prevent it from going up to 0.3 M, which would be deleterious.

Szent-Györgyi: I believe that certain muscles, such as insect muscle, crab muscle, and heart muscle, do not contain adenylic deaminase, so it is unlikely that deaminase has an obligatory role in the contraction process.

Anglemier: What function might tropomyosin have in muscle?

Szent-Györgyi: There is some evidence that tropomyosin is located in the Z band. Crystalline tropomyosin has the same type of quadrangular arrangement which characterizes the Z band in electron micrographs. It is difficult to extract F-actin free of tropomyosin, but there is no good independent evidence as yet that tropomyosin participates in the thin filament of muscle. Ebashi (S. Ebashi, 1963; S. Ebashi and F. Ebashi, 1964) proposed that tropomyosin may also function to make the actomyosin sensitive toward the presence or removal of Ca. Well-purified actomyosin (reconstituted actomyosin) can split ATP and can superprecipitate even at Ca concentrations as low as 10^{-7} M. If a component from muscle is added to the system or it is present in natural actomyosin, then the system will be very sensitive to the withdrawal of Ca. Ebashi's preparation showed similarities to tropomyosin in amino acid composition. Albert Szent-Györgyi and Kaminer (1964) also reported another protein, called "metin," and Ebashi considered that part of his active principle may be a portion of metin; the other part may be tropomyosin. In summary, very little is positively known of the function of tropomyosin.

Mommaerts: The new Ebashi protein may be just the beginning of the discovery of many new muscle proteins.

Pearson: Are there any configurational or structural differences between fibrillar proteins from red and white fibers?

Mommaerts: There is no information at this date on structural differences between proteins of these fiber types. It has been shown that myosin from red, or slowly twitching, muscle (including the heart) has a lower adenosine triphosphatase activity than myosin from white, or fast twitching muscle.

King: What is the effect of postmortem state (prerigor, rigor, postrigor, "old postrigor") of the muscle from which an actomyosin extract is prepared on the ability of actomyosin to be superprecipitated by ATP — as a function of ionic strength, Ca level, etc.?

Szent-Györgyi: I think that the behavior of purified extracted actomyosin will be independent of the state of muscle from which it was obtained, provided that it has not been attacked by proteolytic enzymes in "post-rigor" or "old postrigor."

The state of muscle will influence greatly the extractability of actomyosin, the actin content of the extract, and possibly the extractability of other impurities which may cling rather tenaciously to myosin or actomyosin. Though I must say this question to my knowledge has not been rigorously examined.

Pearson: Different myoglobins vary in minor structural details. Is it possible that the structure of myosin, and possibly actin, may vary?

Szent-Györgyi: Yes. Differences in amino acid composition, adenosine triphosphatase activity, and ease of denaturation have been reported for cardiac, and different skeletal muscle myosins. (See Kay, 1965; Barany *et al.*, 1965; Barany *et al.*, 1964; Seidel *et al.*, 1964.) Some differences in amino acid content have also been reported for actin obtained from various species. (See Carsten, 1965; Carsten and Katz, 1964.)

Pearson: What is the nature of the cross bridges in a filament?

Szent-Györgyi: The cross bridges extend from the thick filaments and probably represent part of the heavy meromyosin end of the individual myosin molecules making up the thick filaments.

Olcott: Is there any information on the chemical nature of the actin-myosin bonds which are made and broken during contraction and relaxation? Could the sulfhydryl-disulfide bonds be involved in this reaction?

Szent-Györgyi: There is very little known about the chemical nature of the bonds. However, we know that when actin and myosin are mixed, the resulting linkage can be broken by pyrophosphate and Mg; so there is probably an electrostatic interaction.

Anglemier: Would you please elaborate further on the nature of the cross linkages established between actin and myosin in the formation of actomyosin?

Szent-Györgyi: When actomyosin is formed in absence of ATP, the bond between actin and myosin is probably electrostatic and definitely not a covalent one. The link can be broken, not only by ATP or other nucleotide triphosphates, but by inorganic pyrophosphate or polyphosphates if Mg is present.

The bond between actin and myosin may be quite different when actomyosin is formed at low ionic strength in presence of ATP at conditions where actomyosin formation leads to contraction. This is one of the important questions for which at present there is no direct answer. The formation of a transient covalent link as part of the contraction cycle, which has been suggested by H. M. Levy and D. E. Koshland, Jr. (1959), is a possibility. The clarification of the nature of the bond between actin and myosin in the contraction cycle is one of the most important steps in our understanding of contraction.

Mommaerts: I have never found any disulfide bonds, but that does not mean they are not there. There is a problem which keeps tormenting me: We know that muscles contract because the cells contract, the cells contract because the fibrils contract, the fibrils contract because the sarcomeres contract, the sarcomeres contract because the filaments slide, and why do the filaments slide? The filaments slide because there are tiny muscles that pull them! The farther one goes in the analysis of a problem, the more essential it is to understand the vital mechanism.

Davies: Although it is true that there is no conclusive evidence on this question, a theory has been published that can explain a large number of events occurring during muscle contraction (Davies, 1963).

Anglemier: Is it reasonable to assume that the chemical and physical events occurring in muscle during maximum contraction are quite similar to those encountered in full rigor?

Szent-Györgyi: No. The similarity is that both in rigor and in contraction cross links between actin and myosin are formed. In rigor nothing more happens: the cycle does not proceed, and the system is frozen at this step. In contraction the cycle proceeds to completion. Undergoing the chemical reactions, mostly unknown, which make up the cycle, the cross link will be broken and reformed as the cycle is repeated many times during a twitch. The similarity between rigor and contraction, then, is that in both cases cross linkages are formed with the mechanical consequences of increased resistance to stretch, viscosity, and elastic modulus.

Anglemier: Is the degree of severity of rigor mortis mainly dependent upon the number of cross linkages formed between the actin and myosin filaments during the formation of actomyosin?

Szent-Györgyi: Yes, in the sense that all the thick filaments will have to be cross-linked to the thin filaments. My guess would be that in practice when the degree of severity of rigor mortis is measured, it is an expression of the uneven depletion of ATP at various parts of the muscle, which would result in cross-linked and noncross-linked parts. The results measuring hardness may also be influenced by whether or not contracture has preceded rigor.

Pearson: Could a Ca chelator be used to prevent the onset of rigor mortis?

Szent-Györgyi: A Ca chelator may perhaps delay rigor mortis by delaying the breakdown of ATP. Once the ATP level is below a certain level one would expect rigor mortis to develop. I do not know how far this question has been studied.

Pearson: Is there any information available concerning the resolution of rigor mortis?

Szent-Györgyi: I think that the actomyosin link itself could persist for a long time unless extreme pH or some reaction product should cause its dissociation. I would guess that proteolysis is involved in the resolution of rigor mortis, if resolution does occur.

Bendall: I find it very difficult to believe that resolution of rigor mortis occurs.

Marsh: We were unable to detect any change in the extensibility of bovine muscle strips, even when the samples were left as long as seven days at about 8–9 C. There was a slight tendency for the muscle to stretch back towards its original length, but there was no change at all in the extensibility.

Pearson: Could changes in the structure of fibrillar proteins possibly be related to the tenderness of the tissue?

Mommaerts: Such a relation was established by the classical investigation by Deutsche: when muscle hardens after death, the myosin becomes inextractable. This and similar observations point to the fact that, post-mortem, there are changes in the interconnections between the muscle proteins, expressing themselves in a diminished access to solvents, and correlated with a change in the gross physical properties of the tissue.

Sink: Would you comment on muscle relaxants as they affect rigor mortis and sarcomere length?

Mommaerts: If we see a tendency to add interesting pharmacological agents, then we may be in for some difficulty. I do not think that we should consider using pharmacological agents for these purposes, unless we are first assured of their safety.

Olcott: Some fish muscle contains very large amounts (5%) of imidazole compounds such as histidine and anserine. What might these substances do other than act as a buffer?

Bendall: Dr. Davey (1960) has shown that muscles which depend primarily on rapid activity and are likely to become anaerobic (white muscle) also generally contain large quantities of carnosine and anserine. Red muscles, which depend on aerobic metabolism and do not easily develop oxygen debts, contain very low amounts of carnosine and anserine. For example, chicken breast contains a considerable amount and pigeon breast contains very little of these compounds. It appears that carnosine and anserine might act as buffers. The sperm whale has an enormous amount of anserine. It has a great need for a buffer, because it dives for a long time, during which it accumulates a considerable amount of lactic acid in its muscles.

Pearson: It has been established that myosin acts as an emulsifier of fat in sausage manufacturing. What conditions could be imposed that would improve the solubility of myosin and thereby increase emulsification?

Szent-Györgyi: An ionic strength higher than 0.3 could be used, but I doubt if this would be appropriate for practical purposes.

Lauck: Is there some role for inorganic pyrophosphate in muscle contraction?

Szent-Györgyi: Myosin is definitely an adenosine triphosphatase which hydrolyzes only the last phosphate of ATP, so I doubt that there is any role for pyrophosphate.

Davies: We have examined muscle for its pyrophosphate content. Pyrophosphate is not present in any significant amount, and certainly is not created during muscle contraction.

Pearson: Would you please clarify the term "myogen" as related to the term "sarcoplasmic proteins"?

Mommaerts: Myogen was a term applied to a preparative entity: the proteins prepared from a press-juice of saline-perfused muscle, or from an aqueous extract from such muscle, and consisting of the water-soluble proteins so obtainable. That this is heterogeneous became especially evident through electrophoretic studies. The fraction is now regarded as consisting of the various glycolytic and other enzymes which are not structure-bound, although some structural compartmentalization may well occur among them.

References

Bailey, K. 1954. Structure proteins. II. Muscle, p. 951. *In* H. Neurath and K. Bailey (eds), *The Proteins*, Vol. 2, Pt. B. Academic Press, New York.

Barany, M., D. Barany, T. Reckard, and A. Volpe. 1965. Myosin of fast and slow muscles of rabbit. *Arch. Biochem. Biophys. 109*:185.

Barany, M., E. Gaetjens, K. Barany, and E. Karp. 1964. Comparative studies of rabbit cardiac and skeletal myosins. *Arch. Biochem. Biophys. 106*:280.

Bendall, J. R., and C. L. Davey. 1957. Ammonia liberation during rigor mortis and its relation to changes in the adenine and inosine nucleotides of rabbit muscle. *Biochim. Biophys. Acta 26*:93.

Carsten, M. E. 1965. A study of uterine actin. *Biochemistry 4*:1049.

Carsten, M. E., and A. M. Katz. 1964. Actin: a comparative study. *Biochim. Biophys. Acta 90*:534.

Davey, C. L. 1960. The significance of carnosine and anserine in striated muscle. *Arch. Biochem. Biophys. 89*:303.

Davies, R. E. 1963. A molecular theory of muscle contraction: calcium-dependent contractions with hydrogen bond formation plus ATP-dependent extensions of part of the myosin-actin cross-bridges. *Nature 199*:1068.

Ebashi, S. 1963. A new protein factor promoting contraction actomyosin. *Nature* 200:1010.

Ebashi, S., and F. Ebashi 1964. A new protein component participating in the superprecipitation of myosin B. *J. Biochem.* (Tokyo) 55:604.

Hamm, R. 1960. Biochemistry and meat hydration. *Advance. Food Res.* 10:355.

Huxley, A. F. 1964. Muscle. *Annu. Rev. Physiol.* 26:131.

Huxley, H. E. 1953a. Electron-microscope studies on the organization of the filaments in striated muscle. *Biochim. Biophys. Acta* 12:387.

————. 1953b. X-ray analysis and the problem of muscle. *Proc. Roy. Soc.* (London), B, 141:59.

Huxley, H. E., and J. Hanson. 1954. Changes in the cross-striations of muscle during contraction and stretch and their structural interpretation. *Nature* 173:973.

————. 1957. Quantitative studies on the structure of cross-striated myofibrils. I. Investigations by interference microscopy. *Biochim. Biophys. Acta* 23:229.

————. 1960. The molecular basis of contraction in cross-striated muscles, p. 183. *In* G. H. Bourne (ed.), *The Structure and Function of Muscle*, Vol. 1. Academic Press, New York.

Kay, C. M. 1965. Physico-chemical studies on cardiac and skeletal myosin A, p. 93. *In* W. M. Paul, E. E. Daniel, E. M. Kay, and G. Monckton (eds.), *Muscle*. Pergamon Press, London.

Levy, H. M., and D. E. Koshland, Jr. 1959. Mechanism of hydrolysis of adenosine-triphosphate by muscle proteins and its relation to muscular contraction. *J. Biol. Chem.* 234:1102.

Seidel, J. C., F. A. Sreter, M. M. Thompson, and J. Gergely. 1964. Comparative studies of myofibrils, myosin, and actomyosin from red and white rabbit skeletal muscle. *Biochem. Biophys. Res Commun.* 17:662.

Stephens, R. E. 1965. Analysis of muscle contraction by ultra-violet microbeam disruption of sarcomere structure. *J. Cell Biol.* 25:129.

Szent-Györgyi, A. G., and W. H. Johnson. 1964. An alternative theory for contraction of striated muscles, p. 485. *In* J. Gergely (ed.), *Biochemistry of Muscle Contraction*. Little, Brown & Co., Boston.

Szent-Györgyi, A., and B. Kaminer. 1964. Metin and metactomyosin. *Proc. Nat. Acad. Sci.* 50:1033.

Wierbicki, E., L. E. Kunkle, V. R. Cahill, and F. E. Deatherage. 1956. Post mortem changes in meat and their possible relation to tenderness together with some comparisons of meat from heifers, bulls, steers, and diethylstilbestrol treated bulls and steers. *Food Technol.* 10:80.

PART V

Connective Tissue Proteins in Muscle

Chapter 21

Collagen

K. A. PIEZ

The most ubiquitous of all proteins in the animal kingdom is probably collagen. It is the major structural material of the simplest multicellular animals, the sponges, and it performs similar functions in species representing most of the phyla. In higher animals it is found in a variety of tissues, including not only skin, tendon, and bone, where it is the major protein, but many others where it has less quantitative significance. In each case it performs a vital function which can be described (e.g., for skin, tendon, and bone, respectively) as containing, connecting, or supporting other tissues.

That collagen is so widely utilized indicates that it plays its role with considerable success. It may not be an exaggeration to say that the development of multicellular animals depended upon the development of collagen. For multicellular animals to have an advantage over single cells, the cells must be physically contained and connected or they could not work together for the common good. Of course, nature has accomplished the same end in other ways. For example, many animals with exoskeletons, such as insects and mollusks, contain little or no collagen. But the fact remains that for many of the simpler animals as well as those in the higher phyla, collagen plays a central role.

Collagen is found in several places in muscle. Most obvious are the tendons, which by connecting muscle to bone transmit the contracting force of a muscle to the movement of a part of the body. This is illustrated in Figure 21.1, which shows an X-ray of a turkey leg, an example chosen because the leg tendons are calcified and therefore readily revealed by X-ray. One can see clearly how the tendons function to connect each individual muscle to a given bone. Collagen is also a major constituent of the reticular sheath of muscle fibers and of septa between muscles.

Collagen may be defined in several ways. Since, as will be discussed, the basic feature of all collagens is the triple chain backbone structure, one convenient definition is the wide angle X-ray diffraction pattern

Fig. 21.1. — X-ray of adult turkey leg, showing relationship of tendons to muscle. The tendons are calcified (except where they pass over the joints) and are therefore readily visible. From Likins, Piez, and Kunde, 1960; copyright © 1960 by the American Association for the Advancement of Science.

which shows specific reflections. These can be related to atomic spacings in the backbone structure common to all collagens. Another way to define collagen is by its amino acid chemistry. All collagens have a high glycine content which represents close to one-third of the total residues. Also present are two amino acids which are unique (or nearly so) to collagen — hydroxyproline and hydroxylysine. However, except for glycine, the amounts of these and other amino acids vary over a wide range. Compositions of some typical collagens, including both invertebrate (Piez and Gross, 1959) and vertebrate collagens (Piez, Eigner, and Lewis, 1963), are given in Table 21.1. It can be seen that there are tissue-specific as well as species-specific differences.

The properties of a tissue are derived in part from the properties of the molecules of which the tissue is composed and in part from the way the molecules are arranged. The factors which determine the position, size,

TABLE 21.1

Amino acid composition of some typical collagens (residues/1000 total residues)

Amino Acid	Sponge [a]	Metridium [b]	Carp swim bladder [c]	Rat skin [c]	Rat tail tendon [c]
3-Hydroxyproline	. . .	. . .	0.6	0.9	4.2
4-Hydroxyproline	94	49	76	92	90
Aspartic acid	97	80	47	46	45
Threonine	27	39	28	20	20
Serine	24	54	37	43	43
Glutamic acid	86	94	71	71	71
Proline	73	63	116	121	122
Glycine	323	311	333	331	331
Alanine	94	70	125	106	107
Cystine	6.0	3.2	0	0	0
Valine	24	34	18	24	23
Methionine	3.1	8.8	16	7.8	8.4
Isoleucine	17	23	10	11	10
Leucine	24	37	20	24	24
Tyrosine	4.0	7.9	3.4	2.4	3.9
Phenylalanine	10	12	13	11	12
Hydroxylysine	24	25	7.0	5.7	6.6
Lysine	24	27	26	28	27
Histidine	3.2	5.1	3.6	4.9	4.1
Arginine	43	57	52	51	50
Amide nitrogen	(90)	(71)	(40)	(41)	(40)

[a] Spongin B (see K. A. Piez and J. Gross, "The amino acid composition and morphology of some invertebrate and vertebrate collagens," *Biochim. Biophys. Acta 34* [*1959*]:24.)

[b] Sea anemone (see *ibid.*)

[c] K. A. Piez, E. A. Eigner, and M. S. Lewis, "The chromatographic separation and amino acid composition of the subunits of several collagens," *Biochemistry 2(1963)*:58.

and direction of collagen fibrils are not well understood, but the problem should at least be mentioned. Figure 21.2 shows diagrammatically several levels of structure from molecules to tissue morphology. The layered arrangement in which the fibrils are approximately parallel in any one layer but at right angles to adjacent layers is typical of cornea and of skin from some of the lower vertebrates. In tendon, the fibrils are all parallel, giving rise to fibers. In mammalian skin, the fibrils are largely disordered

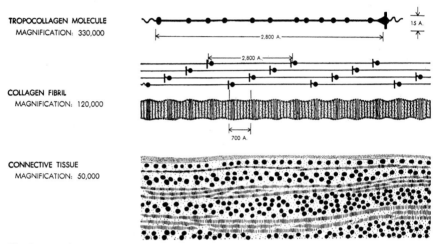

TROPOCOLLAGEN MOLECULE
MAGNIFICATION: 330,000

COLLAGEN FIBRIL
MAGNIFICATION: 120,000

CONNECTIVE TISSUE
MAGNIFICATION: 50,000

Fig. 21.2. — Diagrammatic representation of the relationship of the collagen molecule to morphology of the tissue. Proceeding from top to bottom are shown the asymmetric collagen molecule which has a polarized structure and alternating polar and nonpolar regions, the manner in which molecules are packed in an overlapping array, the appearance of a fibril in which characteristic banding is produced by the overlapping of the molecules and the alignment of polar and nonpolar regions, and a cross section of a tissue showing an example of how fibrils may be arranged in an organized manner. From Gross, 1961; copyright © 1961 by *Scientific American, Inc.*; all rights reserved.

without any orderly packing. Each of these arrangements presumably has a specific role in tissue function.

The individual fibrils, which are typically several hundred Ångstroms in diameter, are composed of aggregates of collagen molecules in which the axes are parallel but the ends overlap in a regular manner to produce typical banded fibrils. The major repeat of about 700 Å results from overlapping by multiples of approximately one-quarter the length of the molecule. Fine banding within the major repeats, which can be made visible by the use of appropriate stains, arises from the alignment of alternating polar and nonpolar regions on adjacent molecules. The aggregation of collagen molecules into fibrils is a phenomenon which apparently results entirely from the nature of the molecule. It occurs spontaneously in vitro in purified solutions of collagen at physiologic pH, temperature, and ionic strength (Gross and Kirk, 1958). Although nearly all collagens show this property, a few are found as unbanded fibrils in vivo.

The collagen molecule has been shown by physical chemical measurements (see the review by Harrington and von Hippel, 1961) and by electron microscopy to be approximately a cylinder about 2800 Å long and 14 Å in diameter with a molecular weight of about 300,000. This may be compared in axial ratio to a 1-inch hose 17 feet long. The representation of the molecule in Figure 21.2 is meant to indicate that the structure is polarized. That is, the details of structure vary from point to point along the molecule.

The molecule is three-stranded, each strand being in a modified polyproline helix which has a repeat distance of about 3 Å and three amino acids per repeat. The three strands are then wound together in ropelike fashion to produce a triple helix with a repeat of the order of 100 Å. This is illustrated in Figure 21.3, which shows one repeat of the triple helix. The structure is stabilized by a regular array of interchain hydrogen bonds, together with stereochemical restrictions which derive from the high content of pyrrolidine rings (proline and hydroxyproline) found in collagen.

There are a number of consequences of this structure. Perhaps the most important is that the polypeptide backbones are tightly packed so that every third position must be a glycine residue, as there is no room for a side chain. That this is the case has been confirmed by chemical studies. Although any amino acid can presumably occupy the other positions, the amino acid side chains must be largely directed to the outside of the mole-

Fig. 21.3. — Projection of a portion of the backbone structure of the collagen molecule drawn from the coordinates of Ramachandran (1963). The amino acids are represented by their α carbon atoms. The three chains are indicated by different symbols. One chain (*circles*) begins (*left*) behind the plane of the page, proceeds around to the front, and reappears at the back after one turn of the major helix. The other two chains begin in front of the plane of the page and follow the major helix of the first chain, separated from it and one another by one-third of a repeat. Though not readily apparent from this representation, each chain exists in a minor helix with three amino acid residues per turn. The filled symbols represent the amino acids which are in the center of the structure and must therefore be glycine. The portion shown here represents about one twenty-fifth of the length of the molecule. The upper and lower lines (14 Å apart) represent the approximate outside of the molecule, the space being filled by amino acid side chains.

cule. This means that the properties of amino acids, which are largely responsible for the properties of proteins, in the case of collagen must be utilized primarily for intermolecular interactions. This is exactly as would be expected, because the major function of collagen is to form fibrils which are nothing more than a specific type of intermolecular aggregate.

Although noncovalent bonds are sufficient to explain fibril formation, they apparently do not provide the long-term stability necessary for the stresses to which connective tissues may be subjected. In all tissues examined, interchain covalent cross links have been found. It is not possible to analyze for cross-link content directly since the chemical nature of the cross link is not understood, but to a first approximation the degree to which collagen can be extracted from a tissue by cold neutral salt solutions or dilute acid solutions is a measure of covalent cross linking. In this way it has been found that there is some correlation between the degree of cross linking and function. For example, Achilles tendon, which has the strength of a steel cable, is almost completely insoluble, while fish swim bladder, which is essentially a resting tissue, gives a high yield of extractable collagen. Skin is intermediate in degree of cross linking and is a convenient tissue to study because cross linking occurs at a relatively slow rate.

When a solution of native collagen is denatured by heating or the action of substances such as urea or potassium thiocyanate the chains of the molecule uncoil and dissociate. It has been shown that such denatured products consist of several molecular weight classes. This is illustrated in the ultracentrifuge pattern in Figure 21.4, showing three boundaries, which are called the α, β, and γ components in order of increasing rate of sedimentation. The α component is almost certainly a single chain of which there are three in each collagen molecule. It has a molecular weight of about 100,000 or one-third the molecular weight of native collagen. The β and γ components represent dimers and trimers respectively of α chains and are formed by covalent cross links.

This would be a relatively simple structure if it were not for the fact that the three α chains are not identical. This can be shown by chromatography of denatured collagen on carboxymethyl cellulose (Piez et al., 1963). Chromatograms of denatured pigskin collagen are shown in Figure 21.5. Protein which behaves like α chains in the ultracentrifuge is found in two peaks, designated $\alpha 1$ and $\alpha 2$, which in a variety of collagens are present in a ratio of 2:1 and have different amino acid compositions. This suggests that the collagen molecule contains two chains of the $\alpha 1$ type and one of the $\alpha 2$ type, a conclusion which is consistent with the amino acid composition of native collagen. Furthermore, in this kind of sample prepared by salt or acid extraction there are in general two kinds of β components.

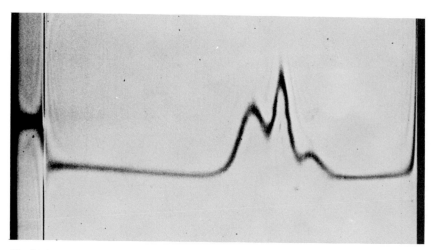

Fig. 21.4. — Photograph taken through Schlieren optics of denatured dogfish skin collagen after sedimentation for 160 min at 59,780 rpm. The boundaries, in the direction of sedimentation (left to right), represent the α, β, and γ components. The β and γ components are covalently linked dimers and trimers of the single chain α components. From Lewis and Piez, 1964.

These have been identified by amino acid composition and molecular weight determination as dimers containing two chains of the $\alpha 1$ type or one each of $\alpha 1$ and $\alpha 2$. These arise by intramolecular covalent crosslinks and are designated β_{11} and β_{12}.

The chromatograms in Figure 21.5 illustrate another point. Cold neutral salt solutions will extract a small amount of collagen which isotope studies have shown represents largely newly synthesized collagen. The larger amount of collagen which can be obtained by extraction with dilute acid is older collagen. It can be seen from the chromatograms that the content of β component is considerably higher in acid-extracted collagen than in salt-extracted collagen, indicating that cross linking is a slow process in skin. However, this is not necessarily the case in other tissues. For example, rat tail tendon yields almost no salt-extractable collagen, even from young animals, but gives a good yield of acid-extractable collagen; bone collagen in general can be extracted by neither salt nor acid solutions, even after decalcification. Therefore both the degree and rate of cross linking are characteristic of the tissue and may vary with age. These properties presumably bear an important relationship to function.

That the two chains designated $\alpha 1$ are in fact identical cannot be concluded from the evidence so far presented. That they may not be is indicated by studies on a collagen from codfish skin (Piez, 1964). When the α components are separated from β and γ components by molecular

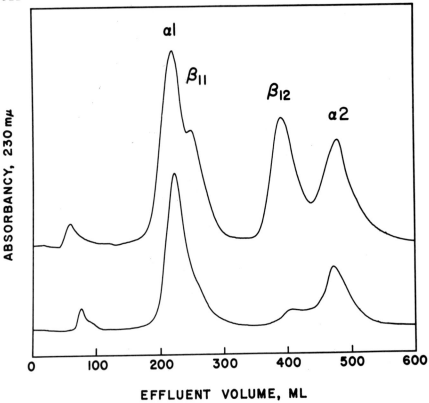

Fig. 21.5. — Chromatogram of denatured pigskin collagen obtained by salt extraction (*lower trace*) and acid extraction (*upper trace*). The collagen was chromatographed on a column of carboxymethyl cellulose at 40 C employing a salt gradient at *p*H 4.8. Protein concentration in the effluent was monitored continuously with a flow cell in a spectro-photometer. From Piez, Bornstein, Lewis, and Martin, 1965.

permeation chromatography and then chromatographed on carboxy-methyl cellulose, three peaks are observed with different amino acid compositions. Each a chain, designated $a1$, $a2$, and $a3$, is present in equal amounts, and analysis of the β fraction shows the presence of the expected covalently linked dimers. It is clear from the amino acid compositions (Table 21.2) that though all three are closely related they have distinctive features, a fact which suggests that they must be made as separate proteins.

Whether the $a1$ fraction of other collagens contains two different kinds of a chains which happen to have similar chromatographic properties is not yet clear. It might be expected from genetic considerations that a property as fundamental as this would be common to all collagens.

Most of the studies done on collagen begin with an extractable collagen.

Since this represents only a fraction of the total collagen the question is often asked whether the results obtained are applicable to nonextractable collagen. Because of the way proteins are synthesized it appears certain that nonextractable collagen is derived from the same monomeric unit as extractable collagen; they could not readily have different precursors. However, it is clear that cross linking occurs after synthesis of the polypeptide chains and even after the protein is deposited extracellularly as fibrils. There may conceivably be other time-dependent changes as well.

Cross linking in normally nonextractable collagen can be studied by extracting under conditions where denaturation occurs. For example, if salt and acid extraction is followed by extraction with 5 M guanidine, an additional portion of collagen can be obtained. When examined in the ultracentrifuge or by chromatography it is found that the proportion of β component in this fraction is higher than the theoretical limit of two-thirds which could be obtained if cross links were only intramolecular. Furthermore a new component can be identified, the covalently linked dimer of the α2 chain (Bornstein, Martin, and Piez, 1964). Since each

TABLE 21.2

Amino acid composition of codfish skin collagen and its constituent α chains (residues/1000 total residues)

Amino acid [a]	Collagen	α1	α2	α3
4-Hydroxyproline	56	55	52	58
Aspartic acid	52	50	54	51
Threonine	24.5	23.4	26.9	24.5
Serine	73	70	73	73
Glutamic acid	73	76	62	78
Proline	97	98	97	96
Glycine	339	339	348	347
Alanine	109	119	107	101
Valine	17.4	15.5	19.5	20.1
Methionine	18.2	16.7	18.3	16.8
Isoleucine	9.3	10.8	9.2	8.9
Leucine	20.9	18.8	24.4	17.5
Tyrosine	4.2	1.8	4.7	2.6
Phenylalanine	10.8	13.2	9.1	11.0
Hydroxylysine	6.5	5.5	9.5	5.3
Lysine	27.9	31.3	20.6	30.3
Histidine	8.5	5.2	11.5	7.0
Arginine	53	51	54	51
Tryptophane [b]	...	0	0	1.0
Amide nitrogen	(46)	(43)	(46)	(54)

[a] No chromatographic evidence was seen (<1 residue/1000) for 3-hydroxyproline or cystine.

[b] Determined by measurements of UV spectra.

collagen molecule contains only one $a2$ chain, this component (β_{22}) could arise only from an intermolecular cross link. A chromatogram of a guanidine-extracted collagen is shown in Figure 21.6. The β_{22} component was identified by amino acid composition and sedimentation in the ultracentrifuge.

It is apparent from this kind of study that cross linking proceeds both intra- and intermolecularly by what is probably a single continuous process. Figure 21.7 shows diagrammatically the process in its early stages. Functional groups on the protein, as yet unidentified, form interchain

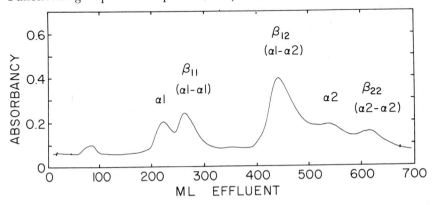

Fig. 21.6. — Chromatogram of denatured human skin collagen obtained by extraction with 5 M guanidine (see Fig. 21.5 for conditions). From Bornstein, Martin, and Piez, 1964; copyright © 1964 by American Association for the Advancement of Science.

cross links. Recent studies which will not be discussed here indicate that the cross link involves groups at one end of the molecule and, further, that this is the N-terminal end of all three a chains. All possible components appear to be formed, though not always in a completely random manner. In some tissues preferential cross linking may serve as a mechanism to control the properties of the tissue.

That cross linking imparts important properties to the tissue has been shown by studies on lathyrism. This is a toxic condition that is expressed by a variety of connective tissue deformities. It can be induced in experimental animals by feeding β-amino-propionitrile or several related substances. In growing animals the connective tissues lose tensile strength and the proportion of extractable collagen increases dramatically. Isotope and analytical studies have shown that this is accompanied by a cessation of cross linking (Martin, Piez, and Lewis, 1963). The extractable collagen contains very little β component.

Since the study of collagen structure is presently at a very active stage, the discussion here has been limited to those areas where the interpreta-

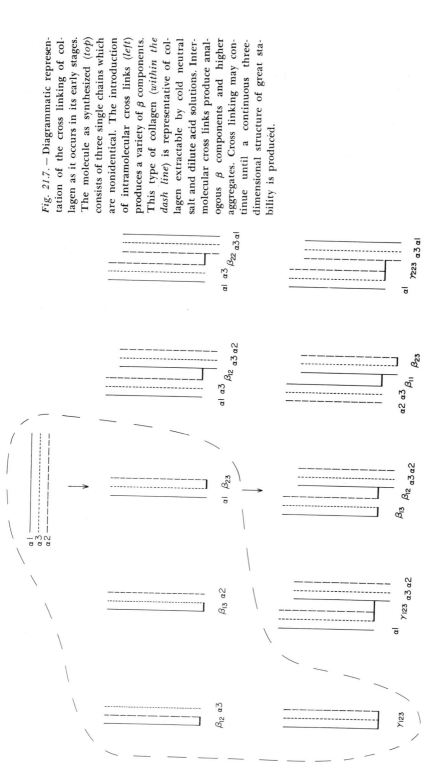

Fig. 21.7. – Diagrammatic representation of the cross linking of collagen as it occurs in its early stages. The molecule as synthesized (*top*) consists of three single chains which are nonidentical. The introduction of intramolecular cross links (*left*) produces a variety of β components. This type of collagen (*within the dash line*) is representative of collagen extractable by cold neutral salt and dilute acid solutions. Intermolecular cross links produce analogous β components and higher aggregates. Cross linking may continue until a continuous three-dimensional structure of great stability is produced.

tions are reasonably certain. There are, however, several aspects of collagen structure which promise to be of great importance to an understanding of function. These include the possible presence of intrachain subunits joined by nonpeptide (perhaps ester) bonds, the role of aldehyde groups in cross linking, and the distribution of amino acids along the chains. The eventual aim is to have a complete three-dimensional picture of the collagen molecule. Though unquestionably difficult, this no longer seems impossible.

References

Bornstein, P., G. R. Martin, and K. A. Piez. 1964. Intermolecular crosslinking of collagen and the identification of a new beta-component. *Science 144:*1220.

Gross, J. 1961. Collagen. *Scientific American 204:*121.

Gross, J., and D. Kirk. 1958. The heat precipitation of collagen from neutral salt solutions: some rate-regulating factors. *J. Biol. Chem. 233:*355.

Harrington, W., and P. H. von Hippel. 1961. The structure of collagen and gelatin. *Advance. Protein Chem. 16:*1.

Lewis, M. S., and K. A. Piez. 1964. The characterization of collagen from the skin of the dogfish shark, *Squalus acanthias. J. Biol. Chem. 239:*3336.

Likins, R. C., K. A. Piez, and M. L. Kunde. 1960. Mineralization of turkey leg tendon. III. Chemical nature of the protein and mineral phases, p. 143. *In* R. Sognnaes (ed.), *Calcification in Biological Systems.* Amer. Ass. Advance. Sci., Washington, D.C.

Martin, G. R., K. A. Piez, and M. S. Lewis, 1963. The incorporation of [14C] glycine in the subunits of collagens from normal and lathyritic animals. *Biochim. Biophys. Acta 69:*472.

Piez, K. A. 1964. Nonidentity of the three α chains in codfish skin collagen. *J. Biol. Chem. 239:*PC4315.

Piez, K. A., P. Bornstein, M. S. Lewis, and G. R. Martin. 1965. The preparation and properties of single and cross-linked chains from vertebrate collagens. In *Proc. NATO Advance. Stud. Inst. on the Structure and Function of Connective and Skeletal Tissues.* (In press.)

Piez, K. A., E. A. Eigner, and M. S. Lewis. 1963. The chromatographic separation and amino acid composition of the subunits of several collagens. *Biochemistry 2:*58.

Piez, K. A., and J. Gross. 1959. The amino acid composition and morphology of some invertebrate and vertebrate collagens. *Biochim. Biophys. Acta 34:*24.

Ramachandran, G. N. 1963. Molecular structure of collagen, p. 127. *In* D. A. Hall (ed.), *International Review of Connective Tissue Research,* Vol. 1. Academic Press, New York.

Chapter 22

Elastin

S. M. PARTRIDGE

Elastin is a rubberlike protein which is normally present in animal connective tissue in rather small amount; but this protein forms the major part of the tissue in structures such as the walls of arteries and in the elastic ligaments which support the heads of large ruminants. In beef animals there are considerable amounts of elastin in the muscles of the rump, but in other muscles the amount may be quite small and associated mainly with the walls of blood vessels. In the thoracic aorta the elastin is arranged in concentric laminae in such a way as to allow a very high degree of extensibility while still retaining strength. All elastomers so far investigated have the same kind of structure; in rubber and synthetic elastomers the structure is entirely noncrystalline and consists of randomly kinked linear chains cross-linked at intervals by firm chemical bonds. In order to show the typical properties of elastic recoil it is necessary in such a system that the chains between the cross links should be kinetically free and that rotation about the covalent bonds should not be restricted by interchain secondary bonding. It is characteristic of such a system that elastic deformation and recovery is associated with changes in entropy rather than with changes in internal energy. Up to the present time stress-strain observations of strips of elastic ligament have been interpreted in the light of rubber theory (see Hoeve and Flory, 1958). However, it should be noted that elastin requires the presence of about 40% of water before its behavior becomes rubberlike, and interpretation of its structure on the basis of comparison with anhydrous elastomers may lead to oversimplication.

The amino acid composition of elastin (Gotte *et al.*, 1963) is unusual for an animal protein in that the content of hydrophilic side chains is very low, and it was once thought that this was a necessary condition for the formation of a protein elastomer. However it is clear that this is not so since the insect protein resilin is a more nearly perfect elastomer than elastin and contains a very high proportion of hydrophilic side chains (Bailey and Weis-Fogh, 1961). It seems more probable that in both proteins the amino acid sequence between the cross linkages is such that the tendency to form an a helix with internal hydrogen bonds is restricted or totally prevented. Both resilin and elastin contain rather large amounts of proline, and it is possible that a contributory factor towards the lack of ordered structure is the spacing of pyrrolidine rings at fairly close intervals in such a way that the kinks produced in the peptide chains tend to prevent the formation of regular helices.

The first chemical proof of the existence of covalent cross links in elastin arose from an attempt to study its structure by partial degradation with dilute organic acids. The soluble products obtained by treating bovine ligamentum nuchae elastin with hot oxalic acid were shown to consist of multichain units by estimating the average length of the primary chains by an end-group method and combining with this an osmotic measurement of the particle weight (Partridge, Davis, and Adair, 1955; Partridge and Davis, 1955). Some years later, in 1962, my colleagues, Dr. J. Thomas and Mr. D. F. Elsden, and I set out with the idea that if elastin were broken down to the smallest possible peptides by the successive action of a variety of enzymes, then the peptides bearing the cross linkages should, on the whole, be larger than the straight chain peptides, and this might offer a possibility of isolating the cross links from the complex reaction mixture. We found that a number of peptide fractions with rather specific properties could be sifted out by using short columns of sulphonated polystyrene resins with different divinyl-benzene contents. These fractions retained the blue-white fluorescence of the original elastin and showed every sign of a cross-linked structure. Thus the fractions, which had osmotic molecular weights in excess of 1,000, showed the presence of 2 to 4 alpha-carboxyl groups and 2 to 4 alpha-amino groups which could have been engaged with separate peptide chains in the native protein. Further purification and chemical work on these peptide materials showed them to be mixtures of closely related multichain peptides containing mainly glycine, alanine, and proline. Attempts are still being made to isolate homogeneous compounds from these mixtures but the fractionations required are very time-consuming. However, we found that the peptide mixtures gave on acid hydrolysis two hitherto unknown amino acids in very high yield (Partridge, Elsden, and Thomas, 1963). These substances, which we have called desmosine and isodesmosine, have now been characterized chemically (Thomas, Elsden, and Partridge, 1963; Bedford and Katritzky, 1963) and have the structures shown in Figure 22.1a and b.

Both compounds are tetra-carboxylic-tetra-amino acids, and from their structure could form a common link with up to four peptide chains. From analysis of the products of enzyme hydrolysis it is clear that the desmosines

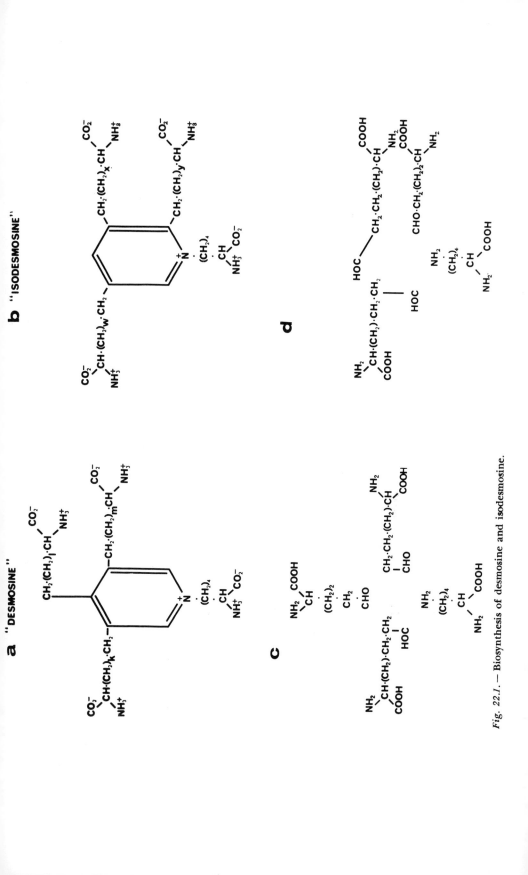

Fig. 22.1. — Biosynthesis of desmosine and isodesmosine.

do, in fact, link together at least two independent chains, but more detailed information must await the isolation of a range of desmosine-containing peptides of proven chemical homogeneity.

Desmosine and isodesmosine contain quaternary pyridinium rings, but unlike derivatives of nicotinic acid they do not undergo reversible oxidation-reduction reactions. On mild oxidation with ferricyanide at alkaline pH the pyridine nucleus is destroyed, yielding several ninhydrin reacting substances, including lysine, as the major component of the mixture. Indeed, if elastin fibers are treated with alkaline ferricyanide at room temperature they go into solution more quickly than with alkali at the same concentration. During the process a large part of the desmosine and isodesmosine is destroyed. This provides further evidence that the insolubility of elastin is due to the presence of the desmosine cross links. It should be noted, however, that peptide bonds are themselves easily ruptured by alkali under oxidizing conditions, and the titration curve of the soluble protein resulting from ferricyanide treatment shows the presence of new acid and basic groups which appear to have resulted from oxidative degradation of peptide bonds other than those concerned with the desmosines.

BIOSYNTHESIS OF ELASTIN

Feeding experiments with labeled amino acids show that the turnover rate for elastin in adult animals is extremely slow (see review: Partridge, 1962); and recently, Walford, Carter, and Schneider (1964) have extended observations on rats for periods of up to 930 days after the injection of ^{14}C lysine. The radioactivity declined until the 120th day (a decline due to growth of the rat), but thereafter it remained constant throughout life. These and other experiments suggest that apart from the repair of fortuitous lesions, the elastic structures of the large blood vessels are retained unchanged once growth has ceased.

No cells specialized for the production of elastin have been identified, but it is generally thought that the fibroblast can be responsible not only for the biosynthesis of collagen and the ground substance mucopolysaccharides, but also for elastin. It has also been suggested that specialized smooth muscle cells can be implicated in the biosynthesis of elastin, but whatever the cell responsible it must be assumed that some kind of soluble pro-elastin is the first product of synthesis and that this is afterwards incorporated into the cross-linked structure of the elastic fiber. In recent years some new information about the biosynthesis of elastin has appeared from what was at the time an unexpected source. Several groups of workers examining copper deficiency among domestic animals in the United States independently reported failures of elastic tissue as an early result of copper deficiency in chickens (O'Dell et al., 1961; Starcher, Hill, and Matrone,

1964) and in pigs (Weissman, Shields, and Carnes, 1963). The usual symptoms include rupture of the aorta or the heart valves, and elastin isolated from these structures swells more, and is more readily soluble in hydrolytic reagents than normal elastin. The amino acid composition of the copper-deficient elastin shows about three times the normal lysine content. It appears that the metabolic failure resulting from copper deficiency may be regarded as a failure in the mechanism of incorporation of a newly formed pro-elastin into the fiber structure, and this at once suggests that it is the synthesis of the pyridinium ring in desmosine and isodesmosine, or a precursor of this structure, that has failed. These considerations, and others, have led us to the expectation that the synthesis of desmosine might proceed by some mechanism similar to the scheme suggested in Figure 22.1c and d. Here it is assumed that at some point during the synthesis, the side chains of three lysine residues lying close together in the tertiary structure are deaminated and oxidized, possibly to the semialdehydes. The aldehydic side chains, which must be stabilized on a suitable steric configuration, then condense with the fourth unmodified lysine side chain. As yet there is nothing to show if the final step, ring formation, requires the mediation of an enzyme system.

In recent experiments, carried out in collaboration with Dr. A. Dorfman's group in Chicago (Partridge *et al.*, 1964), we have fed young rats with U-14C labeled lysine and then isolated the elastin from the aortas. After hydrolysis the specific activities of the isolated desmosine and isodesmosine were compared with lysine isolated from the same sample. The results of two experiments (given in Table 22.1) show that with animals killed 12 hr after the last injection of a course lasting ten days, the specific activity of desmosine and isodesmosine is approximately twice that of the lysine in the same protein sample. This indicates that at least two molecules of lysine are incorporated during the synthesis of both desmosine isomers. However, it was thought that the possibility that four

TABLE 22.1

Incorporation of U-14C lysine into desmosine and isodesmosine

Exp. no.	Labeled precursor	Amino acid isolated	Counts/μmole per min	Counts/μmole ratio to lysine
1	U-14C lysine	lysine	736	1
		desmosine	1,230	1.67
		isodesmosine	1,890	2.57
2	U-14C lysine	lysine	1,190	1
		desmosine	[sample lost]	...
		isodesmosine	2,400	2.01

molecules of lysine are required for the synthesis (as indicated in Fig. 22.1) was not excluded, since in the maturing elastic fiber there may be a considerable lag in time before completion of the full complement of desmosine cross bridges. Further experiments were then carried out in which a concentrated pulse dose of U-^{14}C lysine was given to groups of weanling rats and these were afterwards fed on a normal growth ration ad lib. until they were killed. The groups were sacrificed 0.5 day, 5 days, and 17 days after the last injection. Desmosine, isodesmosine, and lysine were then isolated from the purified aorta elastin and the specific activities determined (Partridge *et al.*, 1965). The results, given in Table 22.2, show that the molar specific activity of the desmosine isomers in-

TABLE 22.2
Incorporation of U-^{14}C lysine into desmosine and isodesmosine

Sample	Count/min	μmoles amino acid	Count/min per μmole	Counts/μmole ratio to lysine
		Group 1 [a]		
Isodesmosine	40.8	.062	660	1.57
Desmosine	45.9	.080	573	1.36
Lysine	176.2	.418	421	1
		Group 3 [b]		
Isodesmosine	91.7	.079	1,150	3.0
Desmosine	83.2	.085	977	2.6
Lysine	199.0	.527	377	1
		Group 4 [c]		
Isodesmosine	108.5	.113	958	4.56
Desmosine	113.0	.125	905	4.30
Lysine	76.7	.366	210	1

[a] Killed 0.5 day after last injection.
[b] Killed 5 days after last injection.
[c] Killed 17 days after last injection.

creased with time after the pulse dose and eventually reached a value rather more than four times that of the lysine isolated from the same sample of elastin. That the figure was fractionally in excess of four was to be expected since there was considerable growth of aorta tissue during the course of the experiments. Since elastin from young animals contains a high lysine-to-desmosine ratio, the activity of lysine is diluted to a greater extent relative to the desmosine isomers.

As indicated earlier, our chemical investigations have resulted in the location of all the carbon atoms in the desmosine isomers except for the methylene groups in the side chains as shown in Figure 22.1*a* and *b.* The demonstration of the biosynthesis of the desmosines from four lysine residues shows that the isomers arise by cyclization of straight-chain 6-carbon units and indicates I and II (Fig. 22.2) as the probable structures of the isomers. While this work was in progress a similar approach was made by Piez and his colleagues, who showed clearly that elastin from chick embryos contains more lysine and less desmosine and isodesmosine than elastin from full-grown birds. Over the age range investigated, the sum of lysine and quarter-desmosine remained nearly constant and there

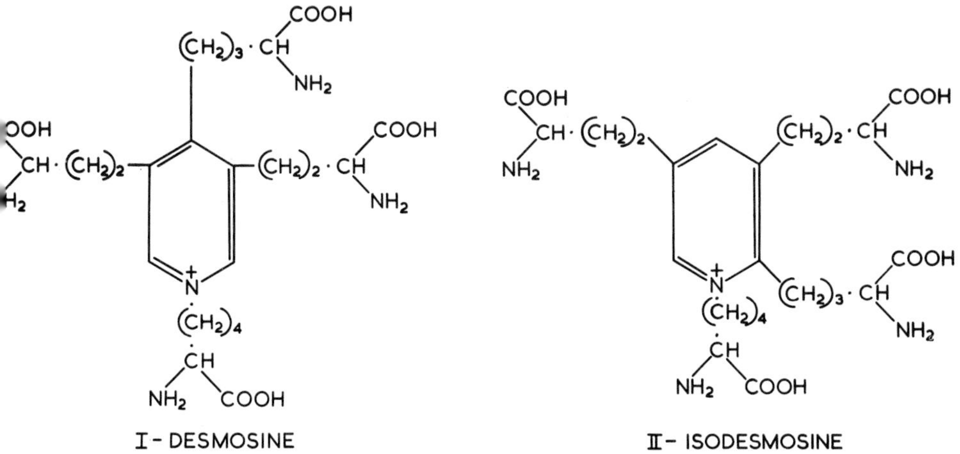

Fig. 22.2. — Structures of desmosine and isodesmosine.

was a smooth transition of the lysine-to-quarter-desmosine ratio with increase in age (Miller, Martin, and Piez, 1964). The same authors reported that in tissue culture experiments with chick embryo aorta, the amount of lysine incorporated into desmosine and isodesmosine increased steadily for some days after the culture had been allowed to take up a quantity of radioactive lysine from the medium. When the aorta tissue was allowed to grow in a medium without labeled lysine for eleven days after the pulse dose of U-^{14}C lysine the specific activity of desmosine and isodesmosine was, as in our own experiments with growing rats, a little over four times that of the lysine isolated from the same sample of elastin.

The incorporation of four molecules of lysine into both desmosine and isodesmosine, and the demonstration that the cyclization process is a slow one, provide an adequate explanation for the observed variation in the composition and physical properties of elastin from animals at different stages of growth. No detailed information is as yet available concerning the stability of the chemical intermediates in the process of formation of the desmosine ring from lysine residues. Semialdehyde intermediates have been proposed in Figure 22.1*c* and *d*; and, as with collagen, aldehyde groups can readily be detected on purified elastin fibers. It appears possible that the aldehyde residues have some stability under physiological conditions, and that the slow process is the condensation to form the quaternary pyridinium ring.

Since copper appears to be involved in the process, we considered it of interest to find out if the lathyrogen, β-amino-propionitrile (BAPN), would inhibit desmosine formation. The formula of this compound ($NH_2CH_2CH_2CN$) would lead one to expect that it might be a potent inhibitor of copper enzyme oxidations, particularly as it is already known to be able to enter cells without much inhibition of general metabolism. In recent experiments in collaboration with Prof. Boyd O'Dell (on sabbatical leave from the University of Missouri) and Dr. R. H. Smith's group at British Glues and Chemicals, Ltd., aortas from young ducklings were grown as organ cultures in roller tubes (O'Dell *et al.*, 1965). During the first two days in culture the medium contained 0.25–0.75 μc of U-^{14}C lysine per ml. The cultures were then continued for 10–12 days without further addition of labeled lysine, but half the culture tubes contained 5×10^{-3} M BAPN. Lysine, desmosine, and isodesmosine were then isolated from the purified elastin as before, and their specific activities determined. In the controls the molar specific activity was about the same as that of lysine, but in the BAPN-treated cultures the specific activity of the desmosines was only about one-tenth that of the lysine. Treatment of the living animal with BAPN yields concordant results. Table 22.3 shows analyses of material provided by O'Dell from feeding experiments with chicks carried out at the University of Missouri. It will be observed that both in copper deficiency and after BAPN feeding the lysine content of the purified elastin is very high and the desmosine content the same

TABLE 22.3

Effect of copper deficiency and BAPN-feeding on the composition of purified chick aorta elastin

Sample	BAPN-fed [a]	Copper deficient [b]	Control 1 [a]	Control 2 [b]
N% (ash- and moisture-free)	17.1	16.6	16.7	16.3
Amino acid residues/1000 residues				
Hydroxy proline	9.5	12.5	10.7	11.2
Isodesmosine	0.9	0.7	0.8	1.1
Desmosine	1.0	0.8	0.9	1.4
Lysine	10.5	17.4	5.3	3.6
Quarter-desmosines	7.3	6.0	6.8	9.8
Lysine + quarter-desmosines	17.8	23.4	12.1	13.4

[a] Purified by formic acid at 40 C.
[b] Purified by 0.1 N NaOH at 95 C.

or slightly reduced. The sum of lysine plus quarter-desmosines is much higher in the copper-deficient or BAPN-treated birds than is found with controls of the same age. The in vitro and in vivo experiments together suggest that in both copper deficiency and lathyrism the interference is concerned with the failure of an oxidative system converting lysine side-chains to an intermediate of desmosine formation.

An effect of lathyrogens in bringing about gross changes in the elastica of the large blood vessels in vivo has already been reported (McCallum, 1958; Zahor, 1964), and McCallum and Paul (1961) have shown by histological methods that BAPN suppresses the formation of new elastic fibers in tissue culture experiments with explants from chick embryo heart. I note that recently Miller, Martin, and Piez (1965) have briefly reported experiments with BAPN, rather similar to our own, which appear to lead to the same conclusions, and observe that these authors are as much intrigued as we are by the apparent parallelism between the cross linking in collagen and elastin which is suggested by the action of BAPN.

At this point it may be permissible to speculate a little about the meaning of the chemical information obtained by others and ourselves to date. Assuming for the present that the scheme shown in Figure 22.1 is basically correct, it is perhaps worth pointing out that in all experiments so far we have analyzed samples of elastin which have been purified either with hot alkali or with anhydrous formic acid at 40 C. In these samples, the lysine content in copper deficiency and in the presence of BAPN is elevated above the normal both in vivo and in vitro. This implies that at least the final reaction of those which lead to the conversion of lysine residues to desmosine and isodesmosine must go on at the surface of the growing fiber and not at the cell. Further, the fall in lysine, with the progress of the cross-linking reaction, is often greater than could be accounted for by the desmosine isomers produced. It thus appears that the cyclization reaction is a slow process and the conversion of the lysine side chains to an intermediate, possibly an α-amino adipic semi-aldehyde residue, is a much faster one. It remains difficult to visualize the condensation reaction itself since the reaction would require the simultaneous apposition of three aldehyde residues and an amino group; such a reaction would normally be extremely slow. We feel that if the reaction indeed follows this course, advantage must be taken of the steric specificity which arises from the tertiary structure of a native protein. With this in mind we have constructed models taking it as a basic concept that the cross-linked polymer arises by condensation reactions on the surface of the globular protein molecules of a soluble pro-elastin. If these molecules are of the same type as hemoglobin, the hydrophobic side chains will be arranged in a relatively water-free environment inside the molecule and

Fig. 22.3. — Structural model of elastin.

the hydrophilic elements, including the side chains of lysine, will be directed towards the surface. Systems of spheres of this sort can touch each other at four, six, eight, or twelve points according to the packing arrangement. If the points of contact each carry two lysine residues close together, we would have a situation ready-made to form a desmosine cross link. The drawing in Figure 22.3 illustrates this arrangement in a single plane, but

Fig. 22.4. — Model of elastin.

of course in an elastomer the cross-linking arrangement must be such as will allow the giant molecule to grow in three dimensions.

The model shown in Figure 22.4 was constructed on the basis that each globular molecule of pro-elastin contains two primary peptide chains and each globular molecule touches its neighbors at four points (directed to the corners of a tetrahedron) where desmosine links are formed. Of course there are many other possibilities, but the present model satisfies the experimental conditions to the extent that:

(1) In the absence of α-helix formation by the primary peptide chains such a model should give a high-angle X-ray diffraction pattern showing only diffuse rings, as observed for fibrous elastin.

(2) The packing arrangement is tetrahedral, and the free space not occupied by the globular molecules could have a value up to 66% depending on how closely their form approaches the sphere. This is not inconsistent with the observation that elastin must be wetted to the extent of at least 40% before it acquires elastic properties (L. Gotte, personal communication). Close-packed or body-centered cubic arrangements would yield densities higher than the values observed for wet elastin fibers.

(3) Elastin shows the enzyme specificity of a native protein, and the

model offers a ready explanation of the resistance of the fiber to many proteolytic enzymes that would otherwise be expected to dissolve it.

(4) The suggested structure would explain the remarkably specific effect of ethanol and a number of higher alcohols as activators of peptide bond hydrolysis by OH^- ions (Robert and Poullain, 1963).

Against the hypothesis it might be argued that elastic extension and recovery would be accompanied by a change in internal energy to the extent that the surface-to-volume ratio of the globular particles is altered during stretching and recovery. However, internal energy changes of a similar kind apply to any system of peptide chains in the presence of water. In the thermodynamic analysis of stress-strain curves obtained with strips of ligamentum nuchae it appears, from the results of several workers, that the elastic force is associated with entropy changes rather than with changes in internal energy. It seems possible, however, that the contribution of the internal energy change could be small, because of the nature and arrangement of the side chains in elastin. It should be observed that internal energy change during stretching may have analogy with the reversible "coacervation" phenomenon observed with soluble α-elastin; this occurs spontaneously on raising the temperature in the range 25–40 C (Partridge, Davis, and Adair, 1955).

References

Bailey, K., and T. Weis-Fogh. 1961. Amino acid composition of a new rubber-like protein, resilin. *Biochim. Biophys. Acta* 48:452.

Bedford, G. R., and A. R. Katritzky. 1963. Proton magnetic resonance spectra of degradation products from elastin. *Nature* 200:652.

Gotte, L., P. Stern, D. F. Elsden, and S. M. Partridge. 1963. The chemistry of connective tissues. 8. The composition of elastin from three bovine tissues. *Biochem. J.* 87:344.

Hoeve, C. A. J., and P. J. Flory. 1958. The elastic properties of elastin. *J. Amer. Chem. Soc.* 80:6523.

McCallum, H. M. 1958. Lathyrism in mice. *Nature* 182:1169.

McCallum, H. M., and J. Paul. 1961. Lathryogenic activity in vitro. *Nature* 192:273.

Miller, E. J., G. R. Martin, and K. A. Piez. 1964. The utilization of lysine in the biosynthesis of elastin crosslinks. *Biochem. Biophys. Res. Commun.* 17:248.

————. 1965. Factors influencing the biosynthesis of elastin crosslinks. *Fed. Proc.* 24(Pt. I):359 (Abstr. No. 1271).

O'Dell, B. L., D. F. Elsden, J. Thomas, S. M. Partridge, R. W. Smith, and R. Palmer. 1965. Inhibition of desmosine biosynthesis by a lathyrogen. *Biochem. J.* 96:35P.

O'Dell, B. L., B. C. Hardwick, G. Reynolds, and J. E. Savage. 1961. Connective tissue defect in the chick resulting from copper deficiency. *Proc. Soc. Exp. Biol. Med. 108*:402.

Partridge, S. M. 1962. Elastin. *Advance. Protein Chem. 17*:227.

Partridge, S. M., and H. F. Davis. 1955. The chemistry of connective tissues. 3. Composition of the soluble proteins derived from elastin. *Biochem. J. 61*:21.

Partridge, S. M., H. F. Davis, and G. S. Adair. 1955. The chemistry of connective tissues. 2. Soluble proteins derived from partial hydrolysis of elastin. *Biochem. J. 61*:11.

Partridge, S. M., D. F. Elsden, and J. Thomas. 1963. Constitution of the cross-linkages in elastin. *Nature 197*:1297.

Partridge, S. M., D. F. Elsden, J. Thomas, A. Dorfman, A. Teiser, and Pei-Lee Ho. 1964. Biosynthesis of the desmosine and isodesmosine cross-bridges in elastin. *Biochem. J. 93*:30c.

———. 1965. Incorporation of labelled lysine into the desmosine cross-bridges of elastin. *Nature 209*:399.

Robert, L., and N. Poullain. 1963. Etudes sur la structure de l'elastine et le mode d'action de l'elastase. I. Nouvelle méthode de préparation de dérives solubles de l'elastine. *Bull. Soc. Chem. Biol. 45*:1317.

Starcher, B., C. H. Hill, and G. Matrone. 1964. Importance of dietary copper in the formation of aortic elastin. *J. Nutr. 82*:318.

Thomas, J., D. F. Elsden, and S. M. Partridge. 1963. Partial structure of two major degradation products from the cross-linkages in elastin. *Nature 200*:651.

Walford, R. L., P. K. Carter, and R. B. Schneider. 1964. Stability of labeled aortic elastic tissue and pregnancy in the rat. *Arch. Pathol. 78*:43.

Weissman, N., G. S. Shields, and W. H. Carnes. 1963. Cardiovascular studies on copper-deficient swine. IV. Content and solubility of the aortic elastin, collagen and hexosamine. *J. Biol. Chem. 238*:3115.

Zahor, Z. 1964. Experimental vascular lathyrism and its application in investigations of experimental atherosclerosis. *Rev. Czech. Med. 10*:58.

Chapter 23

Summary and Discussion of Part V

PANEL MEMBERS: A. VEIS, *Chairman*
T. H. DONNELLY
D. E. GOLL
R. L. HENRICKSON
P. F. HOPPER

Veis: The presence of connective tissues in muscle is undesirable from the standpoint of its use as a food. The proteins collagen and elastin are not "complete" in terms of nutritive value. They do not contain all the essential amino acids. Nevertheless, they are rich sources of other amino acids and serve as much more than "inert diluents" in foods. The undesirable feature of their presence resides in their physical properties, as related to the qualities they impart to the texture of the muscle.

As Dr. Partridge pointed out in Chapter 22, elastin exhibits a distinct rubberlike elasticity, whereas because of its highly cross-linked nature it has a very low degree of solubility. Mature collagen fibers likewise are highly cross-linked and of low solubility. However, in marked contrast to elastin, the collagen fibrils are essentially inextensible, 5% to 10% elongations being maximal in the major structural elements such as the tendons. In the reticular sheaths, mentioned by Dr. Piez in Chapter 21, the collagen fibrils are formed into very complex branched networks, which are associated with some lipid, and these networks have an even more limited range of permissible mechanical distortion prior to actual rupture.

Collagen fibers formed by in vitro precipitation, as described by Dr. Piez, have all the typical electron miscroscopic order of native insoluble collagen, but they do not have high wet strengths. Moderate tensile stress is sufficient to elongate the fibers, with concomitant decrease in diameter; that is, the microfibrils and individual tropocollagen monomer units *slip* along each other. Thus, the forces between molecules in the fibrils are not particularly strong, and the high tensile strength of native collagen does not depend on properties intrinsic to the individual molecules. Many experiments have shown that two factors are essentially involved in the

341

structure stabilization: (1) the fiber weave and (2) the system of intermolecular cross linkages. The principal efforts of my own laboratory, at Northwestern University, have been directed at the description of the number, chemical nature, and distribution of these intermolecular cross linkages in mature collagens. The essential result I wish to emphasize is that in mature insoluble collagen almost all the cross linking appears to be of intermolecular character: the intramolecular modes of polymerization described by Dr. Piez and emphasized in the chromatograms shown are essentially irrelevant in terms of structure stabilization.

Some very interesting studies being carried out in the laboratories of F. O. Schmitt, at Massachusetts Institute of Technology, and of Tomio Nishihara, at the Japan Leather Company, suggest very strongly that the intermolecular cross linkages reside in "noncollagen" peptide attachments to the basic rodlike collagen structure. Schmitt has called these attachments "telopeptides" and believes that they are involved in regulating tissue turnover. I would go a step further, based on some of our own recent work comparing skin and dentin collagen, and speculate that the nature of these peptide attachments is intimately involved in tissue differentiation.

Nishihara has found that mature collagens can be solubilized by treatment with pepsin. Schmitt and his colleagues have used pepsin, trypsin, chymotrypsin, and most notably, pronase for the same purpose. The enzyme-solubilized collagens have all the physical characteristics of native soluble collagen, but, upon denaturation, are devoid of the higher molecular weight components (β, γ, and higher polymers) or at least have much lower amounts of these. The interaction properties of the enzyme treated collagens are altered so that aggregation and polymerization are inhibited.

It seems to me that the most fruitful area for understanding the behavior of collagen lies in the study of the cross-linking sites or peptide attachments. We are actively involved in this with regard to the role of such peptides in the mineralization of collagen matrices, but another area of great interest is the control of the physical properties of collagen systems by limited enzymatic treatment.

DISCUSSION

Donnelly: Would Dr. Piez elaborate on his statement that the interchain cross links are situated toward the end of the collagen chain?

Piez: There are two experiments which I will use as evidence for this statement. The first experiment involves the use of the enzyme which was isolated by Gross and Nagi (1966). This enzyme has the ability to cut the collagen molecule into two pieces — one about 25% and the other about 75% of the molecule. These are called TC^B and TC^A, respectively. This is similar to the action of pepsin on gamma globulin. If we assume that the collagen molecule has three chains, each extending the full length of the molecule, the enzyme must cut through all three. If the molecule is heated to uncoil the chains, pieces with molecular weights of about 25,000 and 75,000 are obtained. These pieces can be isolated and characterized. In addition, pieces of 150,000 molecular weight, formed from a cross link somewhere near the end of the molecule, are also obtained. One does not find 50,000 molecular weight pieces which would be formed if the cross links were located in the TC^B of the molecule; so that locates the cross link somewhere in TC^A. The second experiment has already been mentioned by Dr. Veis. If collagen is treated with a proteolytic enzyme like chymotrypsin, the betas are converted to alphas, except that the alphas are slightly modified. A few amino acids have been lost from the polypeptide chain. The simplest way that I can imagine that these events could occur and still retain a component which is very similar to the original alpha, would be to cut off the end of the molecule and its cross link. Through this process one would ultimately have chains which are just slightly modified from the original ones. I think this process could occur only if the cross link were at the end.

Donnelly: This explanation does not seem to exclude all possibilities.

Piez: One never excludes all possibilities. However, the only other real possibility is that the enzyme cuts the cross link itself. Almost any proteolytic enzyme will do this, and it seems unlikely that all proteolytic enzymes would have that kind of specificity for apparently nonpeptide cross links. Moreover, evidence exists that amino acids are released and polypeptide chains are modified.

Veis: The enzymes that cut out the cross links do not necessarily have to work on the cross links, but instead may work on regions right around the cross links.

Goll: Would Dr. Piez comment on his present views of the structure of the a strand of tropocollagen?

Piez: There are in existence two models which suggest 4, 5, 6, or maybe 7 subunits per a chain. The easiest way to imagine making a polypeptide chain of any size would be by connecting amino acids. Smaller pieces, however, may first be synthesized and then later joined together.

Hopper: In the renaturation of collagen, is the structure identical with native collagen?

Piez: Collagen renatured from a chains, as done by Drs. Kühn and Engel in Munich, or from γ component, as done by Veis and others, has essentially the same properties as native collagen and forms fibrils and SLS aggregates. However, the slightly lower optical rotation and viscosity and the slightly broader melting curve of renatured collagen suggest that the structure is not quite perfect. This may be very critical in vivo. Fibril formation in vivo occurs under conditions not very different from those which will denature collagen.

Sherman: Your slides on amino acid composition of collagen showed no cystine or cysteine. Are these amino acids present in collagen, and is there a possibility that disulfide bridging may be a means of cross linking?

Piez: Careful analyses of many collagens from vertebrate species have failed to demonstrate the presence of cysteine or cystine. The sensitivity of the analytical methods would show as little as one disulfide bridge per molecule. However, there are invertebrate collagens which contain cystine. It has been shown by Harrington that there are disulfide cross links in *Ascaris* cuticle collagen which are an important part of the structure.

Paynter: What evidence, if any, is there to show that collagen chains after having been separated by acid or alkali solubilization return to their original structure upon neutralization of the solution, or could this be a random recombination?

Piez: Acid or alkali under appropriate conditions can solubilize collagen without altering the chain structure. This is merely a disaggregation which is reversible. If extremes of pH are employed, the chain is lost and there may also be cleavage of covalent bonds. This is irreversible except under special circumstances. The recombination is then random. The special circumstances are those employed by Kühn and Engel. They have renatured collagen from denatured a chains by a slow cooling of warm solutions or by annealing to obtain collagen very similar to native collagen.

Sink: Does collagen contract with a concomitant change in its banding pattern and periodicity?

Piez: When collagen fibers are heated in an aqueous environment they shrink at 60–65 C to about one-third of their original length. This is the same process that occurs in solution at 35–40 C and has been referred to here as denaturation. All structure is lost. This is reflected in the loss of the characteristic band pattern of collagen fibers as seen in the electron microscope.

Goll: Petruska and Hodge have recently proposed some modifications in the packing of tropocollagen molecules in collagen fibers, and, on the basis of Fourier patterns, have suggested that there might be subunits in the a strands. Have you, in your work, seen any evidence for the existence of the subunits postulated by Hodge?

Piez: Petruska and Hodge have suggested that the a chains are composed of identical subunits arranged in a linear fashion and joined by hydroxylamine-sensitive bonds. Their evidence is certainly suggestive. However, this model is not compatible with other data. For example, peptides isolated after chemical cleavage with cyanogen bromide or after digestion with the tadpole enzyme have amino acid compositions which show a decided nonuniform distribution of amino acids. More direct evidence has been provided by Kühn, who has renatured $\alpha1$ chains in the absence of $\alpha2$ chains. The SLS aggregates prepared from the renatured collagen are indistinguishable from normal SLS. Since the Petruska-Hodge model requires that the SLS band pattern of collagen be the sum of the contributions of the $\alpha1$ and $\alpha2$ chains, the presence of only one kind of chain should give a very different band pattern. Since it does not, the model seems to be incorrect.

Donnelly: Would you comment about the role of nonpeptide primary bonds, such as ester linkages, in determining collagen structure?

Piez: There is good evidence from Gallop's laboratory and confirmed by others that there are bonds, perhaps twelve per molecule, which behave like ester bonds in their reactivity toward hydroxylamine and similar reagents. I readily accept this, but whether the bond is actually an ester and what its role is remains speculative until small peptides containing these bonds can be isolated and fully characterized. The presumption is that they join intrachain subunits.

Donnelly: The appearance of your sedimentation diagram (Fig. 21.4) suggests that the component in the center peak is either more homogeneous or has a lower diffusion constant than the other two peaks. How much attention has been given to molecular weight homogeneity in these components?

Piez: The sedimentation velocity pattern shows the a, β, and γ components, which have molecular weights of about 100,000, 200,000, and 300,000. The higher the molecular weight, the lower the diffusion constant and the sharper the peak. This is why the β component (the center peak) forms a sharper boundary than the a component. The peak representing the γ component is presumably too small to see any additional sharpening.

Lewis and I have studied molecular weight homogeneity of the a and β components. We are convinced they are homogeneous if isolated and studied under conditions where degradation is minimized. However, this is difficult to do, particularly with the β component.

Hopper: Is there any specific information known on the irradiation degradation of the collagen molecule?

Partridge: A considerable amount of work has been carried out on this question at the Low Temperature Research Station at Cambridge, England. Bailey, Bendall, and Rhodes (1962) showed that the hydrothermal shrinkage temperature of collagen decreased progressively with dose if wet rat-tail tendon collagen was exposed to ionizing radiations. Later, Bailey and Tromans (1964) described an electron microscope study of irradiated collagen. With doses of 10 Mrads or above, a gradual destruction of the fibril band-pattern occurred. The effect appeared to be due to a disruption of the hydrogen bonds which give stability to the structure, and resulted in the swelling of the fibers and increased uptake of water. A further study by Bailey, Rhodes, and Cater (1964) indicated that a considerable decrease in solubility occurred on irradiated wet fibers, and this was probably due to the formation of intermolecular cross links.

Wierbicki: Irradiation of precooked meat is related to degradation of connective tissue resulting in improved tenderness and, occasionally, in a friable texture; and it has also been shown to cause a release of hydroxyproline (Wierbicki and Heiligman, 1964).

Henrickson: Dr. Partridge, you indicated that there is an increase in the amount of elastin as muscular activity increases and also as animals become more mature. Do you think that the elastin synthesis is accelerated per se or could it be derived from collagen?

Partridge: I do not think it is possible for elastin to be derived from collagen because elastin has a peculiar amino acid composition. Elastin contains more valine than any other known protein. If one took all of the valine from collagen and converted it without loss into elastin, only a 10% or 11% yield of elastin would be realized. In regard to the question of animal growth, we know that elastin is metabolically very inert from labeling experiments. Fresh elastin is probably added to existing elastic tissue as an animal grows. This can be observed in the ligamentum nuchae. The ligamentum nuchae of young cows is composed of many fibrils surrounded by cells, and as the animal ages these fibrils increase in size until the cells eventually disappear. This structure then remains, apparently without alteration, until death.

Henrickson: Is there a difference in the elastin of very young compared to very old animals?

Partridge: The lysine content is much higher and the desmosine content is much lower in young elastin as compared to old elastin. The time interval required for cross-link formation is something like 10–14 days. In the very young animal the elastic structure contains a greater proportion of new elastin, whereas an older animal perhaps adds only a very small fraction of its total elastin over a period of days.

Kauffman: Is there any evidence to suggest that a form of chemical bonding exists between elastin and collagen as a function of structure in muscle? If so, how might this be associated with advancing physiological age?

Partridge: So far, nobody has suggested that collagen and elastin can be bonded together covalently. Admittedly, the last traces of collagen are very difficult to remove from the elastin of some tissues, such as the blood vessels, but I believe this to be due to a process of occlusion of small collagen fibrils by the growing elastin. It seems that the presence of large amounts of elastin intermingled with collagen tends to reduce the ease with which the collagen can be extracted by hot water.

Goll: Work on the rate of elastin digestion with elastase has shown that rate of digestion increases with an increase in chronological age. This is in direct contradiction to most work that has been done on collagen and rate of collagen digestion. Would you care to suggest any reason why this might be so?

Partridge: I have seen some reports indicating that the rate of elastase digestion of elastin increases with increasing chronological age, but so far, we have not experimented in this direction. The effect could, of course, be due to more effective screening by ground substance mucopolysaccharides in the young tissue. It is, of course, known that very considerable changes occur in the ground substance as elastic tissue ages.

Johnson: What is the effect of habitual exercise on elastin and collagen in muscle?

Partridge: I do not think that connective tissue responds to exercise as rapidly as muscle, but undoubtedly there is a very real effect of movement on fibrogenesis of connective tissue elements. It is known that during artificially induced hypertension the diameter of the larger blood vessels increases. This increase must be brought about by a process of remodeling, which is not at present understood.

Lalich: There is histological evidence that β-amino-propionitrile inhibits the synthesis of elastin. Dr. Partridge indicated that there is an inhibition of desmosine and isodesmosine synthesis, but I am curious about total elastin synthesis.

Partridge: It is true that the total amount of elastin in lathyrism is less than normal. This is probably due to the fact that cross links do not form and that the proto-elastin is therefore not cross linked to the structure of the growing fiber and possibly diffuses out and disappears through the lymph.

Hoekstra: Dr. Partridge, is it correct that BAPN also affects the cross linking of collagen and the synthesis or turnover of mucopolysaccharides? If this is correct, how do you rationalize this with your effects of BAPN on elastin?

Partridge: I do not know how far the synthesis and turnover of mucopolysaccharides is directly affected by BAPN. Of course, there is always the possibility of such an effect arising by general inanition. At present,

I have no views as to how BAPN could affect the structure of the mucopolysaccharides or their protein complexes.

Piez: There would seem to be some common step, presumably in the
biosynthesis of aldehydes, in both collagen and elastin, where a lathrogen
has its effect.

Donnelly: Soluble proto-elastin has been postulated as the probable
source of elastin. Has this material ever been isolated and has the structure been elaborated?

Partridge: Quite a number of workers have attempted to isolate proto-
elastin in the last few years, including ourselves; but this appears to be a
difficult problem. I think that a large part of the soluble collagen that
can be extracted from collagenous tissues really exists as fibrous structures
which have not yet been cross linked. The situation with elastin is rather
different. There is probably quite a short path between the elastin-pro-
ducing cell and the growing elastic fiber. The total amount of proto-elastin
in young tissue may be very small indeed.

Hamm: Dr. Piez, if the acidic groups in collagen are determined by the
dye-binding method of Frankel-Conrat and Cooper (1944) — binding safranin at about pH 11 — only one-half or one-third of the total acidic groups
react. The acidic groups are available, for binding safranin, only after denaturation or heat denaturation. Is there any explanation for this observation? Could hydrogen bonding between the acidic groups and the hydroxyl
groups of hydroxyproline be involved in this regard?

Piez: In the aggregate the intermolecular interactions may be such that
these groups are simply not available for titration. It is also possible that
this is a kinetic phenomenon and not really one of availability. These
groups might become available if given enough time.

Veis: Titration data show that all the carboxyl groups are available to
direct titration of fibers, although as Dr. Hamm said the safranin binding
does give you a lower availability. I think there may be a steric hindrance
of binding, although the binding sites are accessible to hydrogen ions. The
same observation has been made with basic groups (binding to Orange G)
where a similar partial blocking occurs.

MacKenzie: Could the presence of a large proportion of hydrophobic
side chains facilitate the flexing of a cross-linked structure in an aqueous
medium?

Partridge: I think this could be important with elastin. However, I
should make reference to a similar protein called resilin, which was discovered by Anderson and Weis-Fogh (1964) in the wing hinges of dragon-
flies. This protein apparently has a structure similar to elastin and is an
extremely good elastomer, but it has a high content of polar side chains.

The cross links in resilin have been identified as dityrosine and trityrosine by Anderson (1964).

Piez: Another important aspect of valine is its ability to prevent α-helix formation.

Hopper: Have any other mineral deficiencies produced the same type of inhibition of elastin formation as that demonstrated in copper deficiency?

Partridge: Of course, heavy metals interact with each other in a very complicated way, but so far as I know, copper is the only element which has so far been directly implicated in elastin fibrogenesis.

Hopper: Would it be possible by careful control of the mineral composition of animal feed to significantly alter the texture and tenderness of various muscles such as the rump muscle?

Partridge: I am quite sure that it would be possible to affect the texture of meat by inducing copper deficiency or lathyrism, but I do not think this would be a good thing to do, because it would affect the health and the efficiency of the animal as a muscle producer. Another approach to the problem of tenderness would be by producing as much dilution of the connective tissue network as possible. The aim would be to feed the animal a diet leading to very rapid growth immediately before killing, and in this way the connective tissue network would be packed with muscle protein, sarcoplasmic proteins, fat, and, of course, water.

Hopper: Considerable work has been undertaken on the effect of stress factors on the properties of muscle tissue. Is similar information available on connective tissue?

Partridge: It is rather hard to know what factors should be considered under the heading of "stress." Of course, connective tissue formation is under the control of hormones and these are bound to have at least a long-term effect. The water content of the intercellular space is also important. Apart from this, I do not think that much is known about the subject.

Bendall: When collagen is calcified, how is the Ca deposited?

Piez: In turkey tendon and in reconstituted collagen fibers the Ca is laid down as apatite, which initially is oriented along the banding. The work of Petruska and Hodge (1964; see also Glimcher, 1959) indicates that this may occur in what is known as the hole region of the fibril (a region in which there is a space in the protein structure).

Charpentier: My colleague, Dr. Boccard, has found a close relationship between urinary hydroxyproline excretion and collagen content of muscle in the case of young bulls. How is this observation related to collagen metabolism?

Piez: Urinary hydroxyproline excretion is apparently related to the rate of collagen turnover.

References

Anderson, S. O. 1964. The cross-links in resilin identified as dityrosine and trityrosine. *Biochim. Biophys. Acta 93:*213.

Anderson, S. O., and T. Weis-Fogh. 1964. Resilin: a rubberlike protein in arthropod cuticle. *Advance. Insect Physiol. 2:*1.

Bailey, A. J., J. R. Bendall, and D. N. Rhodes. 1962. The effect of irradiation on the shrinkage temperature of collagen. *Int. J. Appl. Radiat. Isotopes. 13:*131.

Bailey, A. J., D. N. Rhodes, and C. W. Cater. 1964. Irradiation-induced cross-linking of collagen. *Radiat. Res. 22:*606.

Bailey, A. J., and W. J. Tromans. 1964. Effects of ionizing radiation on the ultrastructure of collagen fibrils. *Radiat. Res. 23:*145.

Frankel-Conrat, H., and H. Cooper. 1944. Use of dye for the determination of acidic and basic groups in proteins. *J. Biol. Chem. 154:*239.

Glimcher, M. J. 1959. The macromolecular aggregation state of collagen and biological specificity in calcification, p. 97. *In* I. H. Page (ed.), *Connective Tissue, Thrombosis and Atherosclerosis.* Academic Press, New York.

Gross, J., and Y. Nagi. 1965. Specific degradation of the collagen molecule by tadpole collagenolytic enzyme. *Proc. Nat. Acad. Sci. 54:*1197.

Petruska, J. A., and A. J. Hodge. 1964. A subunit model for the tropocollagen macromolecule. *Proc. Nat. Acad. Sci. 51:*871.

Wierbicki, E., and F. Heiligman. 1964. *Proc. 16th Res. Conf. AMIF* (University of Chicago) Circular No. 76.

PART VI

Response of Muscle to Physical and Chemical Treatment

Chapter 24

Behavior of Muscle Subjected to Freezing and Thawing

B. J. LUYET

The effects of freezing on muscle may differ greatly depending on the state of the tissue and on the mode of freezing.

When muscle is exposed to freezing temperatures, it may be in one of three principal states: *prerigor, postrigor,* or *cooked.* Since, according to universal modern practice, muscle is not eaten unless it is cooked, the effects of cooking acquire a primary practical importance to the food technologist. But any cooked muscle has lost its physiological properties; its protoplasm is coagulated, its proteins are denatured, and the muscle is dead. Therefore, in this book, which places emphasis on physiological properties, the study of freezing of cooked muscle becomes a matter of lesser interest. The same should be said, with some reservation, of postrigor muscle (ordinary meat as sold at the butcher shop); it has lost some of its physiological properties. Thus, I shall examine the effects of freezing and thawing on the functional behavior and the structure of *prerigor* muscle; and I will limit myself to some brief comparisons between prerigor and postrigor muscle, as such, or as they become when subjected to cooking and freezing-thawing, or to freezing-thawing and cooking.

As for the mode of freezing, three factors call for special consideration: the freezing rate, the temperature reached, and the thawing rate. A section of this chapter will be devoted to the effects of these factors.

A glance at the phenomenon designated as "thaw-rigor" is perhaps the best introduction to the study of the effects of freezing and thawing on muscle, for the events usually described under that name probably represent the most drastic form of an injurious action which can be produced in milder forms by less severe treatments.

Thus, I will examine successively (1) the gross characteristics of a typical case of thaw-rigor, (2) the sequence of events in the process of thaw-rigor when muscle fibers are subjected to less injurious freeze-thaw treatments,

(3) the effects of the principal factors which control the degree of injury
or of resistance to injury, (4) some phases in the mechanism of structural
disintegration resulting from freezing and thawing. Then, in a final section, I shall compare the ultrastructure of prerigor and postrigor muscles
which have or have not undergone the freeze-thawing or the cooking
treatments.

Gross characteristics of a typical case of thaw-rigor

It has been observed that frozen muscle undergoes, upon being thawed,
an intense, irreversible shortening. This phenomenon has been designated as "thaw-rigor." Its essential characteristics are as follows: (1) the
muscle may shorten to 20% of its original length — a greater contraction
than is obtained with any other form of physiological stimulation; (2) it
swells considerably; (3) it exudes an acid fluid, as much as 35% of the
original weight (Kaminer, 1962); (4) it undergoes a structural disorganization: its striae become jumbled into a mass of "irregular bands," and it
passes from a quasi-transparent to a turbid state, a change indicative of
precipitation, flocculation, and/or coagulation; (5) it exhibits the same
chemical and enzymatic reactions that are observed in rigor mortis (see
Bendall, 1960).

The differences in appearance between the normal and the frozen-and-
thawed prerigor muscle fibers are shown in Figure 24.1; the degree of
shortening and swelling, in Figure 24.2; the exudation of fluid, in Figure
24.3; the presence of irregular bands, in Figure 24.4.

Fig. 24.1. — Effect of freezing and thawing on a prerigor
muscle fiber. Photo. 1: normal, unfrozen fiber; photo. 2:
same fiber after freezing and thawing. × 135.

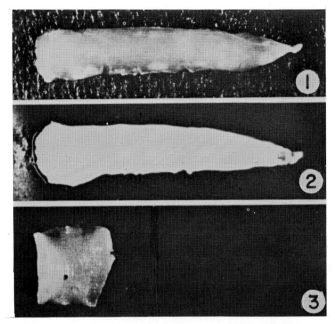

Fig. 24.2. — Extent of thaw-rigor shortening in the sartorius muscle of the frog. *Photo. 1:* freshly excised muscle; *photo. 2:* same muscle in the frozen state; *photo. 3:* same after thawing. × 2.1.

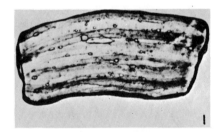

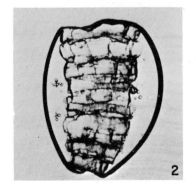

Fig. 24.3. — Shortening, swelling, and exudation of fluid in a frozen-and-thawed bundle of muscle fibers mounted in paraffin oil. *Photo. 1:* bundle of unfrozen fibers; *photo. 2:* same bundle after freezing and thawing. The exuded fluid, being nonmiscible with the oil, forms a conspicuous drop. × 45. From Luyet, Rapatz, and Gehenio, 1965; with permission of *Biodynamica*.

Fig. 24.4. — Appearance, in the phase contrast microscope, of dense irregular bands in porcine muscle fibers after freezing and thawing. From Cassens, Briskey, and Hoekstra, 1963; with permission of *Biodynamica*.

The sequence of events in cases of milder thaw-rigor effects

If, instead of treating muscle fibers in such a way that they undergo the drastic thaw-rigor effect (i.e., by relatively rapid freezing to very low temperatures and relatively slow thawing), one subjects them to a more moderate treatment, intermediate stages become apparent which reveal some features of the intimate mechanism of the injurious action of freezing and thawing.

Thus, freezing segments of single fibers at −5 C to −10 C and thawing them in air at room temperatures permit one to distinguish four stages in the thaw-rigor effect, diagrammed in Figure 24.5. The last stage seems to involve the passage of the muscle from its normal state, as shown in Figure 24.1 (*photo. 1*), to the disorganized state shown in Figure 24.1 (*photo. 2*). It also involves the passage from a regularly arranged system of striations to the irregular bands of which the mode of formation will be described hereafter.

Effects of the principal factors of injury

The predominant factor in determining the results of the freeze-thaw cycle seems to be the thawing rate. To obtain with segments of single fibers a rapid irreversible contracture of which the pattern is of the type shown in the lower curve of Figure 24.5, the proved method is apparently to thaw slowly in air a segment frozen at very low temperatures. Thawing rapidly a segment frozen in the same manner gives the four-stage pattern of injury shown in the upper curve of Figure 24.5.

Another important factor is the lowest temperature reached in the course of freezing. Freezing at −30 C, or below, followed by slow thawing, leads, as was just said, to the pattern represented in the lower curve of Figure 24.5, whereas freezing at −5 C, followed by slow thawing, yields

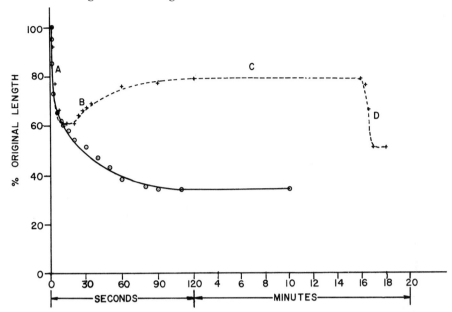

Fig. 24.5. — Behavior of segments of muscle fibers frozen and thawed under various conditions. *Lower curve:* rapid, irreversible shortening after abrupt cooling to very low temperatures followed by slow thawing. *Upper curve:* four-step pattern obtained after slow freezing at high subzero temperatures: *A*, sudden shortening; *B*, partial relaxation; *C*, latent phase in which the length remains constant; and *D*, final irreversible shortening. (For more complete information see Luyet, Rapatz, and Gehenio, 1965, from which the data of this graph are excerpted, with permission of *Biodynamica*.)

the four-stage pattern, and freezing at −2 C yields a pattern in which the reactions are attenuated, but which seems to be of the same type as that obtained at −5 C.

The freezing rate apparently exerts a significant action in controlling the degree of injury. According to Luyet and Thoennes (1938), after a very rapid freezing to very low temperatures, followed by very rapid thawing, the muscle fibers are still capable of responding to electric stimulation. But Thoennes (1940) could not obtain any more response from those fibers 23 min after thawing. Apparently, by that time, the fibers had passed from the latent stage into the final contracture stage. However, this point has not yet been confirmed by actual observations.

Another factor which is of particular significance from the practical point of view is the bulk of the material frozen. When, as in commercial practice, a whole carcass, or a large muscle, like the longissimus dorsi, is frozen in air, the rate of freezing varies with the depth, and the individual fibers are subjected to all sorts of restrictions by their neighbors. The situation is very complex, and observations made on single fibers are not transferable to the cases of freezing of whole muscles.

Finally, one should consider the condition of the muscle at the time of freezing. The tissue is entering gradually into rigor and its response will be gradually attenuated. In attempts at freezing slowly entire muscles, this factor has often been overlooked and the results reported are confusing.

Structural disintegration resulting from freezing and thawing

As was stated above, the behavior of frozen and thawed prerigor muscle involves a four-step process which leads to disorganized tissue characterized by irregular "contracture bands."

The mode of formation of these bands has been the object of queries by food scientists. Bendall and Wismer-Pedersen (1962) attributed the accumulation of dense material in the bands to a precipitation of sarcoplasmic proteins. Cassens, Briskey, and Hoekstra (1963), in electron-microscope studies in which they observed "the continuity of some myofibrils through the dense areas," suggested that the dark irregular bands result from a "violent contraction" which "piled up the myofilaments or parts of the myofilaments from different sarcomeres."

This problem was investigated further with the electron microscope in our laboratory (Amer. Found. Biol. Res., Madison, Wis.). In the case of chicken muscle, our essential findings can be summarized as follows: (1) Muscle treated for thaw-rigor shows two kinds of transversal bands — the well-known irregular bands (Figs. 24.4, and 24.6, at *IB*) and a kind in which transversal lines (apparently the Z lines) are separated by myofilaments running from one such line to the next (Fig. 24.6, at *NB*). This latter kind, which I call narrow bands, apparently correspond to the type described by several authors as sarcomeres in the contracted or supercontracted state. (2) One can follow (see Fig. 24.6) the passage from the regular narrow bands (*NB*) to the irregular bands (*IB*) by an aggregation of the material concentrated around the assumed Z lines. The latter can be seen to come gradually closer to one another and then to merge into the irregular band (*IB*). The merging of the regular into the irregular bands was recorded in motion pictures with the light microscope.

Ultrastructure of muscle subjected to various treatments

One may remark, to begin with, that the ultrastructure of the postrigor untreated muscle differs relatively little from that of the prerigor untreated. Except for some contraction, the slow passage into rigor mortis does not produce much conspicuous structural change.

In general, one would expect dead muscle to behave as a purely physical system and to be least affected by the treatment applied. In fact, postrigor

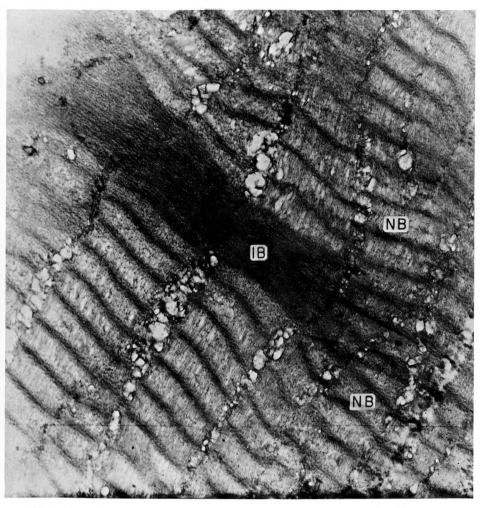

Fig. 24.6. — Electron micrograph of a longitudinal section through an irregular band (*IB*) across four adjacent fibrils, showing a convergence of the narrow bands (*NB*) into the irregular band. × 16,000. From Menz and Luyet, 1965; with permission of *Biodynamica*.

and cooked muscles do not, like prerigor, contract, relax, and undergo the final shortening upon thawing. However, one should not conclude that all treatments are innocuous on postrigor tissue. Cooking exerts a marked effect on it, as shown in Figure 24.7, in which the pattern of striations in a cooked postrigor muscle is compared with the pattern in a control postrigor specimen. It appears that the contents of the fibrils have undergone a packing upon coagulation, as a result of which the material split along

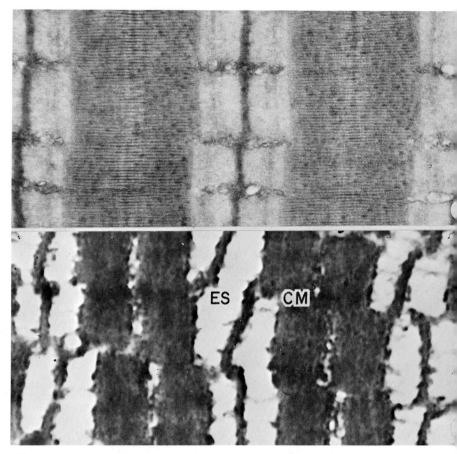

Fig. 24.7. — Electron micrograph of a longitudinal section of a chicken muscle showing the effects of cooking on tissue in the postrigor state. *Photo. 1:* uncooked postrigor specimen; *photo. 2:* cooked postrigor fiber with empty spaces (*ES*) in the region of the former I bands and condensed material (*CM*) in the region of A bands. $\times$ 37,000.

the I band, where there is now an empty space (*ES*), and became concentrated (*CM*) at the place of the former A band and on the Z line.

In contrast with this effect on postrigor tissue, cooking exerts a really devastating action on prerigor muscle. The original pattern of striations is hardly recognizable, or not recognizable at all, as illustrated in Figure 24.8, in which a prerigor untreated specimen is compared with a prerigor cooked one. Thus, the two treatments which cause the most drastic changes are cooking and freezing-thawing when applied to prerigor muscle.

Freezing-and-thawing of previously cooked postrigor tissue does not

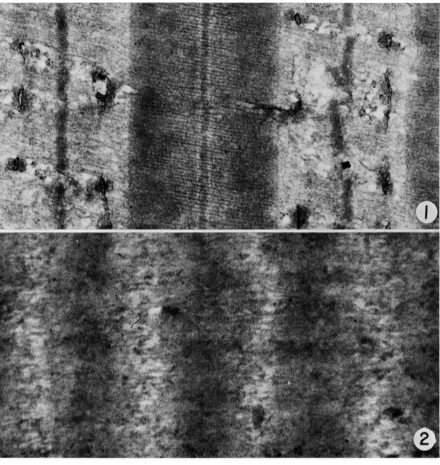

Fig. 24.8. — Electron micrograph of a longitudinal section of a chicken muscle showing the effects of cooking on tissues in the prerigor state. *Photo. 1:* untreated prerigor specimen; *photo. 2:* cooked prerigor fiber, in which the original pattern of striations is not recognizable. × 37,000.

alter greatly the pattern acquired by the cooked, nonfrozen material. Nor does freezing-and-thawing of cooked prerigor tissue change much the pattern resulting from cooking alone. Apparently material which is firmly coagulated has acquired resistance against further structural disturbance by freezing.

Cooking previously frozen postrigor or prerigor tissue produces changes of the type caused by cooking of nonfrozen postrigor tissue, which were shown in Figure 24.7.

ACKNOWLEDGMENTS

The author wishes to acknowledge with thanks the contribution of his colleagues, Drs. G. Rapatz and L. Menz; most of the photographs reproduced in this paper were taken by them or under their direction. Financial support for the research on which the paper is based was received from the Campbell Soup Co. and the U.S. Department of Agriculture, and is gratefully acknowledged.

References

Bendall, J. R. 1960. Post-mortem changes in muscle, p. 227. *In* G. H. Bourne (ed.), *The Structure and Function of Muscle*, Vol. 3. Academic Press, New York.

Bendall, J. R., and J. Wismer-Pedersen. 1962. Some properties of the fibrillar proteins of normal watery pork muscle. *J. Food Sci. 27*:144.

Cassens, R. G., E. J. Briskey, and W. G. Hoekstra. 1963. Similarity in the contracture bands occurring in thaw-rigor and other violent treatments of muscle. *Biodynamica 9*:165.

Kaminer, B. 1962. Water loss during contracture of muscle. *J. Physiol. 46*:131.

Luyet, B., G. L. Rapatz, and P. M. Gehenio. 1965. Observations on the sequence of events encountered in the passage of muscle fibers into "thaw rigor." *Biodynamica 9*:283.

Luyet, B., and G. Thoennes. 1938. La reviviscence de fibres musculaires vitrifiées dans l'air liquide. *Compt. Rend. Acad. Sci. 207*:1256.

Menz, L. J., and B. Luyet. 1965. Electron microscope study of the mechanism of formation of "irregular bands" in muscle undergoing thaw rigor. *Biodynamica 9*:305.

Thoennes, G. 1940. Properties of muscle fibers subjected to vitrification by extremely rapid cooling. *Biodynamica 3*:145.

Chapter 25

Heating of Muscle Systems

R. HAMM

The influence of heat on a muscle system (muscle here being regarded as food) encompasses many alterations. However, the most drastic changes in meat during heating are those that involve the muscle proteins. The shrinkage of tissue and the release of juice are caused by changes in the fibrillar proteins; the discoloration of muscle and the loss of many muscle enzymes are the result of denaturation of the sarcoplasmic proteins. This review will be restricted to changes in muscle proteins, particularly of mammalian muscle.

Muscle can be regarded as a complex of different proteins. Therefore, the question arises as to whether basic knowledge on the influence of heating muscle tissue can be obtained from studying heat denaturation of the isolated muscle proteins. The denaturation of myosin and actomyosin has often been studied by measuring the adenosine triphosphatase activity of these proteins. In myosin this activity is completely destroyed by short heating at 37 C (Engelhardt, 1946; Hashimoto *et al.*, 1959; Nanninga, 1962).

At temperatures as low as 30 C, small fragments are split off from the myosin molecule (Hashimoto *et al.*, 1959). Such investigations, however, cannot provide sufficient information about the influence of heating of muscle tissue, because the most remarkable changes in the tissue occur at higher temperatures, namely, between 40 C and 60 C. It should also be noted that pure proteins in solution or as gels may act in a different way from the same proteins localized within the myofibrils. The difference can be attributed to the special steric position of each protein, their relatively high concentration in the tissue, and the protective nature of accompanying tissue proteins. For these reasons it appears necessary to study the influence of heating on the muscle proteins *in situ*, that is in the muscle tissue or in the myofibrils.

Prior to discussing changes in the muscle proteins, it is essential that the term "denaturation" as used in this review be defined. Kauzmann's (1956) definition of denaturation as any process that alters or destroys secondary or tertiary structures in a polymer may be the best. However, it would seem that the formation and cleavage of intermolecular disulfide bonds should also be included in the definition of the denaturation process. There is no doubt that the term is not very exact, because it does not mean the same thing to different investigators. It may be better to adopt Colvin's (1964) proposition and drop the word "denaturation" from the language of protein chemistry and to describe explicitly the changes observed experimentally.

CHEMICAL CHANGES

Solubility of fibrillar proteins

Fibrillar protein (actomyosin) solubility is decreased by heating the tissue to 40 C. However, the greatest decrease in solubility occurs at temperatures between 40 C and 60 C. Above 60 C the fibrillar proteins become almost insoluble (Table 25.3). Those fibrillar proteins which are still soluble at 40 C seem to be changed by additional heating, as evidenced by decreases in the viscosity number and ATP-sensitivity (Table 25.1).

TABLE 25.1

Influence of mild heating on the viscosity number (Z) and ATP-sensitivity of beef muscle proteins, extracted by phosphate buffer at high ionic strength.

Heating temperature	Extract from coarsely ground muscle, containing mainly myosin, with small amount of actin			Extract from thoroughly minced muscle, containing mainly actomyosin	
	Relative viscosity	Z	ATP-sensitivity	Z	ATP-sensitivity
20 C	2.598	0.103	20	0.461	158
40 C	1.582	0.069	13	0.240	115
60 C	1.095	....	..	....	...

Source: R. Hamm and F. E. Deatherage, "Changes in hydration, solubility and charges of muscle proteins during heating of meat," *Food Research 25(1960):587.*

Alterations in pH, IP, and dye-binding

It is known that the pH of muscle tissue increases during heating (see Figs. 25.1 and 25.10; also Bendall, 1946; Wierbicki, Kunkle, and Deatherage, 1957). According to Bendall and Wismer-Pedersen (1962), the pH shift in myofibrils from 5.4 to 6.0 during heating represents the binding of 12 protons per 100,000 g protein, or a pH increase of about 0.3 unit in the intact muscle with all its natural buffers present. The change of the pH of tissue and myofibrils caused by heating depends on the initial pH. It shows a maximum at a tissue pH of about 5.0 (Hamm and Deatherage,

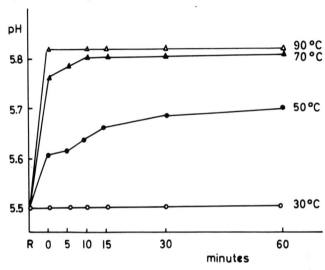

Fig. 25.1. — Influence of heating on the *p*H of beef muscle. From Hamm and Iwata, 1962.

1960); at this *p*H the buffer capacity of muscle is at a minimum. At initial adjusted *p*H values < 4.5 and > 7, heating causes a decrease in *p*H (Bendall, 1947; Savic and Karan-Djurdjic, 1958; Hamm and Deatherage, 1960; Van Logtestijn, 1964).

The *p*H changes that occur during heating may be caused by charge changes, or hydrogen bonding, or both, within the myofibrillar proteins, because such *p*H changes occur not only in the tissue, but also in the myofibrils. Some insight into the charge changes and intermolecular cross linking is given by a study of the dependence of water-holding capacity of muscle tissue on the *p*H (Hamm, 1960). The *p*H at which the water-holding capacity is minimal (5.0 in the native muscle) corresponds approximately to the isoelectric point (IP) of actomyosin. In these experiments the tissue was heated at its normal *p*H, and subsequent to heating the *p*H was adjusted by addition of acid or base. Heating at 40–45 C decreases the water-holding capacity of the tissue in the isoelectric range only (Fig. 25.2). It is important that the muscle does not lose its water-holding capacity at *p*H values < 4.5 and > 7.0. This indicates that in heating up to 40 C the dehydration and shrinkage cannot be caused by the formation of stable cross linkages. It is probable that the release of juice and shrinking of tissue in this range of temperatures are produced by a certain unfolding of peptide chains. These changes may cause the formation of new hydrogen bonds around the IP of actomyosin. Addition of weak acid or base breaks these linkages and restores the hydration. Heating from 40 C

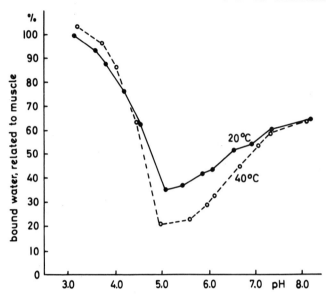

Fig. 25.2. — Influence of *p*H on the water-holding capacity of native (●——●) and mildly heated (○---○, 40 C) beef muscle. From Hamm and Deatherage, 1960.

to 50 C results in new cross linkages which apparently cannot be split off by increasing the *p*H up to 8.0; however, these linkages ("acid-unstable" cross linkages) are unstable against acidification to *p*H 3.0 (Fig. 25.3). Only at temperatures above 50 C do "acid-stable" cross linkages arise (Hamm and Deatherage, 1960). The formation of a tight protein network linked by such bonds increases with rising temperature.

With increasing temperature, the IP of tissue (minimum of water-holding capacity) is shifted to a higher *p*H (see Figs. 25.3 and 25.4; also Hamm and Deatherage, 1960; Shimizu, Fujita, and Simidu, 1960; Anglemier, el-Badani, and Cain, 1964; Hamm, unpublished, 1965). Therefore the positive net charge of myofibrillar proteins is increased. The IP shift to a higher *p*H during heating has been observed with other proteins and is generally explained by splitting of hydrogen bonds which should release additional positive charges (Segal, 1963). However, an increase in positively charged protein-groups, caused by heating the tissue, could not be confirmed by the titration method (Connell and Howgate, 1964). These workers could not find any significant influence of heating on the titratable charged groups of myofibrils.

During heat-coagulation of tissue, myofibrils, and actomyosin, the number of dye-binding acidic groups of proteins decreases (see Fig. 25.10; also Hamm and Deatherage, 1960; Bendall and Wismer-Pedersen, 1962;

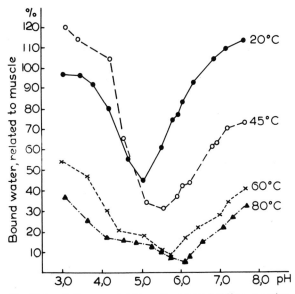

Fig. 25.3. — Influence of *p*H on the water-holding capacity of beef muscle after heating at different temperatures. From Hamm and Deatherage, 1960.

Hamm, 1963). But there is no real change in the acidic groups, because heating of myofibrils at 70 C does not influence the content of glutamic acid, aspartic acid, tyrosine, and cysteine (Hamm, 1963; it should be mentioned that the other amino acids of muscle are not affected by heating up to 80 C; see Beuk, Chornock, and Rice, 1948; Schweigert *et al.*, 1949; Greenwood, Kraybill, and Schweigert, 1951). Coagulation of muscle proteins only reduces the availability of acidic groups for binding safranine cations. After thorough mincing and homogenizing of the heated myofibrils almost all acidic groups are able to bind safranine. Therefore, the increase in the positive net charge of the myofibrillar proteins and the shift of IP during heating cannot be caused by a decrease in acidic groups, as was originally suggested (Hamm and Deatherage, 1960). Recent results (Hamm, unpublished, 1965), obtained by studying the influence of *p*H on the number of dye-binding charged groups of myofibrils, may provide the explanation (Fig. 25.4). The IP of the myofibrillar proteins, which is marked by a minimum of bound dye (intersecting point of curves in Fig. 25.4) is shifted to a higher *p*H upon heating. The most remarkable changes in dye-binding occur between *p*H 5.5 and 7. The *p*K of the imidazolium group of histidine falls in this *p*H range. The increase in available dye-binding imidazolium groups (around *p*H 5) lowers the number of available dye-binding acidic groups (around *p*H 6) because of the formation of salt-

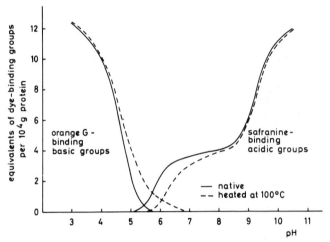

Fig. 25.4. — Influence of *p*H on the amount of orange G-binding basic groups and safranine-binding acidic groups of native and heated (100 C) myofibrils.

like cross linkages between acidic and imidazolium groups. With increasing *p*H, the imidazolium groups are discharged and cannot influence the number of available acidic groups either in the native or in the heated myofibrils. Apparently some imidazolium groups of histidine, which are masked in the native myofibrils, are released by unfolding of actomyosin during heating. The observed release of 10 to 15 imidazolium groups per 100,000 g protein during heating explains the shift and the increase in *p*H. Heating of tissue and myofibrils at temperatures above 80 C results in a loss of dye-binding basic groups (at 120 C: 1.9 ± 1.4 g equivalents per 10^4 g protein; see Hamm, 1963).

Browning reaction

It is possible that this decrease in basic groups is related to *Maillard reactions*. Browning of muscle proteins begins at about 90 C and increases with rising temperature and time of heating. Initially the browning reactions may contribute to a favorable taste, but later they result in an undesirable bitter taste. Furthermore, they cause a decrease in digestibility and in the content of essential amino acids such as lysine (Donoso *et al.*, 1962). The amount of brown color development is related to the level of reducing sugars in the tissue (Pearson *et al.*, 1962).

Ion binding

The denaturation of myofibrillar proteins during heating of tissue is connected with a release of protein-bound alkaline earth metals (see Table

TABLE 25.2

Influence of heating on the binding of cations by the water-insoluble proteins of beef muscle, expressed in μmoles bound cation per g protein.

Muscle state	Mg	Ca
Native	13.0 ± 5.0	4.4 ± 0.7
Heated at 90 C for 30 min	2.2 ± 1.8	1.0 ± 0.5

Source: R. Hamm, "Chemische und physikalische Veränderungen beim Erhitzen von Fleisch. II. Mitt. Einfluss des Erhitzens auf den Bindungszustand von Magnesium, Calcium und Phosphat," *Z. Lebensm. Untersuch. Forsch. 117(1962)*:113.

25.2 and Fig. 25.5; also Wierbicki *et al.*, 1957; Hamm, 1962*b*; el-Badani, Anglemier, and Cain, 1964). Apparently the binding of cations by muscle proteins, as chelates, is related to a certain spatial structure of the peptide chains. Unfolding of the peptide chains caused by heat denaturation lowers the sequestering power of muscle proteins. It is interesting that the binding of zinc by muscle proteins is increased by heat (el-Badani *et al.*, 1964). The release of available imidazolium groups brought about by heating the protein may be responsible for the enhanced binding of zinc.

The binding of phosphate should be mentioned in a discussion of the influence of heating on the ion-binding properties of muscle proteins. At temperatures above 90 C free inorganic orthophosphate is released, and determines the change in tissue conductivity as a result of heating (Fig.

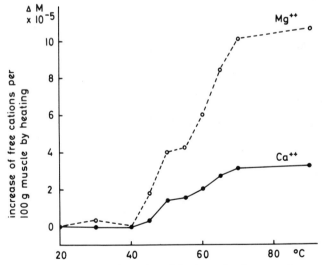

Fig. 25.5. — Influence of heating of beef muscle tissue on the release of protein-bound Ca and Mg. From Hamm, 1962*b*.

25.6). Of the phosphate released, 80% originates from low-molecular weight compounds (hydrolysis of phosphoric esters). However, about 20% of it was bound to muscle proteins. The amount of phosphate bound to the coagulated proteins drops from 59 μmoles to 36 μmoles per g protein upon heating the tissue from 90 C to 120 C (Hamm, 1962b).

Reactions of sulfhydryl groups

It is well known that information about conformational changes of proteins resulting from denaturation is obtained from changes in the availability of sulfhydryl groups. An unfolding of peptide chains increases the availability of some sulfhydryl groups for certain sulfhydryl reagents. All sulfhydryl groups that are present in tissue, myofibrils, or actomyosin can be determined by reaction with $AgNO_3$ and amperometric titration, whereas N-ethyl-maleimide (NEM) reacts only with easily available sulfhydryl groups (Hamm and Hofmann, 1965).

Heating of myofibrils to 70 C results in an increased number of sulfhydryl groups reacting with NEM (Fig. 25.7). Apparently heat denaturation causes an unfolding of the peptide chains and, therefore, a release of reactive sulfhydryl groups which were hidden within the folded structure of the native protein.

The number of sulfhydryl groups in myofibrils reacting with $AgNO_3$ is not affected by heating up to 70 C (Fig. 25.8). This is understandable because all sulfhydryl groups in the native protein are able to react with $AgNO_3$ under the experimental conditions used. From this result one can conclude that the process of heat coagulation of beef muscle taking place

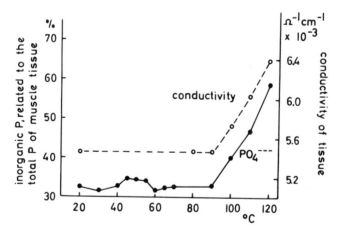

Fig. 25.6. — Influence of heating on the amount of free orthophosphate and the conductivity of beef muscle tissue. From Hamm, 1962b.

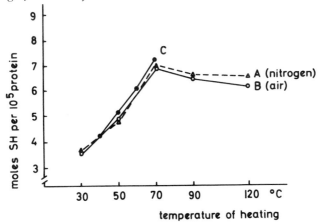

Fig. 25.7. — Influence of heating (30 min) of myofibrils on the amount of sulfhydryl groups reacting with NEM. From Hamm and Hofmann, 1965.

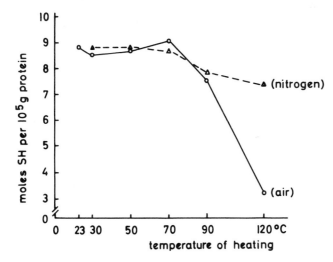

Fig. 25.8. — Influence of heating (30 min) of myofibrils on the amount of sulfhydryl groups reacting with $AgNO_3$. From Hamm and Hofmann, 1965.

between 40 C and 60 C is not accompanied by the formation of new disulfide bonds between the protein molecules. However, the heating of myofibrils to the temperatures which are commonly employed for canning meat (110–120 C), considerably decreases the number of sulfhydryl groups reacting with $AgNO_3$ (Fig. 25.8). This effect is greater in the presence of air than for nitrogen or argon. Apparently the decreased number of sulfhydryl groups at high temperatures is due to an oxidation process.

If myofibrils heated at 120 C for 30 min are treated with NaBH$_4$, almost the same number of sulfhydryl groups is found to react with AgNO$_3$ after reduction as in the reduced unheated myofibrils (Hamm and Hofmann, 1965). This result clearly shows that the decreased number of sulfhydryl groups from heating under these conditions is caused for the most part by oxidation to disulfide groups. The increase in the toughness of meat known to be caused by prolonged cooking may be due to such a formation of intermolecular disulfide linkages between the peptide chains of the actomyosin. However, if the myofibrils are heated at 120 C for a longer time, e.g., for 5 hr, the number of sulfhydryl groups determined after reduction by NaBH$_4$ is considerably less than in the reduced unheated samples (Hamm and Hofmann, 1965). Therefore, it appears that some sulfhydryl and disulfide groups are destroyed under these conditions of heating.

Formation of odoriferous compounds

Of all the reactions which may be responsible for the destruction of sulfhydryl groups, the formation of H$_2$S is most prominent (Fraczak and Pajdowski, 1955; Yueh and Strong, 1960; Hornstein, Crowe, and Sulzbacher, 1960). The formation of H$_2$S from myofibrils begins at about 80 C and increases exponentially with rising temperature (Fig. 25.9). The formation of H$_2$S increases with increasing time of heating, also. Heating of the total beef muscle tissue up to 120 C for 30 min caused the formation

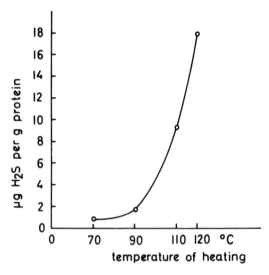

Fig. 25.9. — Influence of heating (30 min) on the formation of H$_2$S from myofibrils. From Hamm and Hofmann, 1965.

of 18.9 ± 0.5 μg H_2S per g protein. This is almost the same amount of H_2S formed by heating the myofibrils (18.3 ± 0.5 μg). Therefore, nearly all of the H_2S released during heating originates from the structural proteins and not from water-soluble substances (e.g., cysteine or glutathione) present in the sarcoplasm. After blocking the sulfhydryl groups of the native myofibrils by reaction with $AgNO_3$ or NEM, heating at 120 C no longer causes the formation of H_2S (Hamm and Hofmann, 1965). These results show that H_2S originates from the easily reacting sulfhydryl groups of the myofibrillar proteins and not from disulfide groups or methionine. Fraczak and Pajdowski (1955) and recently Mecchi, Pippen, and Lineweaver (1964) have suggested that H_2S developed during the heating of meat may originate from the sulfhydryl groups of the muscle proteins. Our experiments demonstrate that this is indeed the case. Most of the results reported on the sulfhydryl-disulfide system could also be obtained with actomyosin. According to Johnson and Vickery (1964), the amount of H_2S developed during heating of postrigor muscle increases with increasing pH of the tissue. There is no agreement as to whether or not volatile mercaptans arise during heating of meat. Some investigators have identified methane, ethane, propane, and butane-thiol by gas-chromatography after heating at 122 C (Kramlich and Pearson, 1958; Brennan and Bernhard, 1964); other authors could not find mercaptans (Yueh and Strong, 1960; Luh *et al.*, 1964). Perhaps different results are obtained with different meats and different temperatures of heating. Of course, the formation of H_2S, mercaptans, and ammonia (Smorodintsev, 1952) during the heating of muscle systems at relatively high temperatures entails a loss of essential amino acids such as methionine, cysteine, etc. (Donoso *et al.*, 1962).

Enzyme systems

In consideration of denaturation of muscle proteins, the influence of heating on muscle enzymes should not be forgotten. The thermal treatment of muscle results in a loss of its enzymatic activity. In the canning of meat it is important not only to destroy the microorganisms but also to eliminate the activity of muscle enzymes, because these enzymes — particularly the proteinases — may spoil the meat. The stability of the numerous muscle enzymes against heating is quite different. The proteinases are inactivated at 70–73 C (Chiambalero, Johnson, and Drake, 1959; Frumkin, Pawlowa, and Dosorez, 1962). The activity of phosphatases of muscle shows a similar behavior (Körmendy and Gantner, 1960). The adenosine triphosphatase activity of actomyosin is much less stable; it can be completely eliminated by brief heating of muscle tissue at 45 C (Nemitz and Partmann, 1959). Glutamic-oxalacetic-transaminase, however, is very stable and exhibits remarkable activity even in muscle heated for 60 min at 70 C (Gantner and Hamm, 1964).

Noncontinuous heating effects

The effect of temperature on the different changes during heating of muscle does not present a continuous process, but shows a characteristic step between 50 C and 55 C. In this range of temperature the changes are delayed or even slightly reversed (Hamm and Deatherage, 1960). This is true for the increase in pH, the decrease in water-holding capacity, and easily available dye-binding acidic groups (Fig. 25.10). Such a delay is also shown in the release of protein-bound Ca and Mg during the heating of muscle (Fig. 25.5). It is interesting that the heating of pure actomyosin also

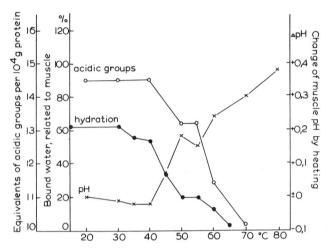

Fig. 25.10. — Influence of heating on water-holding capacity, pH, and easily available dye-binding acidic groups of beef muscle. From Hamm and Deatherage, 1960.

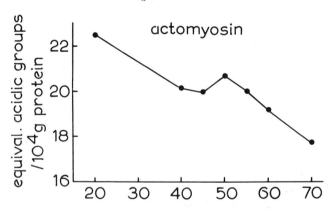

Fig. 25.11. — Influence of heating on the amount of easily available dye-binding acidic groups of actomyosin. From Hamm, 1963.

shows a stepwise denaturation process (Fig. 25.11). Apparently, between 50 C and 55 C a reorientation of the myofibrillar proteins occurs which parallels the coagulation process.

Heat denaturation mechanisms

The results obtained with the myofibrillar proteins suggest a mechanism of heat denaturation of muscle tissue as follows. Between 35 C and 50 C the actomyosin molecules are unfolded. At about 35 C coagulation begins, caused by the aggregation of the unfolded molecules and accompanied by the formation of new, relatively unstable cross linkages. Between 50 C and 70 C the unfolding as well as the coagulation are continued. In this temperature range a tight protein network linked by relatively stable bonds is formed. This process is due neither to the formation of disulfide bonds by the oxidation of sulfhydryl groups nor to the formation of salt linkages, but perhaps to new hydrogen bonds, to some disulfide-sulfhydryl exchange, and/or to interactions between nonpolar side chains. It should be mentioned that not in every case does unfolding of the peptide helix precede the coagulation process. Coagulation of proteins may occur without preceding unfolding, particularly in the isoelectric range of pH, because at the IP the lack of intramolecular electrostatic repulsion impedes the unfolding of the helix whereas the lack of intermolecular electrostatic repulsion at the IP promotes coagulation (Jaenicke, 1965). However, during the heating of the myofibrils, unfolding and coagulation appear to be closely connected. At temperatures above 70 C, unfolding appears to be complete. The oxidation of sulfhydryl groups to disulfide groups begins and is continued with rising temperature. Above 80 C sulfhydryl groups of actomyosin are transformed to H_2S. Further changes of the myofibrillar proteins during heating from 80 C up to 120 C are indicated by the decrease in dye-binding basic groups and the release of protein-bound Ca and Mg.

PHYSICAL CHANGES

Coagulation of myofibrillar proteins

The colloidal-chemical changes in tissue during heating are mainly a result of the coagulation of myofibrillar proteins. This process of coagulation can be followed by measuring the compressibility of tissue (Fig. 25.12). As these curves indicate, coagulation (increase of rigidity) begins between 30 C and 40 C and is almost complete at 55 C. Coagulation of isolated myosin also begins at 35 C (Greenstein and Edsall, 1940). According to Locker (1956), at 53 C 82%–92% of pure myosin is coagulated, and at least four subunits of the myosin molecule are split off in a soluble state.

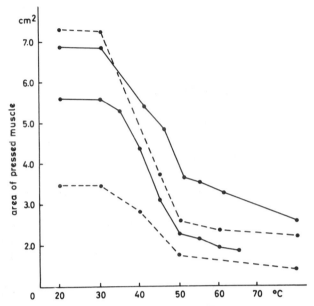

Fig. 25.12. — Influence of heating on the rigidity (area of pressed tissue) of beef muscle (four different animals). From Hamm and Deatherage, 1960.

Water-holding capacity

The coagulation of the myofibrillar proteins by heat-denaturation causes the release of juice because the proteins lose a great deal of their water-holding capacity (see Figs. 25.13 and 25.14; also Wierbicki *et al.*, 1957; Hamm and Deatherage, 1960; Hamm and Iwata, 1962). Parallel with coagulation, the decrease in water-holding capacity begins at about 35 C and occurs primarily between 40 C and 50 C. At 60 C the coagulation and subsequent release of juice are not yet completed, but continue to a small extent with increasing temperature. The influence of thermal treatment on the water-holding capacity of muscle mainly concerns water which is not "hydration-water" but which is "free" in the physical-chemical sense of this term and which is immobilized within the network of protein filaments. During coagulation of the fibrillar muscle proteins, a great part of this water becomes freely movable and is released from the tissue. It is interesting that the mono- and multimolecular layers of "hydration-water," bound to the polar groups of the muscle proteins, are not influenced by heat coagulation. This is shown by the absorption isotherms of native and heated muscle tissue (Fig. 25.15).

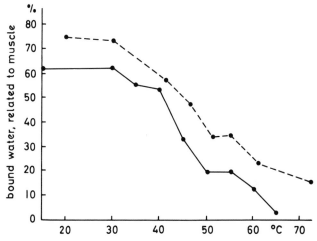

Fig. 25.13. — Influence of heating on the water-holding capacity of beef muscle. From Hamm and Deatherage, 1960.

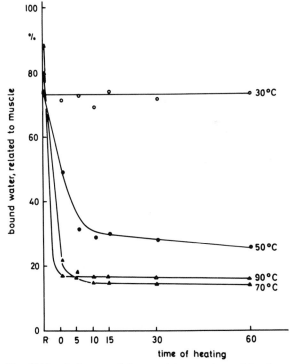

Fig. 25.14. — Influence of time and temperature of heating on the water-holding capacity of beef muscle. *R–O*: decrease of water-holding capacity during heating from 20 C up to the given temperature. From Hamm and Iwata, 1962.

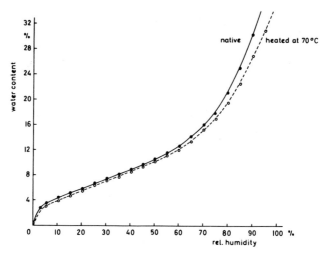

Fig. 25.15. — Absorption isotherms of native (●——●) and pre-heated (○---○, 70 C) freeze-dehydrated beef muscle tissue. From Hamm, 1962*a*.

Denaturation of globular proteins

Of course, the water-soluble globular proteins of the sarcoplasm are changed by heating of muscle. If the temperature reaches 62 C, most of the sarcoplasmic proteins will be denatured (Bendall, 1964). The decrease in solubility of these proteins during heating shows that most of them coagulate between 40 C and 60 C (Table 25.3). At 50 C a large part of these proteins is still soluble; at 66 C a small part of the globular muscle proteins is not yet coagulated, whereas at 80 C they all became insoluble (Hashimoto and Yasui, 1957). Experiments in our laboratory have revealed

TABLE 25.3
Influence of heating of beef muscle on the solubility of structural and globular proteins

Heating temperature	Extractable protein, in % of protein extracted from the native tissue	
	Globular proteins	Myofibrillar proteins
20 C	100	100
40 C	85.6	69
60 C	23.4	2
80 C	0.7	12*

* Increase probably due to the transformation of the collagen of connective tissue to gelatin.

Source: R. Hamm and F. E. Deatherage, "Changes in hydration, solubility and charges of muscle proteins during heating of meat," *Food Research 25(1960)*:587.

that the proteins migrating in an electric field with the greatest velocity (anodic and cathodic) are denatured most quickly (Grau and Lee, 1963). Scopes (1964) has observed that the denaturation of sarcoplasmic proteins decreases the solubility of myofibrillar proteins. According to Bendall and Wismer-Pedersen (1962), the fibrillar proteins of heat-coagulated tissue are probably covered by a layer of denatured sarcoplasmic proteins that is firmly bound to the surface of the myofilaments.

Meat tenderness

If tenderness of meat is increased by cooking, this cannot be caused by changes in muscle proteins, because heat-denaturation of the myofibrillar proteins results in a tightening and stiffening of structure, provided that no exceptionally high temperatures and long heating times are used. Increasing tenderness during cooking must be caused by the fact that the collagen of connective tissue is changed. Tendon collagen shrinks at temperatures above 63 C. At higher temperatures, collagen is transformed to water-soluble gelatin; cross linkages between adjacent peptide chains are split causing a shortening and disintegration of the collagen molecules (Idson and Braswell, 1957). The formation of gelatin, which is partially dissolved in the released juice, may be essentially responsible for softening and disintegration of tissue. Therefore, the tenderness of cooked meat is dependent on the content of connective tissue in the muscle (Sanderson and Vail, 1963). During cooking, the meat first becomes tougher because of changes in the muscle proteins; then, after a longer period of heating, it becomes more tender because of the transformation of collagen to gelatin (Tuorny and Lechnir, 1964). The temperature at which the collagen becomes soluble (forming gelatin) greatly depends on the age of the animal (Fig. 25.16). Furthermore, the resistance of collagen to heating is quite different in the various muscles, e.g., low in the longissimus dorsi, high in the semitendinosus (Ziemba, 1961). Unlike collagen, elastin cannot be heat-denatured because the polypeptide chains are already as randomly orientated as possible; consequently, this protein is one of the few to remain in the native form after cooking (Bendall, 1964).

Color

The change in color of muscle during heating is caused by the denaturation of the protein component of myoglobin, which coagulates at about 65 C (Fig. 25.17). Some nonextractable brown pigments of cooked beef are probably identical with denatured globin-nicotinamide-hemichromes (see Luh *et al.*, 1964). Denaturation of myoglobin in muscle is considerable at temperatures (65 C and below) where thermal denaturation of the pigment is negligible in pure solution (Bernofsky, Fox, and Schweigert, 1959).

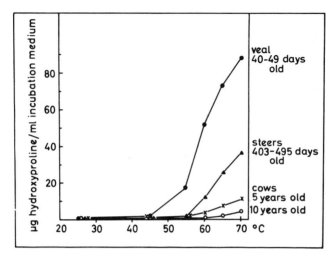

Fig. 25.16. — Influence of heating on the solubility of connective tissue isolated from muscles of beef animals of different age. From Goll, Hoekstra, and Bray, 1964.

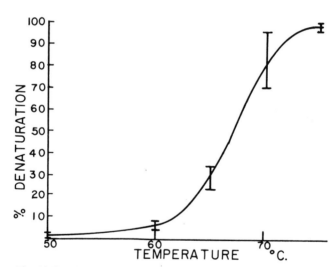

Fig. 25.17. — Percent denaturation of metmyoglobin at *p*H 5.5, 1 hr heating. From Siedler and Schweigert, 1959; copyright © 1959 by American Chemical Society.

In cooked meat, pigment denaturation at these temperatures may be the result of enzyme action or coprecipitation.

SUMMARY

It can be concluded that the physical and chemical changes of muscle during heating occur in different steps.

At 20–30 C: No changes occur in the colloidal-chemical properties of tissue or in the solubility and ion-binding of muscle proteins. The adenosine triphosphatase activity of myosin decreases at 30 C.

At 30–50 C: Some changes in the myofibrillar proteins occur, influencing water-holding capacity and rigidity of tissue, solubility, pH, IP, number of easily available sulfhydryl groups and dye-binding acidic groups and the capacity of muscle proteins for binding Ca^{++} and Mg^{++}. The shift in IP and increase in pH are probably due to an increase in available imidazolium groups. The adenosine triphosphatase is completely inactivated. The changes in myofibrillar proteins in this range of temperature include two steps: an unfolding of peptide chains and the formation of relatively unstable cross linkages resulting in a tighter network of protein structure within the isoelectric range of pH. Between 30 C and 40 C these changes are relatively small. A small part of the sarcoplasmic proteins is also denatured.

At 50–55 C: In this range of temperature a rearrangement of the myofibrillar proteins occurs causing a delay in the changes of water-holding capacity, pH, easily available dye-binding acidic groups, and protein-bound Ca^{++} and Mg^{++}. At these temperatures new cross linkages begin to form which are quite stable and cannot be split by addition of weak base or acid. The denaturation of sarcoplasmic protein is continued.

At 55–80 C: Most of the changes occurring between 40 C and 50 C are continued to a lesser extent. At 65 C most of the myofibrillar and globular muscle proteins are coagulated. Collagen shrinks at temperatures around 63 C and may be partially transformed to gelatin at higher temperatures.

Above 80 C: The formation of disulfide bonds by oxidation of the sulfhydryl groups of actomyosin begins between 70 C and 90 C and is continued with increasing temperature. Above 90 C H_2S is split off from the sulfhydryl groups of actomyosin. Further changes in the muscle proteins during heating to 120 C result in a decrease of dye-binding basic groups and protein-bound Ca^{++} and Mg^{++}. Maillard reactions begin at about 90 C and are continued with increasing temperature and time of heating. Collagen is transformed to gelatin, causing an increase of tenderness.

Some influences of heating on muscle systems have not been mentioned, e.g., the change in digestibility, the decrease in vitamins, and the development of the flavor of cooked meat. It is hoped that this review has made it clear that the influence of heating on muscle systems is an interesting field of meat research which is very broad and quite important for the practice of processing meat. But, fortunately, it is still possible to cook a piece of meat without knowledge of the denaturation process.

References

Anglemier, A. F., A. A. el-Badani, and R. F. Cain. 1964. Effect of irradiation and pre-irradiation treatments on beef muscle proteins. *J. Food Sci.* 29:837.

Bendall, J. R. 1946. The effect of cooking on the creatine, creatinine, phosphorus, nitrogen and pH values of raw lean beef. *Chem. Ind.* (London) 63:71.

————. 1947. The effect of heat denaturation on the base-binding capacity of beef-muscle press-juice. *Proc. Roy. Soc.* (London), B, 134:272.

————. 1964. Meat proteins, p. 225. *In* H. W. Schulz and A. F. Anglemier (eds.), *Proteins and Their Reactions.* Avi Publishing Co. Inc., Westport, Conn.

Bendall, J. R., and J. Wismer-Pedersen. 1962. Some properties of the fibrillar proteins of normal and watery pork muscle. *J. Food Sci.* 27:144.

Bernofsky, C., J. P. Fox, and B. S. Schweigert. 1959. Biochemistry of myoglobin. VII. The effect of cooking on myohemoglobin in beef muscle. *Food Res.* 24:339.

Beuk, J. F., F. W. Chornock, and E. E. Rice. 1948. The effect of severe heat treatment upon the amino acids of fresh and cured pork. *J. Biol. Chem.* 175:291.

Brennan, M. J., and R. A. Bernhard. 1964. Headspace constituents of canned beef. *Food Technol.* 18:743.

Chiambalero, C. J., A. Johnson, and M. P. Drake. 1959. A time temperature relationship for heat-enzyme inactivation of radiation-sterilized beef and pork. *J. Agr. Food Chem.* 7:782.

Colvin, J. R. 1964. Denaturation: a requiem, p. 69. *In* H. W. Schulz and A. F. Anglemier (eds.), *Proteins and Their Reactions.* Avi Publishing Co. Inc., Westport, Conn.

Connell, J. J., and P. F. Howgate. 1964. The hydrogen ion titration curves of native, heat-coagulated and frozen-stored myofibrils of cod and beef. *J. Food Sci.* 29:717.

Donoso, G., O. A. M. Lewis, D. S. Miller, and P. R. Payne. 1962. Effect of heat treatment on the nutritive value of proteins. Chemical and balance studies. *J. Sci. Food Agr.* 13:192.

El-Badani, A. A., A. F. Anglemier, and R. F. Cain. 1964. Effects of soaking in water, thermal enzyme inactivation and irradiation on the textural factors of beef. *Food Technol.* 18:1807.

Engelhardt, V. A. 1946. Adenosine triphosphatase properties of myosin. *Advance. Enzymol.* 6:147.

Fraczak, R., and Z. Pajdowski. 1955. The decomposition of sulfhydryl groups in meat by thermal processing. *Przemysl Spozywczy* 9:334.

Frumkin, M., G. Pawlowa, and D. Dosorez. 1962. Change of the proteolytic activity of irradiated meat during storage and heating. Paper read at 8th Conf. Europe. Meat Res. Workers (Moscow).

Gantner, G., and R. Hamm. 1964. Transaminasen des Fleisches. I. Mitt. Extra-hierbarkeit und Eigenschaften von Transaminasen (GOT und GPT) aus Schweinemuskel. *Z. Lebensm. Untersuch. Forsch. 126*:1.

Goll, D. E., W. O. Hoekstra, and R. W. Bray. 1964. Age associated changes in bovine muscle connective tissue. I. Exposure to increasing temperature. *J. Food Sci. 29*:515.

Grau, R., and F. A. Lee. 1963. Über den Einfluss der Temperatur auf das Verhalten der Eiweisstoffe des Rindermuskels. *Naturwissenschaften 50*:379.

Greenstein, J. P. and J. Edsall. 1940. The effect of denaturing agents on myosin. I. Sulfhydryl groups as estimated by porphyrindin titration. *J. Biol. Chem. 133*:397.

Greenwood, D. A., H. R. Kraybill, and B. S. Schweigert. 1951. Amino acid composition of fresh and cooked beef cuts. *J. Biol. Chem. 193*:23.

Hamm, R. 1960. Biochemistry of meat hydration. *Advance. Food Res. 10*:355.

———. 1962a. Über das Wasserbindungsvermögen des Säugetiermuskels. VII. Mitt. Zur Theorie der Wasserbindung. *Z. Lebensm. Untersuch. Forsch. 117*:20.

———. 1962b. Chemische und physikalische Veränderungen beim Erhitzen von Fleisch. II. Mitt. Einfluss des Erhitzens auf den Bindungszustand von Magnesium, Calcium und Phosphat. *Z. Lebensm. Untersuch. Forsch. 117*:113.

———. 1963. Ladungsgruppen im Muskeleiweiss und ihre Veränderung bei der Hitzedenaturierung. Paper read at 9th Conf. Europe. Meat Res. Workers (Budapest). (See also dissertation of K. Hofmann: Untersuchung des Einflusses der thermischen Behandlung von Fleisch auf die funktionellen Gruppen der strukturellen Muskelproteine. University of Giessen, Germany. 1964.)

Hamm, R., and F. E. Deatherage. 1960. Changes in hydration, solubility and charges of muscle proteins during heating of meat. *Food Res. 25*:587.

Hamm, R., and K. Hofmann. 1965. Changes in the sulfhydryl and disulfide groups in beef muscle proteins during heating. *Nature 207*:1269.

Hamm, R., and H. Iwata. 1962. Chemische und physikalische Veränderungen beim Erhitzen von Fleisch. I. Wirkung des Erhitzens in Gegenwart von Natriumchlorid auf Wasserbindungsvermögen und pH-Wert. des Rindermuskels. *Z. Lebensm. Untersuch. Forsch. 116*:120.

Hashimoto, Y., T. Fukazawa, R. Niki, H. Kanazawa, and T. Yasui. 1959. Denaturation of myosin A. *Jap. J. Zootech. Sci. 30*:318.

Hashimoto, Y., and T. Yasui. 1957. Researches on the detection of meat by serological tests. *J. Fac. Agr. Hokkaido Univ. 50*:171.

Hornstein, I., R. F. Crowe, and W. L. Sulzbacher. 1960. Flavor chemistry. Constituents of meat flavor: beef. *J. Agr. Food Chem. 8*:65.

Idson, B., and E. Braswell. 1957. Gelatin. *Advance. Food Res. 7*:238.

Jaenicke, R. 1965. Wärmedenaturierung von Eiweiss. Paper read at the 2d European Symposium on Food: "Recent developments in heat treatment" (Frankfurt, Germany). Dechema-Monographien, Vol. 56.

Johnson, A. R., and J. P. Vickery. 1964. Factors affecting the production of hydrogen sulfide from meat during heating. *J. Sci. Food Agr. 15*:695.

Kauzmann, W. 1956. Structural factors in protein denaturation. *J. Cell. Comp. Physiol. 47(suppl. 1)*:113.

Körmendy, L., and G. Gantner. 1960. Über die saure Phosphatase des Fleisches. *Z. Lebensm. Untersuch. Forsch. 113*:13.

Kramlich, W. E., and A. M. Pearson. 1958. Some preliminary studies of meat flavor. *Food Res. 23*:567.

Locker, R. H. 1956. The dissociation of myosin by heat coagulation. *Biochim. Biophys. Acta. 20*:515.

Logtestijn, J. G. van. 1964. Über den Einfluss von Kochsalz und Erhitzen auf den pH-Wert von Fleisch. Paper read at 10th Conf. Europe. Meat Res. Workers (Roskilde, Denmark).

Luh, B. S., G. G. Gonzalez-Acuna, S. Leonard, and M. Simone. 1964. Aseptic canning of foods. VI. Hematin and volatile sulfur compounds in strained beef. *Food Technol. 18*:216.

Mecchi, E. P., E. L. Pippen, and H. Lineweaver. 1964. Origin of hydrogen sulfide in heated chicken muscle. *J. Food Sci. 29*:393.

Nanninga, L. B. 1962. The effect of heating on the cinetic constants of myosin ATPase. *Nature 194*:187.

Nemitz, G., and W. Partmann. 1959. Über die Hitzeinaktivierung des Apyrase-systems der Muskulatur. *Z. Lebensm. Untersuch. Forsch. 109*:121

Pearson, A. M., G. Harrington, R. G. West, and M. E. Spooner. 1962. The browning produced by heating fresh pork. I. The relation of browning intensity to chemical constituents and pH. *J. Food Sci. 27*:177.

Sanderson, M., and G. E. Vail. 1963. Fluid content and tenderness of three muscles of beef cooked to three internal temperatures. *J. Food Sci. 18*:590.

Savic, I., and S. Karan-Djurdjic. 1958. The effect of salting and heating on some properties of meat. Paper read at 4th Conf. Europe. Meat Res. Workers (Cambridge, England).

Schweigert, B. S., B. A. Bennett, and B. T. Guthneck. 1951. Further studies on the amino acid composition of pork and lamb cuts. *J. Biol. Chem. 190*:697.

Schweigert, B. S., B. T. Guthneck, H. R. Kraybill, and D. A. Greenwood. 1949. The amino acid composition of pork and lamb cuts. *J. Biol. Chem. 180*:1077.

Scopes, R. K. 1964. The influence of post mortem conditions on the solubilities of muscle proteins. *Biochem. J. 91*:201.

Segal, L. 1963. Stufenweise Denaturierung an Eiweissen. *Acta Biol. Med. Ger. 10*:488.

Shimizu, Y., I. Fujita, and W. Simidu. 1960. Water retention of fish muscle paste. II. Effect of pH on the water holding capacity. *Bull. Jap. Soc. Fish. 26*:749.

Siedler, A. J. and B. S. Schweigert. 1959. Biochemistry of myoglobin. Effects of heat, nitrate, level, iron salts and reducing agents on formation of denatured nitrosomyoglobin. *J. Agr. Food Chem. 7*:271.

Smorodintsev, A. A. 1952. [Quoted from Ziemba, 1961.]

Tuorny, J. M., and R. J. Lechnir. 1964. Effect of cooking temperature and time on the tenderness of pork. *Food Technol. 18*:219.

Wierbicki, E., L. E. Kunkle, and F. E. Deatherage. 1957. Changes in water-holding capacity and cationic shifts during the heating and freezing and thawing of meat as revealed by a simple centrifugal method for measuring shrinking. *Food Technol. 11:*69.

Yueh, M. H., and F. M. Strong. 1960. Some volatile constituents of cooked beef. *J. Agr. Food Chem. 8:*491.

Ziemba, Z. 1961. Changes of canned meats by the effect of heat treatment. *Przemysl Spozywczy,* No. 1, p. 2.

Chapter 26

Influence of Postmortem Conditions
on Muscle Microbiology

J. M. JAY

The microbiology of meats has received the attention of many investigators dating back to at least 1886, when the question of the origin of bacteria in meats was raised. Studies on the incidence, types, sources, and significance of microorganisms in meats have received the attention of a large number of workers, especially in Great Britain, Australia, New Zealand, and the United States. Ayres (1955, 1960) has provided two excellent reviews on this aspect of meat microbiology, and therefore no further discussion of it will be given in this report. This chapter will deal with the specific effects of rigor mortis associated changes on the status and role of bacteria in meats. Although it would seem worth while to compare bacterial growth in prerigor and postrigor meats, such comparison is not possible, since meat normally does not spoil so rapidly. Some pathogenic bacteria do, indeed, grow in live flesh but the physiology of such growth is not well understood and not sufficiently germane to the present subject. Some aspects of the growth of anaerobic bacteria in live muscle, as opposed to meat, are discussed later in this chapter.

RIGOR MORTIS ASSOCIATED PHENOMENA THAT AFFECT MUSCLE MICROBIOLOGY

There are at least eight changes that occur when muscle is converted to meat which may directly or indirectly affect the development of microorganisms therein. These changes are as follows:

1. Reduction of pH by lactic acid as a result of glycolysis.

2. Cessation of phagocytic functions making possible the growth and spread of bacteria present in the living animals.

3. Lowering of oxidation-reduction potential, making for growth of anaerobes as a result of the cessation of oxygen supply.

4. Accumulation of various metabolites, such as hypoxanthine, ribose,

inorganic phosphate, etc., which are readily utilized by many microorganisms.

5. Combination of actin and myosin to form actomyosin.

6. Autolysis or the breakdown of proteins by cathepsins.

7. Decrease in ATP concentration, which is correlated with a decrease in water-holding capacity (Hamm, 1956) prior to a subsequent increase upon aging.

8. Release by skeletal proteins of calcium and the uptake of other metal ions such as potassium.

Each of these rigor-mortis associated changes will now be discussed in terms of what is known about its particular effect on muscle microbiology.

Effect of pH reduction

Upon the death of a well-rested meat animal, the usual 1% glycogen is converted into lactic acid which directly causes a depression in pH values from around 7.4 to around 5.6, depending upon the type of animal in question. Callow (1949) found the lowest pH values for beef to be 5.1 and the highest 6.2 after rigor mortis. The lowest and highest values for lamb and pork, respectively, were found by Callow to be 5.4 and 6.7, and 5.3 and 6.9. More recently, Briskey (1964) reported that the ultimate pH of pork may be as low as appproximately 5.0 under certain conditions. In the case of beef muscles, the usual pH value attained upon completion of rigor mortis is around 5.6 (Bate-Smith, 1948). The effect of pH values of this magnitude upon microorganisms, especially bacteria, is rather obvious, since the pH optima of most are around neutrality. Many species and strains of spoilage bacteria, however, grow fairly well at and around pH 5.6 (Ingram, 1949). It is well known that meat from fatigued animals spoils faster than that from rested animals and that this is a direct consequence of final pH attained upon completion of rigor. It also points up the importance of minor changes in pH in slowing the growth of spoilage bacteria. It has also been known for some time that halibut, which usually attains an ultimate pH of around 5.6, has better keeping qualities than most other fish, whose ultimate pH values range between 6.2 and 6.6 (Reay and Shewan, 1949). While all reported studies on pH minima for spoilage bacteria have employed the use of nutrient media, it is quite likely that many bacteria that grow at pH values around 5.6 under these conditions will fail to do so when cultured on undenatured meat or meat extracts.

Stoppage of phagocytic action

It is now generally agreed that the flesh of live and healthy slaughter animals is sterile, or at most, contains only a few bacteria under normal conditions. An extensive literature exists on this subject dating back to several German workers in 1886, and it has been reviewed by Ayres (1955). The largest number of bacteria found inside the tissues of live animals occurs in lymph nodes (Adamson, 1949; Lepovetsky, Weiser, and Deatherage, 1953). The latter authors, along with Weiser, Kunkle, and Deatherage (1954), showed that lymph nodes constitute the internal source of bacteria to the deep tissues of postrigor meats. In the live animal these organisms are kept under control by the phagocytic organs and cells, but upon the death of the animal and the cessation of phagocytic activities, these bacteria multiply and finally spread through the tissues. Microorganisms which find their way into blood circulation are filtered out by the reticulo-endothelial system and destroyed, but again, upon the death of the animal, these organisms contaminate the tissues where they develop when other conditions permit.

Lowering of oxidation-reduction (Eh) potential

It has been known for many years that bacteria display varying degrees of sensitivity to the Eh of their growth medium (Hewitt, 1950). With respect to the Eh of prerigor as opposed to postrigor muscles, Barnes and Ingram (1955, 1956) reviewed the subject and undertook a study of the measurement of Eh in muscle over periods of up to 30 hr postmortem, and its effect upon the growth of anaerobic bacteria. These authors found that the Eh of the sternocephalicus muscle of the horse immediately after death was +250 mv, at which time clostridia failed to multiply. At 30 hr postmortem the Eh had fallen to around −130 mv in the absence of bacterial growth. When bacterial growth was allowed to occur, the Eh fell to around −250 mv. Growth of clostridia was observed at Eh values of −36 mv and below. These authors confirmed for horse meat the finding of Robinson *et al.* (1952) for whale meat, that anaerobic bacteria do not multiply until the onset of rigor mortis, because of the high Eh in prerigor meat. It has been known for some time that *Cl. tetani* is unable to initiate the tetanus syndrome until the Eh of the local lesion has been lowered (Fildes, 1929).

The significance of Eh changes to postmortem muscle microbiology stems from the fact that the clostridia are found on meats and sometimes cause spoilage, especially when meats are held at temperatures above the refrigerator range.

Accumulation of metabolites

Upon the completion of rigor mortis, there accumulate from the breakdown of ATP and other rigor-mortis changes numerous metabolites, such as IMP, ADP, ITP, carnosine, anserine, glutathione, carnitine, sarcosin, taurine, creatine, purine bases, amino acids, enzymes, etc. (Bate-Smith, 1948; Whitaker, 1959). The specific effect of these substances on bacterial growth in meats seems not to have been investigated and reported. From the fact that ninhydrin-positive substances tend to decrease as meat spoilage progresses (Saffle *et al.*, 1961; Jay, 1964*b*) and the general lack of evidence for bacterial proteolysis during incipient spoilage (see section below on autolysis), it is quite likely that these substances constitute the primary sources of nutrients for meat spoilage microbes.

Formation of actomyosin

The most obvious physical change that occurs in muscles as a result of rigor mortis is that associated with the stiffening process resulting directly from the union of actin and myosin to form actomyosin. It is not clear at this time just what specific effect this change has on the welfare of spoilage microorganisms. On the basis of molecular size, one might assume that actomyosin is less readily attacked by bacteria than might be either component alone. There is, however, no direct proof of this. From the studies of various investigators on the cause of postmortem tenderization of beef, Whitaker (1959) concluded that actomyosin does not dissociate upon meat aging, especially in the absence of bacterial growth. An answer to this question could be got by preventing the combination of actin and myosin with the use of such compounds as copper glycinate, oxarsan, salyrgan, and others, and then noting the spoilage rate and measuring the protein changes of such meat; but such an approach has not been reported. While a change of such magnitude as the combination of actin and myosin would seem almost certain to have effect on bacterial growth, it is not inconceivable that it is entirely without effect.

Autolysis

It has been reported that upon the completion of the process of rigor mortis there is a breakdown of proteins in the absence of bacterial action which is presumed to be caused by cathepsins (Hoagland, McBryde, and Powick, 1917; Mitchell, Zimmerman, and Hamilton, 1926). Beganovic and Muftic (1958) have stated that autolysis creates favorable conditions for the activity of bacteria. The usual method employed to follow this autolytic process is a measure of changes in nonprotein nitrogen (Bate-Smith, 1948). In a study by Hoagland *et al.*, only a 6% degradation of proteins occurred in beef stored at 0–2.2 C over 180 days. While bacteria were kept down, the authors reported the presence of mold growth but presumed it to be of no importance in the degradation process. Whitaker has reviewed the literature on this subject which shows that some authors support the notion of autolysis upon aging of meats while others are unable to do so. Among this latter group are Deatherage and Harsham (1947), Husaini *et al.* (1950), and Wierbicki *et al.* (1954). Most recently, Bodwell and Pearson (1963) were unable to effect degradation of crude preparations of beef actin, myosin, and actomyosin with partially purified beef muscle cathepsins. These authors suggested that tenderness changes are due to action on soluble proteins of meat rather than to a breakdown of structural proteins.

Studies on protein degradation by beef spoilage bacteria in this laboratory indicate a lack of capacity on the part of the flora of refrigerated meats to bring about such changes. Table 26.1 presents data on the nitrogen changes in ground longissimus dorsi (LD) muscle from a two-year-old standard grade steer held for 17 days at 7 C and allowed to go into frank spoilage, as shown by extract-release volume (ERV) values. The ERV phenomenon has already been described (Jay, 1964b) as a simple and rapid method for detecting spoilage in meats, with values of around 25 and below indicating spoiled beef. It can be seen that the changes in nitrogen from freshness to spoilage were minor. Table 26.2 presents similar results

TABLE 26.1

Percentage of nitrogen changes in longissimus dorsi muscle from two-year-old standard grade Holstein steer in relation to ERV and bacterial numbers (degree of spoilage)

Days held	ERV	Log no. bact.	% Protein	% Amino N	% Heat coag. protein	% TCA sol. N	% Total sol. N	% Moisture
0	53	5.54	..	0.57	0.34	0.03	0.60	69
2	50	5.70	22	0.39	0.62	0.06	0.40	67
6	53	5.54	23	0.45	1.39	0.06	0.57	68
8	53	5.81	26	0.51	3.12	0.04	0.98	69
10	47	6.48	24	0.32	2.55	0.08	0.32	66
14	40	8.89	21	0.42	2.61	0.08	0.61	67
17	22	9.30	22	0.38	2.55	0.09	0.49	68

TABLE 26.2

Percentage of nitrogen changes in rump tip muscle of beef animal in relation to ERV and bacterial numbers

Days	ERV	Log no. bact.	% Protein	% Amino N	% Heat coag. protein	% Total sol. N	Fibrous protein	% Moisture
0	41	5.61	23	0.21	2.49	0.53	2.22	67
2	40	6.34	23	0.69	2.39	0.62	2.21	68
5	43	5.88	..	0.53	2.40	0.50	2.60	67
7	43	8.04	22	0.55	2.39	0.53	3.04	67
9	45	8.91	22	0.44	2.76	0.56	2.29	67
12	41	9.47	23	0.33	3.12	0.71	2.67	68
14	18	9.70	23	0.41	3.10	0.52	2.50	69

on ground beef muscle from rump tip obtained in commercial trade. This meat was held for 14 days also at 7 C.

Data of a similar nature are presented in Table 26.3, where ground beef round muscles were held for 18 days at 7 C. It can be seen that the percentage of protein-nitrogen determined by the procedure of Hamm and Deatherage (1960) remained more or less constant as ERV decreased from 49 to 0. The possible role played by bacterial cell nitrogen in nitrogen determinations on spoiled beef was examined by biuret determinations on both filter-sterilized and nonsterilized ERV extracts, and the results presented in Table 26.3 indicate that the presence of bacteria (in unfiltered extract) apparently does not significantly raise total nitrogen values. If spoilage bacteria utilized significant amounts of protein, one would expect a decrease in protein-nitrogen as meat spoils, since the meat is not freed of its bacteria. If one assumes that the bacteria subsist on nonprotein com-

TABLE 26.3

Effect of spoilage bacteria on the total protein content of beef round muscles. The beef was ground and held at 7 C wrapped in aluminum foil and sampled in duplicate

| Days held | ERV | pH | Biuret (O D)[a] | | % Total N | % Total prot. | % Prot. N | % Act. prot. | % Prot. of NPN |
			Unfil.	Fil.					
0	49	5.75	0.36	0.36	3.37	21.06	2.72	17.00	4.06
3	40	6.30	0.33	0.30	3.48	21.75	2.95	18.44	3.31
5	41	6.10	. . .	. . .	3.25	20.31	2.57	16.06	4.25
7 [b]	28	7.00	0.68	0.56	. . .	. . . .	. . .	. . . .	. . .
10	8	7.40	0.45	0.45	3.44	21.50	2.49	15.56	5.94
18	0	8.10	. . .	. . .	3.51	21.94	2.69	16.81	5.13

[a] Determined on ERV extracts (phosphate buffer, pH 5.8). Unfil = unfiltered; fil = filtered through 0.2 micron Metricel membranes.

[b] First sign of detectable offness (spoilage).

pounds, one might at the same time assume an increase in total protein nitrogen as a result of the conversion of nonprotein nitrogen to bacterial protein nitrogen by the spoilage flora. Data available at this time do not show significant changes in either direction, and the reason for this is not clear. The existence of a phenomenon where succeeding generations of bacteria subsist upon the autolyzed substances of preceding generations of dead bacterial cells would explain this. Although this is only conjecture at present, it is not inconceivable that such actually occurs.

Further evidence for the lack of degradation of beef proteins by bacteria is presented in Tables 26.4 and 26.5. Table 26.4 presents data from all-lean ground beef allowed to spoil at refrigerator temperatures, showing that the content of total soluble protein remains about the same from freshness

TABLE 26.4

Effect of spoilage flora on total soluble protein of beef allowed to spoil at 7 C

Days held	ERV	Log bact. no.	Total soluble protein (O D)[a]
0	37	6.30	0.16
2	37	6.90	0.16
5	5	9.30	0.16
10	5	10.38	0.16
13	3	. . . .	0.17
15	4	10.91	0.16

[a] Extracted with 0.1 N NaOH by the method of D. S. Miyada and A. L. Tappel, "The hydrolysis of beef proteins by various proteolytic enzymes," *Food Res.* 21(1956):217; and measured by the biuret method following the procedure of Judith Torten and J. R. Whitaker, "Evaluation of the biuret and dye-binding methods for protein determination in meats," *J. Food Sci.* 29(1964):168.

TABLE 26.5

Effect of spoilage flora on the sarcoplasmic and total soluble proteins of all-lean beef allowed to spoil at 7 C

Days held	ERV	pH	Sarcoplasmic (O D)[a]	Total soluble protein (O D)[a]
0	58	5.8	0.44	0.16
2	55	5.9	0.32	0.23
5	25	6.3	. . .	0.21
7	4	7.6	0.22	0.13
9	2	8.0	0.21	. . .
19	0	8.5	0.23	0.12
27	0	8.6	0.15	0.22

[a] Extracted by the methods of R. N. Sayre and E. J. Briskey, "Protein solubility as influenced by physiological conditions in the muscle," *J. Food Sci.* 28(1963):675; and measured as in Table 26.4 above. Each value represents triplicate readings.

to spoilage, employing the extraction procedure of Miyada and Tappel (1956). The same level of protein was confirmed by the Kjeldahl method and by paper electrophoresis employing cellulose acetate strips run in barbital buffer at pH 7.7. By the latter method the same bands were present in all extractions from freshness to spoilage and appeared not to reflect differences in concentration.

Essentially the same results for total soluble protein were achieved by another extraction procedure (Sayre and Briskey, 1963) as shown in Table 26.5. In the case of sarcoplasmic proteins, however, a general decrease was found as this meat spoiled, thus indicating that at least some of the sarcoplasmic substances are utilized by the spoilage flora.

The foregoing can be interpreted to mean that the usual spoilage flora of refrigerated beef is not strongly proteolytic. It is a common observation that spoiling beef yields off-odor compounds such as ammonia, hydrogen sulfide, etc. These substances no doubt originate from free amino acids. Nevertheless, it is known that if ground beef is allowed to remain under refrigeration long enough the meat is consumed almost totally by its microbial flora. The loss in weight of two 25-g samples of ground beef tightly wrapped in aluminum foil and held at 7 C for 13 weeks is presented in Figure 26.3. It can be seen that over the 13-week period, at 21.6% loss in weight occurred. This meat was unfit for consumption around the fourth day and displayed the usual off-odors of spoiled beef.

At this point it was of interest to determine the proteolytic capability of beef spoilage bacteria from refrigerated meat. Sixteen different strains were recovered from 5 samples of fresh beef and 17 from a like number of samples of spoiled beef. Some characteristics of these organisms are presented in Table 26.6, along with some well-known proteolytic and nonproteolytic strains. It can be seen that only five strains each from fresh and spoiled beef were capable of digesting the casein of litmus milk, while only one from fresh meat and two from spoiled beef were capable of digest-

TABLE 26.6

Some characteristics of bacteria recovered from fresh and refrigerator-spoiled beef along with six control strains [a]

Characteristic	Fresh beef	Spoiled beef	Strain A	Strain B	Strain C	Strain D	Strain E	Strain F
No. of strains	16	17	1	1	1	1	1	1
Gram positive	5	2	1	..	..	..	..	1
Gram negative	11	15	..	1	1	1	1	..
Rods	13	15	1	1	1	1	1	..
Cocci	3	2	..	..	..	..	..	1
Chromogens	4	1	..	..	1	..	..	1
Nonchromogens	12	16	1	1	..	1	1	..
Gelatinase producers	7	6	1	1	1	1	0	1
Amylase producers	0	0	1	0	0	0	0	0
Litmus milk:								
Digestion	5	5	1	1	1	1	0	0
Coagulation only	2	4	..	..	..	..	..	1
Acid only	1	4	..	..	..	..	1	..
Alkaline only	4	2	..	..	..	..	..	..
Unchanged	4	2	..	..	..	..	..	..
Digestion of								
alkaline egg	1 [b]	2 [c]	1	1	1	0	0	0

[a] Strain A: *Bacillus subtilis* (ATCC 9799); B: *Pseudomonas aeruginosa* (ATCC 10145); C: *Serratia marcescens* (WSU strain); D: *Proteus vulgaris* (WSU 302); E: *Escherichia coli* (ATCC 11229); F: *Staphylococcus aureus* (ATCC 6538).

[b] Partial digestion; not as complete as controls.

[c] Complete digestion by Gram positive rod, partial digestion by Gram negative rod. Fresh beef samples had average ERV of 43 (range: 29 to 47) while spoiled beef had ERV range of 0 to 8, with average of 4.

ing a protein like egg albumin. The specific identity of these organisms will be reported elsewhere, but most belong to the genera of *Proteus*, *Achromobacter*, and *Pseudomonas*, all of which are quite common on beef allowed to spoil at refrigerator temperatures (Ayres, 1960). While most of these bacteria do degrade gelatin in culture media, they seem to lack the capacity to degrade native proteins.

It appears from these findings that beef undergoing refrigerated bacterial spoilage does not undergo proteolysis to any great extent when examined up to several weeks after appearance of the first detectable signs of spoilage. That bacteria do multiply in refrigerated meats is unquestionable, but they apparently do so at the expense of some or all of the many relatively low molecular weight substances present in the sarcoplasm and possibly even at the expense of dead autolyzed bacterial cells and substances excreted from living cells. Indeed, if the usual spoilage flora of refrigerated beef degraded significant numbers and amounts of beef proteins to low molecular weight peptides or amino acids, the spoiling meat would liquefy and drip from its container. Anyone who has observed the spoilage of beef in the refrigerator knows that this does not occur. From all indications, it apparently does not occur as a result of simple autolysis.

It appears, then, that autolysis by cathepsins and proteolysis of beef proteins undergoing refrigerated spoilage are not as extensive as is generally believed.

Change in water-holding capacity (WHC)

Immediately after slaughter, prerigor meat has a very high WHC, which drops markedly within a few hours. Its minimum is reached in 24–48 hr, after which time it increases slowly with aging (Hamm, 1960). The extract-release volume (ERV) phenomenon of beef reported from this laboratory gives results similar to those obtained by the filter-paper press method for determining WHC (Jay, 1964a, 1964b). The phenomenon measured by this technique may or may not be the same as WHC. The two are certainly related, and the correlation between them is usually quite high (Fig. 26.1). An experiment employing ERV on four beef muscles (semitendinosus, semimembranous, biceps femoris, and longissimus dorsi) 2 hr postmortem and continuing over a 5-day period and averaging the results of all, gave results (presented in Fig. 26.2) similar to those of Hamm (1960) for WHC. ERV increased rather sharply the first day of storage and began to decrease thereafter, returning to its original value between the fourth and fifth days of holding at 7 C. It can be seen that ERV decline coincided with the completion of rigor mortis as measured by ultimate pH, which in this case was 5.8. Since it appeared that these muscles, intact, would not spoil

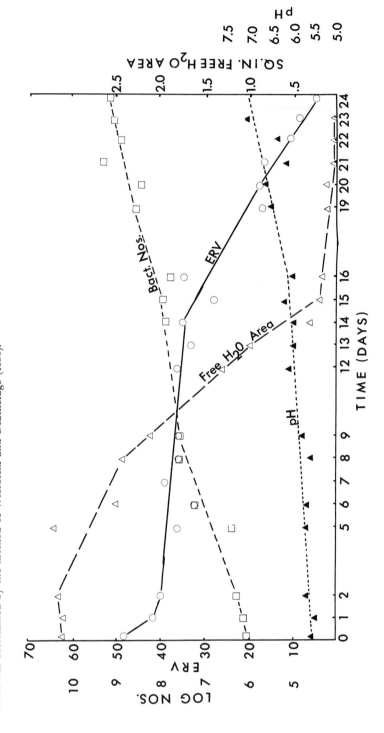

Fig. 26.1. — ERV, WHC, bacterial numbers, and pH of ground longissimus dorsi muscle held at 6 C for 24 days wrapped in aluminum foil. WHC was determined by the method of Wierbicki and Deatherage (1958).

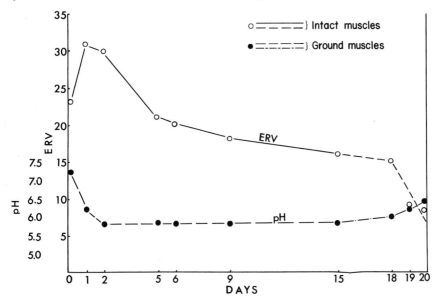

Fig. 26.2. — Averaged ERV and *p*H on LD, ST, SM, and BF muscles from cutter grade cow, from 2 hr to 20 days postmortem. The muscles were held intact on the hindquarter at 7 C up to 15 days and then ground in approximately equal portions. Definite spoilage was evident on 19th day of holding in ground state.

for a very long time, they were comminuted on the 15th day of holding in approximately equal portions and kept at the same temperature until frank spoilage had occurred by the 20th day postmortem. It can be seen that ERV decreased sharply between the 18th and 20th days while *p*H increased to 6.4. This meat was judged unfit for consumption on the 19th day. Referring again to Figure 26.1, it can be seen that ERV decreased rather sharply after the 16th day, when this sample of ground longissimus dorsi muscle was judged to be unfit for consumption. It can be noted also that free-water area on pressing decreased, thus reflecting an increase in WHC as microbial spoilage occurred. The correlation coefficient (*r*) between WHC and *p*H was 0.308; between ERV and *p*H, 0.227; between WHC and bacterial numbers, -0.887 ($P < .001$); between ERV and bacterial numbers, -0.808 ($P < .001$); and between ERV and WHC, 0.743 ($P < .001$), indicating that the response was more to microbial changes than to *p*H increase. The use of free-water area measurement as a rapid technique for determining microbial spoilage in meats has been described elsewhere (Jay, 1965).

The relationship of WHC to ATP, proteases, and metal ions has been reviewed by Hamm (1960). The effect on ERV of these substances and treatments has been shown to be quite similar (Jay, 1964*a*).

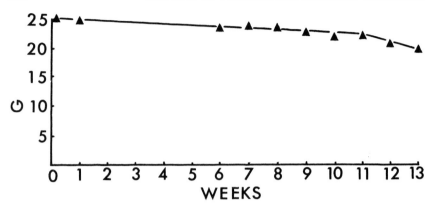

Fig. 26.3. — Effect of spoilage bacteria on the weight loss of refrigerated ground beef held tightly wrapped in aluminum foil.

Just what causes WHC or hydration of beef muscles to increase as bacterial spoilage sets in is not clear at this time. It has been shown that large numbers of bacterial cells per se affect neither ERV nor WHC (Jay, 1964b, 1965). The possibility exists that bacterial polysaccharides might be responsible, but this tends to be negated by the fact that proteases such as trypsin and ficin bring about changes in fresh beef that make it resemble spoiled beef relative to ERV and WHC. The increase in hydration of beef upon bacterial spoilage is further proof of a general lack of complete proteolysis indicated previously, as the larger molecular weight compounds are undoubtedly the site of the hydration phenomenon. While protein degradation apparently does not proceed to the amino acid stage, it could well occur at higher levels to a point where an increase in water-binding sites occurs. This point of view has been expressed by Hamm (1960), and at this time it appears to be the most plausible hypothesis as to why an increase in beef hydration accompanies bacterial spoilage. It is not inconceivable that bacteria which do not degrade proteins completely might produce proteases of a type sufficient to "loosen" the structure of native proteins. The more strongly proteolytic bacteria such as aerobic spore-formers do affect the liquefaction of beef at temperatures above the refrigerator range. These organisms in general lack the capacity to grow at around 7 C.

Exactly how changes in WHC of muscle might affect the growth of microorganisms is not clear at this time. It is tempting to assume that a well-hydrated muscle is more susceptible to microbial attack since microbial proteases require an aqueous milieu for activity. It is not inconceivable that meat proteins are "protected" from enzymatic hydrolysis until they attain a certain state of hydration. It has often been observed in this laboratory that meat spoils "only when it is ready" and this is not always related to observable differences in the microflora. Since metal ions are known to affect WHC and since changes in these elements occur during meat aging, a closer look in this direction seems indicated.

Shifting of metal ions

During the postmortem aging of beef, Na^+ and Ca^{++} are continuously released by the muscle proteins while K^+ is absorbed after the first 24 hr. Mg^{++} are released during the first 24 hr and later between the 6th and 13th days followed by a decrease (Arnold, Wierbicki, and Deatherage, 1956; Wierbicki, Kunkle, and Deatherage, 1957; Wierbicki *et al.*, 1954). The dynamic shifting in meats of metal ions postmortem has been reviewed by Whitaker (1959) and Hamm (1960). It has been known for many years that bacteria require metal ions for growth, as do all living organisms. While meats contain concentrations of metal ions essential for bacterial growth in excessive amounts, there is some question as to whether they are available to spoilage bacteria. For example, Jay, Weiser, and Deatherage (1957*a*, 1957*b*) showed that low concentrations of the tetracycline antibiotics were able to inhibit in beef bacteria which were not inhibited by the same levels in nutrient media. The antibiotic inhibition in beef was overcome by the addition of metal ions such as Mg^{++}, Ca^{++}, and others. Since the tetracyclines possess chelating properties, it was postulated that the antibiotics tied up most of the free ions or those available to bacteria and consequently prevented their growth.

While the cause of increased hydration of beef upon the onset of spoilage is not well understood at this time, as noted previously, there are grounds for suspecting that bacteria in some way upset the metal ion balance. In view of the findings of Bozler (1955) and Hamm (1955, 1958) that partial removal or extraction of Ca^{++} and Mg^{++} from muscles results in an increased WHC, it is reasonabl. to assume that bacterial growth effects a removal of this type, thereby causing the increased WHC associated with spoilage. The increase of pH as meats spoil accounts for some of the increased hydration but certainly not for all. Experimental data on the effects of bacterial growth on meat metal ions seem not to be available. Data of this type seem essential for a complete understanding of the mechanism by which meat spoils, with its associated increased state of hydration.

SUMMARY

There are at least eight rigor mortis associated phenomena that either have or seem to have definite effect upon the growth of bacteria in post-rigor meats: (1) reduction of pH, (2) cessation of phagocytic functions, (3) lowering of redox potential, (4) accumulation of metabolites, (5) formation of actomyosin, (6) autolysis, (7) changes in hydration capacity, and (8) the shifting of metal ions. Evidence to date indicates that beef which is allowed to spoil at refrigerator temperatures does not undergo proteolysis to the extent of formation of significant amounts of nonprotein nitrogen. It appears that the spoilage flora subsists on low molecular weight substances in the sarcoplasm and possibly upon autolyzed bacterial cells. The most obvious change that occurs when beef spoils, aside from the formation of off-odors, is an increase in hydration capacity as measured by both ERV and a filter-paper press method. While the exact cause of this latter phenomenon is not known at this time, it is postulated that a loosening of the native protein structures by bacterial enzymes along with a disturbance of the normal postmortem shifting of metal ions may constitute the basis.

ACKNOWLEDGMENTS

This investigation was supported by Public Health Service Research Grant No. EF-00421, from the Division of Environmental Engineering and Food Protection, National Institutes of Health. The technical assistance of Lynn A. Baril, Jayne C. Bates, and Gwendolyn D. Wright is gratefully acknowledged. Contribution No. 151 from the Department of Biology, College of Liberal Arts, Wayne State University.

References

Adamson, C. A. 1949. A bacteriological study of lymph nodes. *Acta Med. Scand.* 227:1.

Arnold, Nancy, E. Wierbicki, and F. E. Deatherage. 1956. Post mortem changes in the interactions of cations and proteins of beef and their relation to sex and diethylstilbestrol treatment. *Food Technol.* 10:245.

Ayres, J. C. 1955. Microbiological implications in the handling, slaughtering, and dressing of meat animals. *Advance. Food Res.* 6:109.

———. 1960. Temperature relationships and some other characteristics of the microbial flora developing on refrigerated beef. *Food Res.* 25:1.

Barnes, Ella M., and M. Ingram. 1955. Changes in the oxidation-reduction potential of the sterno-cephalicus muscle of the horse after death in relation to the development of bacteria. *J. Sci. Food Agr.* 6:448.

———. 1956. The effect of redox potential on the growth of *Clostridium welchii* strains isolated from horse muscle. *J. Appl. Microbiol.* 19:117.

Bate-Smith, E. C. 1948. The physiology and chemistry of rigor mortis, with special reference to the aging of beef. *Advance. Food Res.* 1:1.

Beganovic, A. H., and A. Muftic. 1958. On chemism of the muscles in connection with postmortem chemical-physical changes in the meat. *Veterinaria* (Sarajevo) 7:369. (English translation from U.S. Dept. of Com.)

Bodwell, C. E., and A. M. Pearson. 1964. Activity of partially purified bovine catheptic enzymes on various natural and synthetic substrates. *J. Food Sci.* 29:602.

Bozler, E. 1955. Binding of calcium and magnesium by the contractile elements. *J. Gen. Physiol.* 38:735.

Briskey, E. J. 1964. Etiological status and associated studies of pale, soft, exudative porcine musculature. *Advance. Food Res.* 13:89.

Callow, E. H. 1949. Science in the imported meat industry. *J. Roy. Sanitary Inst.* 69:35.

Deatherage, F. E., and A. Harsham. 1947. Relation of tenderness of beef to aging time at 33–35°F. *Food Res.* 12:164.

Fildes, P. 1929. Tetanus IX. The oxidation-reduction potential of the subcutaneous tissue fluid of the guinea pig, its effect on infection. *Brit. J. Exp. Pathol.* 10:197.

Hamm, R. 1955. Über die Erdalkalien des Muskels: Ihr Einfluss auf die Muskelhydration und die Bistimmung ihrer Bindungsfestigkeit. *Naturwissenschaften* 42:394.

———. 1956. Über die Wirkung der Adenosintriphosphorsaüre auf Hydratation und Rigiditat des postmortalen Rindermuskels. *Biochem. Z.* 328:309.

———. 1958. Über die Mineralstoffe des Saugetiermuskels. I. Mitt. Magnesium, Calcium, Zink und Eisen und ihre Bedeutung für die Muskelhydratation. *Z. Lebensm. Untersuch. Forsch.* 107:423.

———. 1960. Biochemistry of meat hydration. *Advance. Food Res.* 10:355.

Hamm, R., and F. E. Deatherage. 1960. Changes in hydration, solubility and charges of muscle proteins during heating of meat. *Food Res.* 25:587.

Hewitt, L. F. 1950. *Oxidation-Reduction Potentials in Bacteriology and Biochemistry* (6th ed.). E & S Livingston, Ltd., Edinburgh.

Hoagland, R., C. N. McBryde, and W. C. Powick. 1917. *Changes in fresh beef during cold storage above freezing.* U.S. Dept. Agr. Bull. 433.

Husaini, S. A., F. E. Deatherage, L. E. Kunkle, and H. N. Draudt. 1950. Studies on meat. I. Biochemistry of meat as related to tenderness. *Food Technol.* 4:313.

Ingram, M. 1949. Benjamin Ward Richardson Lecture: Hygiene and Storage. *J. Roy. Sanitary Inst.* 69:39.

Jay, J. M. 1964a. Release of aqueous extracts by beef homogenates, and factors affecting release volume. *Food Technol.* 18:1633.

———. 1964b. Beef microbial quality determined by extract-release volume (ERV). *Food Technol.* 18:1637.

———. 1965. Relationship between water-holding capacity of meats and microbial quality. *Appl. Microbiol.* 13:120.

Jay, J. M., H. H. Weiser, and F. E. Deatherage. 1957a. Studies on the mode of action of chlortetracycline in the preservation of beef. *Appl. Microbiol.* 5:400.

———. 1957b. Further studies on the preservation of beef with chlortetracycline. *Food Technol.* 11:563.

Lepovetsky, B. C., H. H. Weiser, and F. E. Deatherage. 1953. A microbiological study of lymph nodes, bone marrow, and muscle tissue obtained from slaughtered cattle. *Appl. Microbiol.* 1:57.

Mitchell, H. H., R. L. Zimmerman, and T. S. Hamilton. 1926. The determination of the amount of connective tissue in meat. *J. Biol. Chem. 71*:379.

Miyada, D. S., and A. L. Tappel. 1956. The hydrolysis of beef proteins by various proteolytic enzymes. *Food Res. 21*:217.

Reay, G. A., and J. M. Shewan. 1949. The spoilage of fish and its preservation by chilling. *Advance. Food Res. 2*:344.

Robinson, R. H. M., M. Ingram, R. A. M. Case, and J. G. Benstead. 1952. Whale-meat: bacteriology and hygiene. *Spec. Rep. Serv. Food Invest. Board* (London), No. 59.

Saffle, R. L., K. N. May, H. A. Hamid, and J. D. Irby. 1961. Comparing three rapid methods of detecting spoilage in meat. *Food Technol. 15*:465.

Sayre, R. N., and E. J. Briskey. 1963. Protein solubility as influenced by physiological conditions in the muscle. *J. Food Sci. 28*:675.

Torten, Judith, and J. R. Whitaker. 1964. Evaluation of the biuret and dye-binding methods for protein determination in meats. *J. Food Sci. 29*:168.

Weiser, H. H., L. E. Kunkle, and F. E. Deatherage. 1954. The use of antibiotics in meat processing. *Appl. Microbiol. 2*:88.

Whitaker, J. R. 1959. Chemical changes associated with aging of meat with emphasis on the proteins. *Advance. Food Res. 9*:1.

Wierbicki, E., and F. E. Deatherage. 1958. Determination of water-holding capacity of fresh meats. *J. Agr. Food Chem. 6*:387.

Wierbicki, E., L. E. Kunkle, V. R. Cahill, and F. E. Deatherage. 1954. The relation of tenderness to protein alterations during post mortem aging. *Food Technol. 8*:506.

Wierbicki, E., L. E. Kunkle, and F. E. Deatherage. 1957. Changes in the water-holding capacity and cationic shifts during the heating and freezing and thawing of meat as revealed by a simple centrifugal method for measuring shrinkage. *Food Technol. 11*:69.

Chapter 27

Role of Muscle Protein
in Processed Foods

J. C. TRAUTMAN

The role of muscle proteins in processed foods may be grouped into the following functions: water-binding, fat emulsification, color, flavor, texture, and nutrition. Depending upon the particular food product, one or more of these properties of muscle protein will contribute to the products' characterization. For example, protein solubility may have little importance in foods containing cubes of muscle tissue, while it may be extremely important in finely comminuted sausages. In the former, the intact muscle structure characterizes the product. But the manufacture of wieners, for example, involves batter preparation which consists of muscle structure disintegration, protein solubilization and extraction, fat emulsification and binding of added moisture, followed by product-forming in casings, heat processing, cooling, and packaging. The significance of the role of protein in such a product is illustrated in Figure 27.1, where the average composition is plotted.

Without protein, the remaining components would not be recognized as a wiener. Since the protein portion contains approximately 30% water-soluble protein, 30% salt-soluble protein, 30% connective tissue, and 10% nonprotein nitrogen, it is readily apparent that the soluble muscle proteins are largely responsible for the distinctive characteristics of a wiener. The same is true for many other meat products.

The object of this article is to review the role of muscle proteins in processed foods as they are influenced by animal physiology and by the sequence of events which lead to the transformation of muscle into meat. The researcher familiar in this field recognizes that many factors may influence this transformation. However, it becomes readily apparent that postmortem pH is probably one of the most important single factors which determine the ultimate quality of the muscle. For this reason the major emphasis has been placed on the discussion of how pH influences the

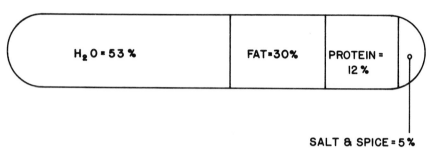

SALT & SPICE = 5%

Fig. 27.1. — Diagrammatic average composition of a wiener.

functions of muscle proteins in processed foods. Although the transformation of living muscle into meat may have many biochemical similarities between species, this discussion will be limited to bovine and porcine muscles.

SOME VARIABLES IN PROCESSED FOODS WHICH MAY BE RELATED TO MUSCLE QUALITY

One of the major manifestations of poor muscle quality as viewed by consumers is the appearance of pale, soft, exudative porcine muscle and dark-cutting bovine muscle. Although these conditions may be similar, they are opposite extremes of abnormal postmortem conditions. The properties of and the conditions leading to pale, soft, exudative porcine muscles have been recently described by E. J. Briskey (1964) as "those physicochemical changes in, or the result of, post-mortem anaerobic glycolysis, rigor mortis, and/or temperature changes." Variability in pH of porcine carcasses shortly after death time is shown in Figure 27.2. The most uniformly consistent feature found to be associated with pale, soft, exudative muscle development was the rapid decrease of pH and lower ultimate pH.

Many other meat food processing problems which may be encountered by manufacturers are associated with muscle quality. A summary of the most common problems would include fat separation or breakdown of stable muscle protein-fat emulsions, water separation in heat-processed meat foods, variable cure color intensity and stability, and poor texture problems such as mushiness in finely comminuted sausages. To the food processor, these problems are baffling because they may appear overnight for no apparent reason, with no change in processing conditions. The following studies in our laboratory (Oscar Mayer & Co., Madison, Wis.) may serve to illustrate the difficulties involved in solving product problems where very little fundamental information exists and the biochemical parameters are not well defined.

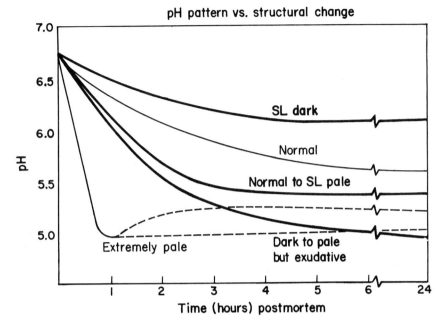

Fig. 27.2. — Variations in postmortem porcine *p*H patterns. From Briskey, 1964.

In the area of finely comminuted sausages, processors may be able to predict from past experience the occurrence of fat separation problems. Many times these problems coincide with seasonal weather changes. V. G. Moss (unpublished, 1961) studied for one year the sausage-making qualities of porcine muscle by statistically sampling 1.5 million hogs. He determined the composition, total heme, labile phosphate, viscosity lag phase, gel strength, fat emulsifying ability, water binding, protein solubility, and *p*H. Despite the fact that the usual manufacturing problems were experienced in production, the only significant statistical variable related to muscle quality that he found was the relationship to climatic changes. Obviously, a great deal more study remains to be done in this area of factors which influence animal physiology. Moss (unpublished, 1963) later studied for 39 weeks the properties of finely comminuted sausage batters and their finished product characteristics. While the product quality varied during this period, he found no significant correlation between product shear press values relating to protein extractability, *p*H, or protein quality. Moss (unpublished, 1963) also found that moisture determinations by either the AOAC or rapid-moisture methods of ham muscle slurries were *p*H dependent.

INFLUENCE OF *p*H ON MUSCLE QUALITY

Since premortem *p*H of healthy animals is rather constant, the influence of *p*H on muscle quality must occur during and after the transformation of muscle into meat. The curves of Figure 27.2 illustrate the rates and extent of *p*H decrease which may be found in porcine muscles. It has been shown by Briskey (1963) and Millo (1964) that a slower rate of reduction in postmortem *p*H results in organoleptically superior meat.

Protein solubility and extraction

Many investigators (Bendall and Wismer-Pedersen, 1962; Briskey, 1964; Goll, Henderson, and Kline, 1964; McLoughlin and Goldspink, 1963; Sayre and Briskey, 1963; Saffle and Galbreath, 1964) have studied the solubility and extractability of soluble muscle proteins as influenced by biological conditions. There is general agreement that the biochemical events during the transformation of muscle into meat do influence protein extractability. However, there is considerable controversy on which proteins are most influenced by these events.

Bendall and Wismer-Pedersen (1962) studied the properties of fibrillar proteins from various postrigor *p*H muscles and found a great decrease in solubility at lower *p*H values when extracted with *p*H 6.5 buffer. At higher rigor temperatures and lower *p*H, they found greater protein contents in the fibrillar muscle components which they interpreted as being due to denatured sarcoplasmic protein. They concluded that this denatured precipitated protein in turn reduced the fibrillar protein solubility. While this may be the mechanism of sarcoplasmic protein insolubility, they also concluded that the fibrillar proteins are unaffected by these same postmortem changes. The sarcoplasmic protein insolubilizing action of postmortem low *p*H has been supported by studies with similar *p*H and carcass temperatures (McLoughlin and Goldspink, 1963; Goldspink and McLoughlin, 1964; Trautman, 1966). Using optical density as a measure of insolubilization, McLoughlin and Goldspink (1963) demonstrated these effects as shown in Figure 27.3. Bendall and Wismer-Pedersen's (1962) conclusion that fibrillar proteins are not altered in watery porcine muscle was based upon water swelling, extraction, and titration observations. This conclusion does not appear to be fully justified on this basis. While these methods have been used to determine protein associated differences, they probably lack the sensitivity necessary to detect subtle changes in the secondary and tertiary structure of fibrillar proteins which manifest themselves in terms of water binding and associated properties. However, as Bendall (personal communication, 1964), has pointed out, it is most difficult to introduce and study controlled rigor mortis conditions into washed prerigor fibrils.

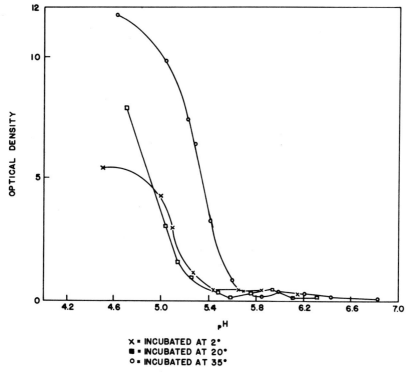

Fig. 27.3. — Effects of *p*H and temperature on the optical density of an extract of sarcoplasmic proteins. From McLoughlin and Goldspink, 1963.

Reduction in fibrillar protein solubility concomitantly with sarcoplasmic protein solubility during rigor has been reported in porcine (Sayre and Briskey, 1963) and in bovine (Goll *et al.*, 1964) muscles. The dissociating action of potassium iodide in phosphate buffer at *p*H 7.4 was utilized to extract the fibrillar proteins and may have overcome the sarcoplasmic protein masking effect observed by Bendall and Wismer-Pedersen. Although the evidence of fibrillar protein alteration is still not conclusive, additional studies (Cassens, Briskey, and Hoekstra, 1963; Trautman, 1966) appear to support the position that fibrillar protein solubility during rigor is influenced by *p*H and temperature. It would be desirable to study the relationship between fibrillar extractability and postrigor muscle *p*H without the additional variables such as buffer, dissociation, and specific ion (Yasui, Sakanishi, and Hashimoto, 1964) effects.

While solubility is essential for extractability, the meat particle size and mechanical action (Trautman, unpublished, 1960) are significant factors in limiting extractability in meat proteins. Specific ions, ionic strength, time, and temperature (Yasui *et al.*, 1964; Trautman, unpublished, 1961) may also influence the quantity of protein extracted. Depending upon the nature of the meat product, both solubility and extractability may be necessary. For example, in cooked cured ham it may be sufficient to solubilize the proteins to enhance water-binding capacity, while in other products (Maas, 1963) it may be essential to extract a portion of the proteins.

Water binding

Water binding by meat is a function of muscle pH, as shown by Dr. Hamm (Chap. 25), and is influenced by microbial growth, as shown by Dr. Jay (Chap. 26). In processed foods, water is considered as normal muscle moisture and as added water. Physiological muscle moisture binding may vary due to rigor mortis conditions and manifest this variation in terms of carcass drip losses which are found in pale, soft, exudative porcine muscles. Poor binding of added moisture in processed meats leads to excessive juice separation in canned hams and similar products.

The muscle component most responsible for water binding has not been fully elucidated. However, interpretation of studies in our laboratory suggest that the fibrillar proteins may bind the majority of water in the system and their efficiency in this property may depend upon carcass pH and be influenced by the extent of change from the superprecipitated to soluble state by sodium chloride concentration. The effects of temperature on water binding by muscle are also important in processed foods and have been reviewed in earlier chapters (Chaps. 24, 25).

INFLUENCE OF pH ON THE PROTEINS IN MUSCLE EXTRACTS

Because of the many difficulties encountered with attempts to control the dynamic state of postmortem glycolysis, investigators have selected the alternate route of study by isolating the soluble proteins from muscle and simulating certain postmortem conditions. Although some of the properties of the soluble proteins may be analogous to their reactions in muscle and meat, model systems must be considered different in at least two respects. First, the model system contains only those proteins which are soluble after limited or extensive postmortem glycolysis. Because the extraction may be considered as a fractionation step of soluble from insoluble protein of the same protein or of mixtures of proteins, the extracts may not be truly representative of meat, especially with respect to molar ratios of myoglobin, actin, myosin, and actomyosin. Second, the fibrillar proteins are studied in high ionic strength solutions versus their potentially soluble or superprecipitated condition in the muscle. Despite these restrictions which must be considered when results are related to intact muscle, many informative studies have been made on model or puri-fied muscle protein systems.

Water-soluble proteins

Solubility. — McLoughlin and Goldspink (1963) and Goldspink and McLoughlin (1964) have studied the effects of pH and simulated glycolysis at various temperatures on water extracts of muscle and measured the solubility as a function of optical density. They found no effect until the pH was lowered to approximately 5.6 where a dramatic decrease was observed which was temperature dependent (Fig. 27.3). They also found that temperatures in the range of 30–37 C accelerated the rate of protein precipitation, and in agreement with many other investigators (Briskey, 1964; Bendall and Wismer-Pedersen, 1962) they concluded that the carcass should be rapidly cooled to at least 22 C before glycolysis had progressed to the extent of lowering the pH to 6.0. Very rapid postmortem cooling in liquid nitrogen has been shown by Borchert and Briskey (1965) to significantly retain the sarcoplasmic solubility. A more direct method of study was made in our laboratory (Trautman, 1966) on the influence of pH on the solubility of water-soluble porcine muscle extracts. These extracts were dialyzed against various phosphate pH buffers, followed by sedimen-tation and determination of soluble and insoluble protein. A typical pH effect is shown in Figure 27.4. These data suggest that changes in the protein solubility initially occur between pH 6.5 and 6.0 and that approxi-mately 50% may be insoluble at pH values found in normally low pH meat (pH 5.2–5.4). These results support the work of McLoughlin and Goldspink (1963) and Bendall and Wismer-Pedersen that sarcoplasmic proteins do precipitate at lower pH values.

As shown in Figure 27.4, not all the water-soluble proteins are insoluble at pH 5.5 to 5.0. These lower pH values may also serve as a separation step and assist in fractionation, as has been reported by Fujimaki and Deather-age (1964). They found at least 14 fractions with ion-exchange cellulose between pH 5 and 10. Fewer sarcoplasmic protein fractions were found in extracts from aged muscles, freeze dried meat, and those meats which had been heated to 50 C. This reduction in soluble fractions was attributed to denaturation.

Color. — When water-soluble muscle extracts are reduced step-wise in pH to 4.5, the most obvious changes are turbidity development and fading of the oxymyoglobin red color (Goldspink and McLoughlin, 1964; Traut-man, 1966). This is in agreement with the findings of Briskey's group and Bendall and Wismer-Pedersen (1962) on intact muscle at low pH. Because extracts of sarcoplasmic proteins become turbid and may precipitate con-comitantly with myoglobin fading upon decreasing pH, the pH effect on

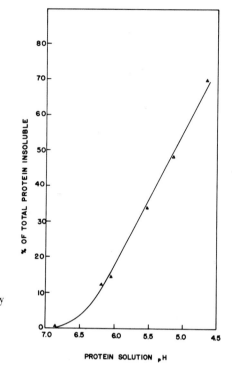

Fig. 27.4. — Effect of *p*H on the solubility of water-soluble proteins.

color was measured in our laboratory (Trautman, 1966) as a function of the free heme content. Using phosphate buffers containing ascorbate ions, various *p*H values were obtained by dialysis. By omitting the acid during the free heme analysis by Hornsey's (1959) method, it was possible to follow the increase in free heme during *p*H decreases. The effect of *p*H on free heme content in water-soluble porcine muscle extracts is shown in Figure 27.5. The release of heme from the protein moiety of extracted myoglobin began above *p*H 6.5 and increased linearly with decreasing *p*H. The loss in visual color also appeared to parallel this increase in free heme. The presence of free heme above *p*H 6.0 was similar, although not as great as reported by Snyder (1963) in crystallized bovine muscle myoglobin at *p*H 6.6. Fronticelli and Bucci (1963) found a similar effect on the release of heme from horse myoglobin at *p*H 5.0 and lower.

The presence of free heme in muscle extracts at lower *p*H suggested that paleness in porcine muscle might be initiated by simple *p*H effects in muscle during rigor mortis. If this were true, then analysis of free heme, total heme, and *p*H of muscle pairs, one prerigor and one postrigor, should establish a relationship between free heme in the muscle and loss in postrigor muscle color. Such a study was made in our laboratory. No free heme

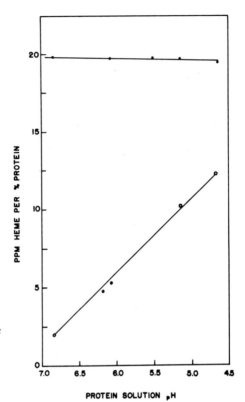

Fig. 27.5. — Effect of *p*H on the heme distribution of water-soluble proteins: ●—●, total heme; O—O, free heme.

was found in any of the muscle pairs. The lack of apparent free heme in the low *p*H, postrigor porcine muscles has prompted a detailed study in our laboratory on other mechanisms to account for the color loss in muscle. Some possible changes under consideration are electron resonance shifts in the heme structure caused by rupturing the bond between the iron of the ferriheme and the F-8 histidyl residue, or splitting of the salt linkages between the heme and the myoglobin moiety. At the present time the loss in color in low *p*H muscles must be considered unresolved.

Salt-soluble proteins

Solubility.—As previously discussed, there is not good agreement on the effect of muscle and meat *p*H upon the solubility of salt-soluble proteins. In attempts to establish more directly the *p*H effect, we chose to isolate and purify salt-soluble proteins from prerigor and postrigor individual porcine ham muscles. Simulated postmortem *p*H values were then obtained by dialysis of these protein solutions against a series of *p*H phosphate buffers. The insolubilizing effect of lower *p*H was determined by

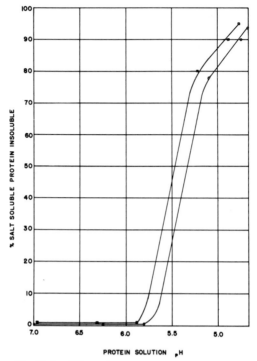

Fig. 27.6. — Effect of *p*H on the solubility of post-rigor salt-soluble protein: O—O, original ham muscle *p*H 5.46; □—□, original ham muscle *p*H 6.51. From Trautman, 1966.

sedimentation and protein distribution. The effect is shown in Figure 27.6, for one of a series of similar experiments. No reduction in solubility was found at *p*H 6.0 and above. However, below *p*H 6.0 a very great decrease in solubility was found and at *p*H 5.0, at least 80% of the proteins had been rendered insoluble. Although this *p*H effect was found with solubilized proteins and while these proteins are considered to be in a superprecipitated state in muscle, observations in our laboratory suggest that this effect may be similar.

Heat gelling. — During a study of methods to measure the more subtle properties of the salt-soluble proteins, we have developed what we call the Least Concentration Endpoint (LCE) test. When applied to solutions of salt-soluble proteins, it appears to have greater sensitivity in evaluating postmortem changes than water binding or extractability. This test consists of heating a series of protein solution dilutions in test tubes to 80 C for 10 min, cooling to 0 C, and evaluating the strength of the coagulum by inverting each tube. The endpoint is that lowest protein concentration which will form a stable gel and remain in the inverted tube. Although the endpoint is arbitrary, the accuracy and reproducibility are excellent.

Using the LCE test we determined the effect of simulated pH and carcass temperatures on prerigor porcine muscle extracts containing both water-soluble and salt-soluble proteins. The results, presented in Figure 27.7, are plotted as a family of curves representing the five heat treatments from 18 C to 41 C. There was very little significant deleterious effect of the heat treatments. The most significant effect was pH. The best LCE

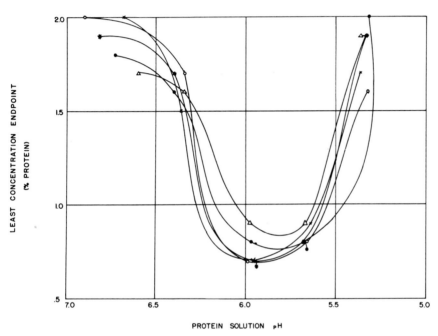

Fig. 27.7. — Effects of pH and temperature on the Least Concentration Endpoint of a prerigor muscle extract containing water-soluble and salt-soluble proteins; heat treatments for 30 min: ×—×, 18 C; O—O, 24 C; *—*, 29 C; ●—●, 35 C; and △—△, 41 C. From Trautman, 1966.

was found between pH 6.0 and 5.7. Below this range a sharp positive slope occurred until the sample gelled into an unworkable condition at pH 5.3 and approximately twice the LCE. Above pH 6.0 the slope of the curves increased in a positive manner to approximately pH 6.75 and again about twice the LCE. The LCE results suggest that there is an optimum pH range in which the soluble proteins gave a more rigid gel. These results parallel the effects found in comminuted sausage manufacture where low pH meat produces a very inferior sausage; also at high pH, extremely prerigor muscle produces a sausage emulsion with very low viscosity.

To determine the effect of simulated carcass *p*H and temperature conditions on purified porcine muscle salt-soluble proteins, a similar range
of *p*H samples was again prepared by dialysis. After each sample had
obtained the desired *p*H, half of each sample was returned to *p*H 6.4 by
further dialysis. The results obtained are presented in Figure 27.8. The
effect of changing the protein *p*H is represented by the solid lines while
the effect of returning the protein solutions to *p*H 6.4–6.5 is represented
by broken lines and arrows. Again the LCE minimum was found in the *p*H

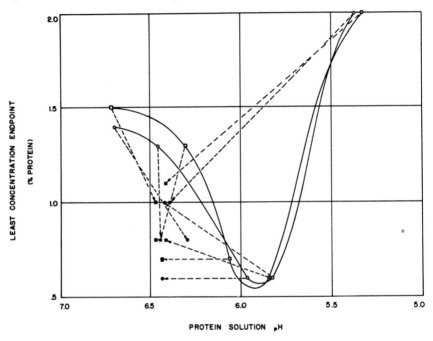

Fig. 27.8. — Effect of *p*H temperature, and *p*H reversal on prerigor salt-soluble protein:
O—O, control; □—□, heated to 18 C for 30 min. Filled symbols with dotted line connecting arrows indicate *p*H reversal effect. From Trautman, 1966.

range of 5.8 to 6.1. Similar sharp positive slope changes were found at
*p*H 5.4 and 6.75, respectively. The effect of returning the *p*H to approximately 6.4 tended to slightly increase the LCE of those samples which were
at *p*H 5.8 to 6.1. An improvement in LCE was found in those samples
which were either above or below this *p*H range. Changing the *p*H appeared to restore partially, but not completely, the LCE of the samples
initially at the *p*H extremes. In other words, the extreme *p*H of 6.75 and
and 5.4 tended to imprint certain properties which were irreversible during subsequent *p*H changes as detected by this heat gelling test. Hamm

(1959) has stated that pH changes from 4.5 to 7.0 of muscle are completely reversible for water-holding capacity of uncooked meat systems. These results suggest that either the heat gelling test is more sensitive than Hamm's water-holding test or that these subtle changes in salt-soluble proteins are masked in the intact meat system when it is heated.

The effects of simulated carcass pH and temperature conditions on purified postrigor porcine muscle salt-soluble proteins were also studied. The postrigor proteins were similar to prerigor proteins in their influence by pH and temperature. However, the postrigor muscle proteins from different muscles did not respond equally at the same dialyzed pH. Since the prerigor salt-soluble proteins had been observed to reflect their prior pH treatments, this difference in response was suggested to have been due to the original postrigor muscle pH.

To test this theory purified salt-soluble proteins were individually prepared from muscles ranging in pH from 6.8 to 5.25, and their LCE values determined. The results obtained are presented in Figure 27.9. A minimum LCE was found in the salt-soluble proteins extracted from postrigor ham

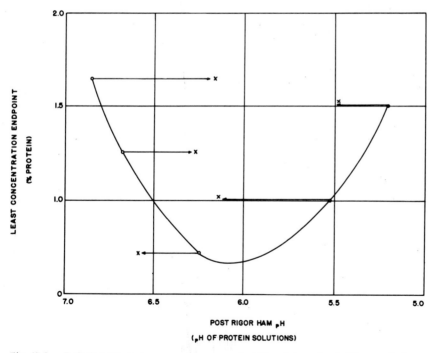

Fig. 27.9. — Relationship between postrigor muscle pH and its salt-soluble protein Least Concentration Endpoint: O—O, muscle pH versus LCE; O→ ✕, direction and magnitude of shift from muscle pH to SSP solution pH at equilibrium dialysis. From Trautman, 1966.

muscles which had pH values in the range of 5.8 to 6.25. The endpoint then increased in a similar manner on both sides of this minimum when the muscle was either higher or lower in pH. There appears to be a very definite relationship between the LCE and the postrigor muscle pH. This indicates that the properties of the salt-soluble proteins are determined by and are characteristic of the glycolytic events during rigor mortis which determines the ultimate muscle pH.

The pH of each protein solution was also plotted in Figure 27.9 with arrows connecting each respective muscle pH. The direction and length of each arrow serves as a measure of the pH shift from muscle to salt-soluble protein solutions. At muscle pH of 6.5 or higher, after exhaustive NaCl dialysis, the salt-soluble proteins had a lower solution pH, while at muscle pH of 6.25 and lower, the solutions had an increase in pH. This shift in pH may explain the differences in response at a given solution pH of salt-soluble proteins obtained from muscles with differing pH. It may also be interpreted as differences in sodium and chloride ion binding capacity as determined by postrigor muscle pH. During an 18-month period following these experiments, 14 similar salt-soluble protein solutions from known muscle pH were studied and found to have LCE which fit this curve.

Mixed pH *solutions.* – The relationship shown in Figure 27.9 explains the range of 0.7 to 1.2 LCE found in our studies of several years ago when we pooled muscles from several carcasses but failed to measure the pH of each muscle. It did not, however, explain the LCE of 0.8 to 0.9 of salt-soluble proteins extracted from large sausage batters which were prepared from muscles ranging in pH 6.6 to 5.4 (Moss, unpublished, 1963).

To study the effect of mixing salt-soluble proteins from known pH muscles, three postrigor muscles representing the normal range (pH 6.8–5.4) were selected for a series of similar experiments. The salt-soluble proteins were individually isolated and the LCE, pH, and adenosine triphosphatase activity were determined on individual solutions and 50/50 mixtures of each. The results of one series of experiments are presented in Table 27.1. The LCE of the individual samples closely followed the relationship shown in Figure 27.9 with respect to their muscle pH. The mixtures of samples D and E resulted in an averaging effect on the LCE. However, when the high pH sample was mixed with the low pH sample, giving sample F, a lower LCE was obtained than either of the individual samples. Since the pH of the latter mixture approximated that of the two former mixtures, pH alone did not account for this effect. This improvement appeared to be similar to observations made several years ago in our laboratory where mixing prerigor and postrigor muscles together resulted in a prerigor electrophoretic pattern of the extract. Analysis at that time indicated that this effect could not be entirely accounted for by the ATP content of the prerigor meat, but probably involved protein complexing. Although the mixing improvement may involve protein complexing, a thorough study of all properties must be made before this phenomenon can be attributed to different rigor mortis conditions causing different protein molecular stoichiometric combinations or alterations.

The adenosine triphosphatase activity of the individual and mixed samples was on the order expected if this activity was primarily a function

TABLE 27.1

The effect of mixing postrigor salt-soluble proteins on their LCE, solution pH, and adenosine triphosphatase activity

Sample	Muscle pH	Protein solution pH	LCE (% protein)	Adenosine triphosphatase activity*
A	6.85	6.01	1.4	2.50
B	6.15	5.80	0.7	1.85
C	5.60	5.61	1.0	0
D	½A + ½B mixture	5.76	1.1	2.20
E	½B + ½C mixture	5.70	0.9	0.90
F	½A + ½C mixture	5.80	0.9	1.20

* μM PO_4 released in 5 min per mg enzyme N.

of ultimate muscle pH and a secondary function of protein solution pH. The activity of the mixed samples supported this position in that it was a numerical average of the activity of the two component proteins. The variability of muscle adenosine triphosphatase activity reported in literature may be the result of pH differences in the sources of fibrillar proteins.

SUMMARY

Muscle protein characteristics and their food manufacturing properties are decidedly influenced by the rate, temperature, and extent of postmortem pH decrease. Decreasing pH reduces salt-soluble protein solubility, heat gelling properties, and adenosine triphosphatase activity; it imprints certain irreversible pH characteristics; and alters the pH shift in solutions at equilibrium dialysis. It also reduces the solubility of water-soluble proteins and releases free heme from protein solutions containing myoglobin. Because mixing postrigor salt-soluble proteins from various pH muscles may lead to anomalous results, it appears desirable to study proteins from individual muscles and characterize each in detail.

References

Bendall, J. R., and J. Wismer-Pedersen. 1962. Some properties of the fibrillar proteins of normal and watery pork muscle. *J. Food Sci.* 27:144.

Borchert, L. L., and E. J. Briskey. 1965. Protein solubility and associated properties of porcine muscle as influenced by partial freezing with liquid nitrogen. *J. Food Sci.* 30:138.

Briskey, E. J. 1963. Influence of ante- and post-mortem handling practices on properties of muscle which are related to tenderness. *Proc. Campbell Soup Co. Meat Tenderness Symp.* (Camden, N.J.), p. 195.

————. 1964. Etiological status and associated studies of pale, soft, exudative porcine musculature. *Advance. Food Res.* 13:89.

Cassens, R. G., E. J. Briskey, and W. G. Hoekstra. 1963. Variation in zinc content and other properties of various porcine muscles. *J. Sci. Food Agr.* 14:427.

Fronticelli, C., and E. Bucci. 1963. Acetone extraction of heme from myoglobin and hemoglobin at acid pH. *Biochim. Biophys. Acta* 79:530.

Fujimaki, M., and F. E. Deatherage. 1964. Chromatographic fractionation of sarcoplasmic proteins of beef skeletal muscle on ion-exchange cellulose. *J. Food Sci.* 29:316.

Goldspink, G., and J. V. McLoughlin. 1964. Studies on pig muscle. 3. The effect of temperature on the solubility of the sarcoplasmic proteins in relation to colour changes in post-rigor muscle. *Irish J. Agr. Res.* 3:9.

Goll, D. E., D. W. Henderson, and E. A. Kline. 1964. Post-mortem changes in physical and chemical properties of bovine muscle. *J. Food Sci.* 29:590.

Hamm, R. 1959. Biochemistry of meat hydration. *Proc. 11th Res. Conf. AMIF* 50:17.

Hornsey, H. C. 1959. The colour of cooked pork. III. Distribution and relationship of pigments, pH and cysteine. *J. Sci. Food Agr.* 10:114.

Maas, R. H. 1963. Processing meat. U.S. Pat. 3,076,713.

McLoughlin, J. V., and G. Goldspink. 1963. Post-mortem changes in the colour of pig longissimus dorsi muscle. *Nature* 198:584.

Millo, Aldo. 1964. Chemical modification in bovine and pig muscles after slaughter. *Vet. Ital.* 15:521.

Saffle, R. L., and J. W. Galbreath. 1964. Quantitative determination of salt-soluble protein in various types of meat. *Food Technol.* 18:119.

Sayre, R. N., and E. J. Briskey. 1963. Protein solubility as influenced by physiological conditions in the muscle. *J. Food Sci.* 28:675.

Snyder, H. E. 1963. Heme dissociation and autoxidation of myoglobin. *Biochim. Biophys. Acta* 69:200.

Trautman, J. C. 1966. Effect of temperature and pH on the soluble proteins of ham. *J. Food Sci.* 31:409.

Yasui, T., M. Sakanishi, and Y. Hashimoto. 1964. Effect of inorganic polyphosphates on the solubility and extractibility of myosin B. *J. Agr. Food Chem.* 12:392.

Chapter 28

Summary and Discussion of Part VI

PANEL MEMBERS: H. LINEWEAVER, *Chairman*
O. FENNEMA
J. McANELLY
R. B. SLEETH
S. MOZERSKY

Lineweaver: The chapters in Part VI have shown clearly that massive differences in dead muscle can be caused by the way the muscle dies. Dr. Luyet (Chap. 24) demonstrated that thaw rigor causes supercontraction, a fact that is undoubtedly related to toughness of thaw-rigor muscle. Evidently the manner of muscle death is not obscured by heat denaturation. He showed us that death of muscle during cooking produces a different denatured structure from that arrived at by cooking muscle that died some other way. Dr. Luyet's demonstration of changes in the ultrastructure of muscle due to freezing, thawing, and heating in the prerigor and postrigor state provides highly valuable fundamental information to those concerned with the mechanisms involved in muscle tenderness. Understanding postmortem muscle changes at the lowest observable level of structure differentiation should help us to devise specific methods to control changes in muscle texture.

The need to understand or control the way muscle dies is perhaps obvious. However, in this connection, Dr. Trautman's observations (Chap. 27) on the salt-soluble protein fraction from muscle is most interesting. He observed that postrigor muscle pH variations, which reflect differences in the glycolytic events during rigor, cause as much as a threefold difference in the amount of salt-soluble protein required to form a gel on heating.

Dr. Jay (Chap. 26) pointed out that pH is an important factor, but only one of several muscle factors that can vary and influence microbial spoilage. There is lack of adequate knowledge on differences in water-holding capacity, autolysis, and other factors that can be influenced by the way the muscle dies.

Dr. Hamm (Chap. 25) reviewed the complexities of the many changes that occur during conversion of muscle to food by cooking. He pointed out that pure proteins in solution or as gels may act in a different way from the same proteins localized within the myofibrils. He thus emphasized the complexity of muscle and the reactions that can or do occur during cooking.

Perhaps then it may be useful to conclude with a comment by Dean R. A. Alberty, of the University of Wisconsin. Dean Alberty referred to the physical chemists' starting point — the ideal system. Drawing from Raoult's law, which holds exactly only for ideal systems, he symbolized the symposium as a perfect solution in which, he hoped, each member's partial pressure would be proportional to his mol fraction. Manifestly, the heterogeneous muscle system is very unlike a perfect solution, nor can we dilute it to approach Raoult's ideal solution. This situation increases the credit we must give to the investigators responsible for the advances reported here on muscle as a subject of scientific study.

DISCUSSION

Fennema: What effect do large organic molecules, such as proteins, have on the structure of water, and what effect may the structure of water have on the properties or the chemical reactivities of proteins?

Hamm: True hydration water, which is bound by the structural proteins, does not seem to be influenced very much by the usual treatment of meat or by rigor mortis. There is a great change in the amount of water which is immobilized within the structure, and this immobilized water appears to be held between the filaments. The immobilization of the water depends on the interaction between the protein molecules. This interaction may depend on attraction of oppositely charged groups or repulsion of groups which have the same charge. It may also be influenced by cross linking or cleavage of linkages in such a way that each increase of cross linkages decreases the amount of immobilized water and each decrease of interactions increases the amount of immobilized water. We do not know what causes the immobilization of the free water in the true chemical and physical sense. It may be that there is some kind of icelike structure induced by nonpolar groups. (See also Klotz, 1962).

Mozersky: In connection with the immobilization of water by a macromolecular network, such immobilization could conceivably be attributed to mucopolysaccharides as well as to proteins; such a system occurs in the vitreous of the eye. Is there any evidence regarding the participation of mucopolysaccharides in this function in muscle?

Hamm: I have no information on the question.

Fennema: In another publication (Jay, 1965), you presented evidence indicating that the changes in free water content are caused by the micro-organisms. Would you care to comment on the possible mechanisms?

Jay: While we do not know the exact cause of the increase in hydration as bovine muscle spoils, the utilization of bovine metal ions by the micro-flora no doubt plays an important role. Since added proteases cause similar changes in free water, the possibility also exists that partial degradation or "loosening" of bovine proteins may be involved.

Fennema: Do microbial-induced changes in free water produce a notice-able change in muscle quality?

Jay: Muscles which spoil to the point of producing low ERV values show a greater degree of tenderness; and, therefore, this quality factor is at least associated with changes in free water.

Donnelly: What was the extracting solution used to define "salt-soluble proteins," and what were the conditions of pH, ionic strength, and voltage gradient under which electrophoresis revealed but one peak for these proteins?

Trautman: The salt-soluble proteins were prepared by extracting finely ground muscle with 0.67 M NaCl for 1 hr at 0 C. This slurry was sedi-mented at 10,000 $\times$ g for 10 min. The supernatant was dialyzed against 0.05 M NaCl for 3 days at 0 C. The superprecipitated salt-soluble proteins were recovered and washed twice with 0.05 M NaCl and resolubilized in electrophoretic buffer, pH 7.35 and ionic strength 0.4. Electrophoresis was conducted at 25 milliamperes with 60 volts. The pattern and Rayleigh fringe indicated a single component.

Sleeth: What details would be brought out in the Least Concentration Endpoint test in the intervals of greatest change, pH 6.4 to 6.0 and pH 5.7 to 5.3?

Trautman: Decrease in pH of prerigor salt-soluble proteins appears to imprint certain properties on the proteins so that subsequent pH changes do not reverse the original pH effect.

Fennema: What effect does the ionic strength and type of ion have on the LCE test?

Trautman: The salt-soluble proteins which are examined by the LCE test must be suspended in sufficient ionic strength to be soluble and yet not too great to cause salting-out. I prefer 0.6 to 1.2 ionic strength NaCl. A deleterious effect was found with most phosphate ions at constant pH while no effect could be found with Ca^{++} up to 0.01 M.

Sleeth: Is the denatured sarcoplasmic protein effect on fibrillar protein solubility observed in thoroughly homogenized tissue?

Trautman: Some question has been raised as to the actual insolubilizing action of denatured sarcoplasmic protein; pH of muscle seems to be important.

Whitaker: What is the effect of water-holding capacity on the color of meat?

Trautman: At constant pH and oxidation-reduction potential, the color of meat appears to be myoglobin concentration dependent.

McAnelly: What is the sensitivity of the LCE test for water-soluble proteins when compared to other tests?

Trautman: The LCE test is not applicable to water-soluble proteins, because they form a very fragile coagulum when heated.

McAnelly: What role do the stroma proteins play in processed foods?

Trautman: It depends upon the type of processed foods being considered. In finely comminuted products the stroma proteins contribute significantly less character to the product than in other coarse-textured products.

McAnelly: Is the extraction of muscle proteins with phosphate buffers leading to possible misconceptions of the role of these proteins in processed meat products?

Trautman: Yes, in at least two ways. First, many of the phosphates are used at pH values other than the meat pH and can introduce erroneous results as shown in Figure 27.8. Second, many phosphates exhibit a specific ion effect. For example, a mixed muscle extract of purified salt-soluble protein had a LCE of 0.8% protein, and when dialyzed against a buffer containing the same 0.67 M NaCl plus 0.01 M pyrophosphate at pH 6.0, a LCE of 1.25% was found.

King: Could you describe in more detail the evidence which led you to suggest that your salt-soluble extracts represented an equilibrium mixture of protein components? How is the equilibrium displaced by pH? What proteins appear (or increase in concentration) as pH is lowered? Did you use moving boundary electrophoresis evidence to support this hypothesis? If so, please give more results or details of evidence.

Trautman: I have suggested that different rigor mortis conditions cause different protein molecular stoichiometric combinations or alterations. The evidence leading to this suggestion includes the reported LCE relationship shown in Figure 27.9 and the mixing effect in Table 27.1. Additional unpublished evidence includes curves on the influence of (1) post-rigor pH on salt-soluble protein viscosity, (2) ionic strength of extractant solutions on the quality and quantity of salt-soluble protein extracted, (3) extraction temperature on the quality and quantity of salt-soluble protein extracted, and (4) a moving boundary electrophoretic comparison of the methods employed in the preparation of salt-soluble solutions. For example, centrifugation to reduce turbidity prior to electrophoresis will change the ratio of myosin and actomyosin in the same prerigor extract. Referring to one experiment, we found 31.6% myosin and 39.5% actomyosin in the sample by Rayleigh fringe calculation while after centrifugation of the same sample 27.3% myosin and 42.9% actomyosin were found.

McAnelly: What possible explanations are there for the statement that meat spoils only "when it is ready" and that this is not always related to observable differences in the microflora?

Jay: We are not always able to predict on the basis of holding temperature, relative humidity, etc., just how long it will take a given sample of fresh bovine tissue to spoil. It appears that certain changes or conditions must occur within the meat itself before the phenomenon of "spoilage" occurs. The spoilage of bovine tissue certainly appears to be more than the mere growth of a certain number of bacteria.

Lauck: Might nucleotide level (ADP, etc.) be a factor in bacterial spoilage of muscle?

Jay: The effect of ADP on bacterial spoilage of muscle has not been published to my knowledge. The antibacterial properties of polyphosphates are probably due to their capacity to chelate metal ions.

McAnelly: Would Dr. Jay comment further on his statement: "It is well known that muscle from fatigued animals spoils faster than that from rested animals and that this is a direct consequence of final pH attained upon completion of rigor."

Jay: The muscles of a well-rested bovine animal contain approximately 1% glycogen which usually forms 1.1% lactic acid as rigor mortis develops (Bate-Smith, 1948). This amount of lactic acid is usually sufficient to lower the pH from 7.4 to about 5.6. If the animal is excited or fatigued prior to slaughter, its glycogen level would be depleted, thereby leaving less for conversion to lactic acid. The over-all effect would be a muscle with a relatively high ultimate pH. At ultimate pH values of 6.0 or above, bacterial growth rate is accelerated.

McAnelly: Have any of the bovine muscle spoilage organisms listed in Table 26.3 been tested to determine their proteolytic digestion capabilities on bovine muscle proteins other than gelatin?

Jay: This activity was measured by extracting 5 g of beef with a total of 20 ml of distilled water and adding 8 ml of filter-sterilized extract to 100 ml of agar-agar (1.5%) at about 45 C. The suspension was poured into petri dishes and streaked with the 34 strains of bacteria. Of the fresh bovine muscle isolates, seven (41%) degraded the bovine muscle proteins, while only 2 (12%) of those from spoiled bovine muscle showed this activity. Protein degradation was determined by flooding the plates (incubated at 30 C for 5 days) with $HgCl_2$ and HCl.

Mozersky: Two types of functional groups were mentioned as being exposed on unfolding of myofibrillar protein due to heating: (a) imidazole and (b) sulfhydryl. Direct evidence implicating these groups would be valuable. Exposure of imidazole was associated with proton binding. If histidine were destroyed, e.g., by radiation, one would then expect to prevent the increase in pH observed on heating. Likewise, if the sulfhydryl groups exposed by heating to 70 C were properly substituted one might prevent the subsequent formation of disulfide bonds and the toughness which occurs on heating to 120 C. Is there direct evidence to support either of these speculations?

Hamm: Regarding imidazole, the idea is a good one, provided that effects of radiation other than the destruction of histidine do not complicate the interpretation of the results. It is difficult to block the imidazolium group specifically. Concerning the sulfhydryl groups, such experiments have not yet been carried out. We intend to follow this proposition.

King: Your results show that heating alters the number of equivalents of acidic and basic groups in beef. However, Connell and Howgate (1964) did not find a change in amount of these groups when cod was heated as you stated in your speech. Could this difference in results be due to a difference in experimental method instead of a species difference? Your dye-binding method may be more sensitive to alterations of molecular configuration on heating than Connell and Howgate's potentiometric titration method.

Hamm: We observed a change of charged groups only in the pH range between 5.5 and 7. If you look at Figure 2 in the paper of Connell and Howgate (1964), you will see a change of charged groups in the same range of pH. You will also see an increase of IP of about 0.5 pH units. This result is in very good agreement with our results. With cod myofibrils, however, Connell and Howgate did not observe a change of IP during heating.

Sleeth: Can the discontinuity of effects of heat on muscle be due to protein structural adjustments preceding denaturation?

Hamm: I do not think so, because unfolding of the actomyosin molecules results in an increase of available sulfhydryl groups. That means the denaturation process starts at temperatures lower than the temperature range of the characteristic step.

McAnnelly: What should cause the collagen in different muscles to show differences in resistance to heating?

Hamm: Recent work reported by F. Hill (1965) strongly indicates an increase in the number or strength of the cross links of intramuscular collagen of cattle and pigs with an increase in chronological age of the animal. These differences in cross linkages may be extremely important in explaining differences in resistance to heat. I would also refer you to three articles by Goll, Hoekstra, and Bray (1964).

Usborne: What is the effect of relatively low heat over a long period of time on the activity of cathepsins and other natural muscle enzymes on tenderizing of muscle?

Hamm: You will find some information in Chiambalero, Johnson, and Drake (1959). They presented data concerning the time-temperature relationship for heat inactivation of proteolytic enzymes in radiation-sterilized beef and pork in the temperature range between 60 C and 77 C. They found, for example, that the enzymes are inactivated after heating at 60 C for 250 min, or at 77 C for 0.4 min. Recently F. C. Parrish (1965) studied the influence of temperature on muscle cathepsins.

SPECIAL DISCUSSION

Davies: The extreme contraction which was demonstrated by Dr. Luyet (Chap. 24) seemed to be similar to that shown with large individual muscle fibers of the giant barnacle (McAlear and Hoyle, 1963; McAlear, Hoyle, and Selverston, 1964). These barnacle fibers were able to contract to 10% of their length. When this extreme contraction occurred, the thick A filaments passed through the Z lines to make a double overlap of the thick filaments. However, when the muscle was damaged or glycerol extracted, the thick filaments were unable to pass through the Z lines and instead crumpled in all directions, making a very obvious contraction band at the level of the Z line. This crumpled material would have been isotropic, which was also one of the observations noted by Dr. Luyet. At the M region, where the double overlap of the actin occurred, the dense contraction band would be anisotropic. Dr. Luyet's observation of an isotropic condition at the Z line and anisotropic condition at the M line seems similar to the findings of Drs. Hoyle and McAlear. One of Dr. Luyet's additional fascinating results was that the muscle which had been frozen at relatively high temperatures (−5 or −10 C) experienced a cycle upon rapid thawing — initially a contraction, then a relaxation, then another contraction. This could perhaps be explained by relatively light damage upon freezing, since at the temperatures used not all the water in the muscle would freeze. Free liquid water would still exist. Consequently, the reticulum may be only slightly damaged rather than severely damaged as in the muscles frozen with liquid nitrogen which just contract when thawed. Upon thawing of the lightly damaged muscles, contraction occurred for a few seconds in the cold until the muscles approached room temperature. Then the sarcoplasmic reticulum (Ca pump) could operate to reaccumulate the Ca which would have been liberated immediately upon thawing at the low temperature. At this low temperature the Ca pump would have been dramatically slowed, but the slight damage would have allowed a leak of Ca. Thus, the initial contraction following the Ca release would be reversed by a temporary relaxation as the reticulum started to pump Ca (warmer temperature). However, due to the damage, the tissue would be using up its energy quite rapidly and after a few minutes the energy stores would be relatively depleted. Excess free Ca would then be present in the muscle. This build-up of Ca would be sufficient to activate the actin-myosin contraction; so the terminal situation should be a further contraction and then a stiffening of the muscle after which no further contraction would occur, because of the absence of a further supply of ATP or other high energy nucleotides. In muscles frozen to $-2\,C$, apparently little damage occurred to the sarcoplasmic reticulum so that no Ca was released and, therefore, contraction was not observed.

Luyet: Would Dr. Davies please elaborate further on the reason for anisotropy of the contraction band CM in supercontracted muscle? The optical properties of the contraction bands about which I raise questions here are not the result of my own observations; they were reported by Huxley and Hanson (1960).

Davies: The M line of supercontracted muscle should consist of thick filaments, thin filaments in a double overlap (therefore containing high concentration of actin), and other electron dense material (probably cross linkages between the myosins themselves; see Huxley, 1965). Even after supercontraction all these filaments should remain parallel at the middle of the sarcomere, and therefore this region should be anisotropic. However, the extreme crumpling that would occur at the level of the Z line would result in an isotropic situation because the thick filaments would now distort and twist in all three dimensions so that there would be no preferential anisotropic situation. If either the thick filaments or the thin filaments were removed, the situation would still be anisotropic at the level of the M lines.

Luyet: Please elaborate further on the development of birefringence at both the I and M band.

Davies: This is perhaps comparable to what happens to a solution of tobacco mosaic virus. The individual rodlike molecules, in a stationary solution, point in all possible directions, so the solution appears isotropic; however, if the solution is poured from a pipette or passed through a tube, flow birefringence develops because all the particles become parallel, making the solution anisotropic. In the M region the rodlike molecules are all parallel, so that this region will appear anisotropic under a polarizing filter, whereas at the Z line the distorted rods will point in all directions just as the rodlike virus particles would point in a free stationary solution and thus this region appears isotropic.

Luyet: What is the composition of the dense line which appears in supercontraction, at the position of the former M line, when the A material is removed?

Davies: Under these conditions of supercontraction there should be a double overlap of the actin. There would probably be four times as many actin filaments as myosin filaments: and even if the myosin filaments were completely removed this would still leave a highly anisotropic arrangement of filaments in the M region, so that the actin itself would, under these circumstances, be contributing to the observed anisotropy even after removal of the A substance.

Another situation which may arise with supercontraction is that the lateral alignment of the thick A filaments gets distorted. Some of the thick filaments are pulled in one direction, some are pulled towards the other Z line, and this can give a pseudo-effect as if the A band had shortened. In fact, the filaments do not shorten but they move off to one side, and this can account for a variety of assymetries where an individual sarcomere may seem more dense to one side than towards the other. This could perhaps explain some of your remarkable pictures.

Bendall: I would like to make a remark about the experiment at −2 C where there appeared to be no contraction when the muscle was thawed. This is because the chemical changes which normally occur during rigor mortis at higher temperatures also do so at the lower temperature, but at a somewhat accelerated rate. Thus, after an hour or two, there is no ATP left, to produce the contractile process when the muscle is thawed. In the frozen state, on the other hand, where normally the muscle would contract at these rates of ATP destruction, it cannot do so, because of the ice crystals. Sometimes, however, it evidently makes the attempt, which results in very great damage to the fibrils.

Marsh: In a study of thaw rigor in ovine muscle, it was found that the very slow thawing which occurred in relatively large samples effectively prevented any signs of thaw shortening. It seems that during this slow thawing sufficient ice crystals remained to act as an internal matrix which resisted all shortening. To demonstrate actual shortening in relatively large unattached samples it was necessary to thaw at very high rates, for instance by immersion in warm saline. If, in addition, skeletal attachments were still present shortening would be completely suppressed. Thaw rigor complications, therefore, are most unlikely to be encountered in the pre-rigor freezing and thawing of meat still attached to the skeleton. In this same study, little exudation of fluid or drip occurred until the shortening exceeded more than about 40% or 45% of the initial length. Beyond this amount of shortening, fluid exudation increased rapidly with further shortening. Kaminer (1962), using frog muscle, found that fluid was exuded in direct proportion to thaw shortening over the shortening range from 0% to very high values. Has Dr. Luyet observed a steady fluid release or a sudden start to fluid release after considerable shortening has already occurred?

Luyet: We have not made any quantitative determination of either the amount of fluid which is exuded or the time at which the exudation of fluid takes place in relation to extent of contraction or expansion.

Marsh: In thaw rigor of ovine muscles kept under tension while thawing there was no development of exudation. If the muscles were released when complete thawing had occurred, but within a few minutes of this taking place, then an immediate and very large contraction took place within seconds and was accompanied by a large amount of exudation. If, however, the muscle was allowed to remain fully thawed for a period of 30 min while still restrained, and it was then released, there was no shortening or fluid exudation.

References

Bate-Smith, E. C. 1948. The physiology and chemistry of rigor mortis with special reference to the aging of beef. *Advance. Food Res.* 1:1.

Chiambalero, C. J., D. A. Johnson, and M. P. Drake, 1959. A time-temperature relationship for heat-enzyme inactivation of radiation-sterilized beef and pork. *J. Agr. Food Chem.* 7:782.

Connell, J. J., and P. F. Howgate. 1964. The hydrogen ion titration curves of native, heat-coagulated and frozen-stored myofibrils of cod and beef. *J. Food Sci.* 29:717.

Goll, D. E., W. G. Hoekstra, and R. W. Bray. 1964. Age-associated changes in bovine muscle connective tissue. I. Rate of hydrolysis by collagenase. II. Exposure to increasing temperature. III. Rate of solubilization at 100° C. *J. Food Sci.* 29:608, 615, 622.

Hill, F. 1965. The solubility of intramuscular collagen in meat animals of various ages. Paper read at 11th Conf. Europe. Meat Res. Workers (Belgrade).

Huxley, H. E. 1965. Structural evidence concerning the mechanism of contraction in striated muscle, p. 3. *In* W. M. Paul, E. E. Daniel, C. M. Kay, and G. Monckton (eds.), *Muscle*. Pergamon Press, Oxford.

Huxley, H. E., and J. Hanson. 1960. The molecular basis of contraction in cross-striated muscles, p. 183. *In* G. H. Bourne (ed.), *The Structure and Function of Muscle*, Vol. 1. Academic Press, New York.

Jay, J. M. 1965. Relationship between water-holding capacity of meats and microbial quality. *J. Appl. Microbiol.* 13:120.

Kaminer, B. 1962. Water loss during contracture of muscle. *J. Gen. Physiol.* 46:131.

Klotz, I. M. 1962. Water, p. 523. *In* M. Kasha and B. Pullman (eds.), *Horizons in Biochemistry.* Academic Press, New York.

McAlear, J. H., and G. Hoyle. 1963. The mechanism of supercontraction of striated muscle fiber of the barnacle (Balanus Nubilus). *J. Cell Biol.* 19:49A, Abstr. 115.

McAlear, J., G. Hoyle, and A. Selverston. 1964. The phenomenon of A band contraction, an artifact of preparation. *J. Cell Biol.* 23:57A.

Parrish, F. C. 1965. Physico-chemical properties of sarcoplasmic and lysosomal cathepsins from porcine and bovine muscle. Ph.D. thesis, Univ. of Missouri Dept. Animal Husbandry.

Index

A band filaments: description, 47; granular appearance, 193; mentioned, 425. *See also* Thick filaments

Acetylcholinesterase: location in muscle, 65

Acid phosphatase, 237

ACTH. *See* Adrenocorticotrophic hormone

Actin: fish, 197; and nucleotides, 281, 292; polymerization process, 281; F-form, 282, 289; G-form, 282, 289; G-F transition, 283; structural alteration, 292; steric limitations during actomyosin formation, 293; F-G transformation and tenderness, 302; mentioned, 281, 287, 300, 408

Actin filaments: polarity of, 290; mentioned, 7, 8. *See also* Thin filaments

Action potential, 10, 14

Actomyosin: fish, 197; contractility of, 280; contraction with ATP, 287; dissociation by irradiation, 302; postmortem state of, 306; isoelectric point, 365; mentioned, 232, 281, 408

Adenosine diphosphate: glycolytic enhancer, 35; rephosphorylation, 35; actin bound, 218; mentioned, 36, 198, 305, 389

Adenosine monophosphate, 198, 268, 305

Adenosine triphosphatase: of fibrils, 258; effect of heat on, 363; mentioned, 197, 213, 233, 373, 417

Adenosine triphosphate: sources of, 11; uses of, 11; plasticizing effect, 213, 300; and contraction, 226, 300; and volume increase, 227; irreversible synaeresis, 228; in restrained strip, 270; mentioned, 198, 208, 268, 277, 305, 389

Adenylic acid: glycolytic regulator, 35

Adenylic deaminase: binding to myosin, 305

ADP. *See* Adenosine diphosphate

Adrenal cortex: effect on muscle, 173–174

Adrenaline: chronic release, 153; preslaughter effect, 153; preslaughter administration, 171; and irregular bands, 253

Adrenocorticotrophic hormone, 138

Age: muscle changes, 22, 23

Alcoholism, 130

Allosteric transition, 283

Ammonia, 305

AMP. *See* Adenosine monophosphate

Androgen: protein anabolic effect, 82; mobilization of amino acids, 101; protein synthetic action, 168; mentioned, 86

Anisotropy, 280, 425

Anserine, 145, 277, 309, 389

Anterior pituitary: function of, 81; mentioned, 86

Antibiotics, 399

Arteriosclerosis, 73

Aryl sulfatases, 237

ATP. *See* Adenosine triphosphate

ATPase. *See* Adenosine triphosphatase

Atrophy: possibility of recreation, 27, 118; neurogenic, 120

β-amino-propionitrile, 324, 334, 347

BAPN. *See* β-amino-propionitrile

Basement membrane, 39, 51

Basophilia, 50, 128

Bernard, C., 137, 145

Biological variation, 251

Birefringence, 426

Blood: carbon dioxide, 189; oxygen, 189

Bruised muscle: and lysosomal enzymes, 241

Büchner, T. *See* Multiple control